Mapping AND Modeling Weather AND Climate with GIS

Edited by

L. Armstrong,　**K.** Butler,　**J.** Settelmaier,　**T.** Vance,　**O.** Wilhelmi

Esri Press
REDLANDS|CALIFORNIA

In memory of Rob Raskin, a true geoinformatics innovator and gentleman.
http://www.aag.org/cs/membership/tributes_memorials/mr/raskin_robert_g.

Contents

Foreword

A fruitful collaboration between geospatial and atmospheric communities

Weather and climate information is innately geospatial. Maps have long been essential to meteorologists and climatologists in their research and operations. Edmond Halley included a map of the trade winds and monsoons in an article he wrote in 1686 (Halley 1686). The map is credited as the first to depict atmospheric phenomena. Since then, maps have been instrumental to producing and communicating weather and climate information. Maps are also the center of geographic information systems (GIS) technologies, so naturally there is great potential in using GIS technology in atmospheric research and operations. *Mapping and Modeling Weather and Climate with GIS* explores the benefits and possibilities that arise when geospatial and atmospheric communities collaborate.

Since early 2000, scientists at the National Center for Atmospheric Research (NCAR) have led the efforts to bring GIS technologies to atmospheric science communities. Through the coordination of the GIS group at NCAR, geospatial and atmospheric communities collaboratively accomplished major milestones, including the creation of the atmospheric data model, GIS tools to ingest multidimensional atmospheric data, and various functions and symbols for weather data rendering. Their progress and accomplishments constitute the foundation of this edited volume. *Mapping and Modeling Weather and Climate with GIS* explores issues that arise when coupling atmospheric data and GIS technologies and demonstrates the relevance of GIS to weather and climate sciences. Chapter authors discuss existing data and software resources and accomplishments and opportunities for cross-fertilization of atmospheric and geospatial sciences beyond data processing and mapping. The book follows the collaborators' journey from data representation and observations to modeling, data-model integration, web services, tools, and resources. This fruitful collaboration has not only improved GIS support for atmospheric communities, but has also resulted in advanced GIS functions in handling multidimensional and time-enabled data, which extends GIS beyond mapping.

GIS development has a long tradition in computer-assisted cartography and with the "layer-cake" conceptual model that brings the map metaphor to the underlying principle of geospatial data organization. Although object-oriented approaches have become the norm of GIS data modeling, maps remain the primary conceptual construct for data handling and analysis in GIS. Accommodating atmospheric data on maps sacrifices the dimensions of altitude and time that are important for modeling. Atmospheric data forces a switch from the map metaphor to the hypercube metaphor, in which maps are slices of the hypercube. NetCDF (Network Common Data Form) and HDF (Hierarchical Data Format) files embed data hypercubes efficiently. From the very beginning, the collaboration between geospatial and atmospheric science communities focused on one of the most important milestones for weather and climate modeling in GIS: the extension of GIS capabilities to handle netCDF and HDF file formats commonly used by atmospheric scientists. These file formats are intrinsically temporal and multidimensional, with variables and values regularly structured and explicitly documented in individual header files. Multidimensional tools that extract and map data from netCDF and HDF files in GIS make it possible to spatially integrate atmospheric data with myriad geospatial data for modeling environmental correlates, spatio-social interactions, risk and impact assessment, and evacuation and mitigation planning.

Parts 1 and 6 of this book provide detailed discussions and technical specifications of netCDF and HDF files and the GIS tools to handle these files and broader atmospheric data. A suite of atmospheric data, including surface observations, weather radar imagery, meteorological satellite imagery, and ocean measurements, can now be handled and analyzed in ArcGIS software and its related software platforms, which is discussed in parts 2 and 3.

Part 3 also discusses the concept of scale, specifically downscaling. GIS software allows us to place weather and climate observations and related atmospheric processes and forecasts into a geographic context. Understanding climate-change effects at local and regional scales can lead to strategic planning and preparation for alleviation and adaptation. Nowadays, local and national television newscasters use street-level weather forecasts to make weather information more relatable to the general public. Similarly, climate models supported by the general circulation models (or global climate models, both abbreviated GCM) operate at the global scale. Various downscaling methods have been developed, and some have been implemented in GIS. The tools developed by DHI, an independent research and development organization, discussed in part 3 are a good example of downscaling analysis of climate change and its effects on communities. Although GIS conceptual models and tools remain subject to the layer-cake constraints, their capabilities to handle multidimensional data offer new resources and possibilities to connect all aspects and interactions of our environments for better understanding and decision making.

Part 5 discusses the important concept of standards, specifically as they relate to web services. Both atmospheric and geospatial communities are active contributors to the Open Geospatial Consortium (OGC), which develops standards that ensure that data and resources from geosciences and environmental sciences are interoperable, sharable, and discoverable across communities. Unidata, one of the University Corporation for Atmospheric Research (UCAR) programs, has been the leading provider and coordinator of data, tools, and support to enhance earth-system education and research. Unidata has been working with OGC to successfully establish netCDF data model standards and extensions for climate and forecast data. In addition to Unidata and NCAR in the United States, National Meteorological Services in Europe and the World Meteorological Organization formed OGC domain working groups for hydrology and for meteorology and oceanography.

Much effort has also been devoted to creating standards for web services such as Web Map Service (WMS) and Web Feature Service (WFS) interface standards. GIS technologies that embrace OGC WMS and WFS standards offer high degrees of flexibility to mash-up online and local resources. Web services also transform ways in which government agencies disseminate information. Traditional file transfer protocol (FTP) allows local computing facilities to download data for display and analysis. WMS and WFS allow users to map, access, and integrate data directly on web browsers, and therefore enable direct communications (graphical, tabular, or text) on multiple computing platforms. Part 5 provides detailed discussions on the kinds of web services for atmospheric and hydrological data available from government agencies and Esri. In addition to information about the public sites at the National Oceanic and Atmospheric Administration (NOAA) and US Geological Survey (USGS), part 5 provides information about web services in military applications. WMS and WFS make such integrations, at least visually, easy in ArcGIS and other GIS technologies that follow OGC standards.

As web technologies advance, the World Wide Web becomes the primary platform for public participation and social interactions. Crowdsourcing and social media mining have gained popularity as effective means for data collection. Crowdsourced volunteered geographic information (VGI) is now a common type of geospatial data particularly effective for event monitoring, including natural hazards. Because the majority of significant natural hazards are weather or climate related, many successful VGI use cases already exist, as discussed in part 2 (chapter 7). In fact, the climate and weather communities have a long history of VGI, or citizen science, with the NOAA National Weather Service Cooperative Observer Network (http://www.nws.noaa.gov/om/coop/), created in 1890, and a number of nonprofit or volunteer spotter networks, such as US Storm Spotter Network (http://stormtask.wix.com/stormspotternetwork) and Spotter Network (http://www.spotternetwork.org), established in the last 10 years. Advances in Web 2.0 and social media provide further opportunities and increased effectiveness of public participation and citizen science with web services, mobile computing, and cloud computing technologies. Beyond VGI, ambient geospatial data relevant to weather and climate information is also available, including sensor networks and social networks. Weather and climate sensor networks provide multitudes of observation data, as discussed in part 2. Social networks are relatively new sources of data to science communities. Geotagged photos may include severe weather phenomena, such as tornado touchdowns or dust bowls, for forecast validations. Geotagged tweets may consist of keywords that indicate urban heat island effects or the progression of a wildfire. Broadly, data mining of such ambient, unstructured, heterogeneous, and massive data is recognized as the "big data" challenge. Atmospheric and geospatial communities clearly have ample opportunities to lead big data research in geoinformatics and beyond.

Mapping and Modeling Weather and Climate with GIS offers both concepts and practices of mapping and modeling weather and climate with GIS. The following chapters chronicle the exciting progress of GIS capabilities for weather and climate applications and include useful lists of data, tools, and resources to support atmospheric and hydrological studies. The book provides a good balance between technical details of current technological implementations and methodological approaches of mapping and modeling for research considerations. Novices who are just beginning to use GIS in weather and climate projects will find this book to be a useful resource. Practitioners will gain a clear picture of the advances of GIS for atmospheric sciences and appreciate the lists of available geospatial resources.

Mapping and Modeling Weather and Climate with GIS is a milestone in the collaboration between atmospheric and geospatial science communities. The growing interest in both communities promises a greater atmospheric–geospatial integration that can lead to exciting new progress in both weather and climate modeling and GIS development.

May Yuan
Ashbel Smith Professor of Geospatial Information Sciences
School of Economic, Political, and Policy Science
University of Texas, Dallas

References

Halley, Edmond. "An Historical Account of the Trade Winds, and Monsoons, Observable in the Seas between and near the Tropicks, with an Attempt to Assign the Phisical Cause of the Said Winds." *Philosophical Transactions* (1683–1775): 153–68. doi:10.1098/rstl.1686.0026.

Acknowledgments

Writing this book has been a truly collaborative exercise. Many people assisted in the creation of this publication. I would like to express our special appreciation and thanks to Tiffany Vance, Kevin Butler, Olga Wilhelmi, Jennifer Boehnert, Steve Kopp, and Jack Settelmaier for their brilliance, limitless knowledge of the subject matter, and for not giving up when moving forward became complicated. Thanks to May Yuan from University of Texas, Dallas, for contributing the foreword; Ted Habermann from The HDF Group for his insightful afterword; and Esri President Jack Dangermond, who realized the importance and limitless potential of GIS in the atmospheric science, climate, and weather community.

I would also like to thank the following agencies, organizations, universities, and companies for their insight and experience and for endorsing and supporting the contributions of their employees: National Center for Atmospheric Research (NCAR), National Oceanic and Atmospheric Administration (NOAA), Jet Propulsion Laboratory (JPL), Unidata, DHI, The HDF Group, Colorado State University, University of South Florida, the Royal Australian Navy, and Axiom Consulting.

I appreciate the support from Esri Press. A special thank you to Christa Campbell, who helped organize the collection of manuscript materials and acted as the liaison between the editors and authors of the book and Esri Press. This was no easy task.

Apart from those previously mentioned, in the course of my work and getting this book written I met many people in the industry I admire for their understanding and vision. I would like to thank the many people who saw this book through: to all those who provided support, agreed that the book was needed, wrote, offered comments, encouraged, reviewed, and assisted in the editing, proofreading, and design.

Lori Armstrong
Esri Global Atmospheric, Climate, and Weather Industry Manager

PART 1

Representations of atmospheric phenomena

Atmospheric data meet all of the criteria for "big data": they are large (high volume), generated or captured frequently (high velocity), and represent a broad range of data types and sources (high variety). Atmospheric data are often multidimensional, meaning they capture information about the third (altitude or depth) and fourth (time) dimensions. For these reasons, the storage of atmospheric data requires file formats not common to GIS or the conversion of data to more traditional GIS file formats. The chapters in part 1 outline both of these approaches.

Chapter 1 describes three file formats for storing atmospheric data: netCDF (Network Common Data Form), HDF (Hierarchical Data Format), and GRIB (Gridded Binary Form). It also introduces OPeNDAP (Open-source Project for a Network Data Access Protocol), which is a web-based protocol for accessing and subsetting multidimensional data stored remotely. Specific ArcGIS tools for natively reading these file formats are described in detail in part 6.

Chapter 2 describes an alternative approach, storing atmospheric data in a geodatabase. Using meteorological data as the example, this section provides a detailed description of how to organize the geodatabase and how to establish and store the relationships among the data elements. This brief introduction to multidimensional data formats should provide you with sufficient information to understand the datasets referenced in subsequent chapters.

Chapter 3 introduces coordinate systems and how the use of these systems affects coordinate values (positional locations). It continues with a discussion of how weather and climate models classify the shape of the earth and what measures are taken when data are in various coordinate systems.

CHAPTER 1

Multidimensional data in ArcGIS

Steve Kopp and Kevin Butler

The atmosphere is a continuous volume of gas extending over 80 km above the earth's surface (Huddart and Stott 2010). The atmosphere has a near-infinite number of locations where measurements could be taken or values modeled. It is not possible to store this near-infinite number of points in a geographic information system (GIS). The atmosphere is not only volumetric, but also dynamic, changing over time. The infinite atmosphere must be abstracted or modeled by a specific data structure to be represented in a GIS. Storing atmospheric data in a GIS requires three spatial dimensions (x, y, and z) at different time periods. The large amount of observed and modeled atmospheric data (discussed in parts 2 and 3) requires data structures that are efficient in terms of storage requirements and access time. Two major formats have emerged to store large quantities of complex scientific data: netCDF (Network Common Data Form) and HDF (Hierarchical Data Format). Conceptually, netCDF and HDF store the data as multidimensional arrays. Arrays of data are intuitive and enable efficient access to data along different dimensions. For example, using the same dataset, you may want to draw a two-dimensional (2D) map of temperature at a particular altitude and time (figure 1.1) or create a line graph of temperature values through time at a single location for a specific altitude (figure 1.2). In the netCDF or HDF file, the data would be represented as a four-dimensional array: temperature(x, y, altitude, time). To generate the 2D map, a program would access the array by iterating over all of the x and y values but holding the altitude and time indices fixed. To access the data for the graph, a program would iterate over the time values while holding all other indices fixed. The ability to efficiently access the data in different ways is a powerful feature of netCDF and HDF.

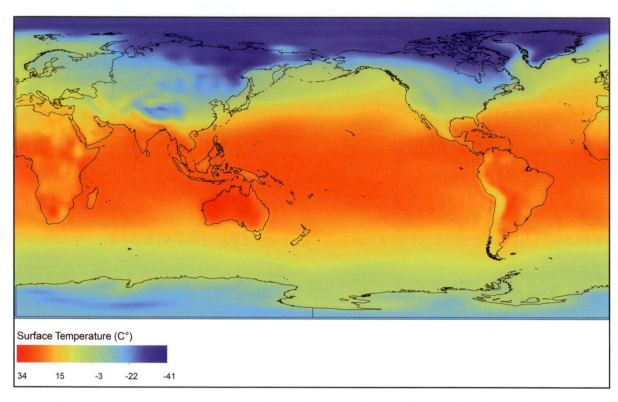

Figure 1.1   Global surface air temperature, 1948. | NCEP reanalysis data provided by NOAA/OAR/ESRL PSD, Boulder, Colorado, USA.

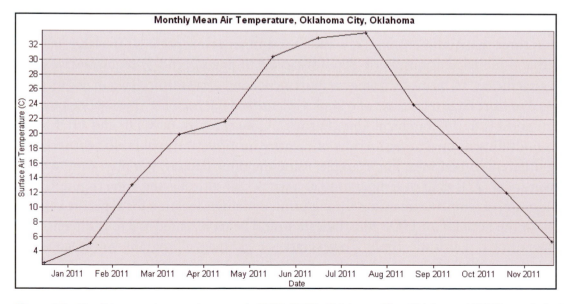

Figure 1.2   Monthly mean temperature graph (2008–2012), Oklahoma City, Oklahoma. | NCEP reanalysis data provided by NOAA/OAR/ESRL PSD, Boulder, Colorado, USA.

The Esri ArcGIS platform provides support for integrating these popular multidimensional data formats into GIS workflows. The tools for accessing netCDF files are described in detail in chapter 20. The next part of this chapter provides background information for three widely used multidimensional file types: netCDF, HDF, and GRIB (Gridded Binary Form). The final section of the chapter provides background on OPeNDAP (Open-source Project for a Network Data Access Protocol), a web-based protocol for accessing multidimensional files.

NetCDF

NetCDF is a multidimensional array–oriented file format widely used in the GIS community. NetCDF has been adopted as a core encoding standard by the Open Geospatial Consortium (OGC). Nearly any type of data can be stored in a netCDF file. The netCDF format is most commonly used in the atmospheric and oceanic sciences. In order to promote sharing and analysis of data among a wide variety of data distributors and consumers, a set of metadata conventions, known as the Climate and Forecast (CF) conventions, were developed for data stored in the netCDF format. One of the major benefits of the netCDF format is that it is self-describing. This means that the netCDF file itself contains metadata information. The CF conventions provide a standard way to describe what each variable represents, its measurement units, and the spatial and temporal properties of the data. Understanding the spatial and temporal properties of the data are prerequisites to integrating the data into a GIS. The CF conventions are an evolving set of guidelines that are revised based on feedback from netCDF users. When netCDF files comply with the CF conventions, it is easier for ArcGIS software to locate the spatial and temporal data in the file and then generate the correct display or animation.

Meteorological observations are collected from numerous stationary observation stations and from moving platforms, such as ships, weather balloons, and satellites. In addition, large volumes of data are produced by numerical weather models for regularly spaced grids at the global scale. These data types can be stored in the netCDF format, but representing them in GIS requires a different approach. All GIS will abstract features or phenomena in the real world into discrete geometries, such as points, lines, polygons, and fields, or continuous fields stored as rasters. To be useful in GIS mapping and analysis workflows, the various types of netCDF data must be represented as one of these "GIS-friendly" data structures. ArcGIS software provides a set of tools to represent atmospheric observations and models as data tables, points, or raster fields. These tools, Make NetCDF Table View, Make NetCDF Feature Layer, and Make NetCDF Raster Layer, read netCDF files and translate their contents into one of the common GIS structures. If the fourth dimension of time is present in the netCDF file, the temporal data are recognized by ArcGIS and can be used to create animations or perform time-series analyses of the data. The GIS format of the data is determined by which tool you select to read the netCDF data and typically depends on the intended form of the visualization or analysis. If the goal is to create a graph for a particular location, the data should be represented as a table in ArcGIS and used as input to the Create Graph Wizard. To use the data as input to a spatial statistics tool, it should be represented in ArcGIS as a set of points (most of the spatial statistics tool require points as input). To use the netCDF data in a hydrology or line-of-sight analysis, the data, if appropriate, should be represented as a raster. One note of caution: In order for the data to be represented as a raster in ArcGIS, it must be regularly tessellated, meaning that the distance between each observation in both the horizontal and vertical directions must be the same. The suite of netCDF tools and examples of their use are described in more detail in chapter 20.

HDF

HDF is a file format widely used in the remote sensing community. Much like netCDF, the majority of the data inside an HDF file is stored as multidimensional arrays. One of the differences between the two formats, not surprisingly, is that HDF supports a hierarchical structure within the file. Data within the HDF file can be organized into groups. Groups can contain one or more datasets. Each of these datasets can contain multidimensional data. There are three different types of HDF files: HDF4, HDF5, and HDF-EOS. Created in the late 1990s, the HDF4 format could not support files larger than 2 gigabytes and lacked support for parallel input and output. HDF5 was created to overcome these limitations as well as to introduce other enhancements. HDF-EOS (Hierarchical Data Format—Earth Observing System) is a special implementation of HDF optimized for the massive data storage requirements of satellite-based remote sensing. HDF-EOS is the standard format used to store data collected from NASA's (National Aeronautics and Space Administration) earth-observing satellites, such as Terra, Aqua, and Aura.

ArcGIS supports reading, visualizing, and analyzing raster data stored in the HDF formats. There are two workflows for processing HDF data in ArcGIS. Recall that many HDF files are hierarchical, meaning they contain many datasets housed in a single file. The first workflow in ArcGIS involves using the Extract Subdataset geoprocessing tool to select and extract the desired data from the HDF file. This tool extracts the raster data from the HDF file and converts it to one of the common GIS raster file formats. The converted raster can be used in any raster-based GIS workflow. The second workflow is more data management oriented. Each NASA satellite produces over a terabyte of information each day. Organizing such large quantities of data can be difficult. One solution is to load the HDF-based satellite data into a mosaic dataset. A mosaic dataset is stored in a geodatabase used to manage a collection of raster datasets. Inside the geodatabase, the mosaic dataset is simply a catalog of rasters. However, when viewed in the ArcMap application of ArcGIS, all of the rasters are dynamically mosaicked to produce a single image (figure 1.3). A mosaic dataset allows you to store, manage, view, and query vast collections of raster data. Mosaic datasets have advanced raster-querying capabilities and processing functions and can also be used as a source for serving image services. Multiple HDF files can be added to a mosaic dataset using the Add Rasters To Mosaic Dataset tool.

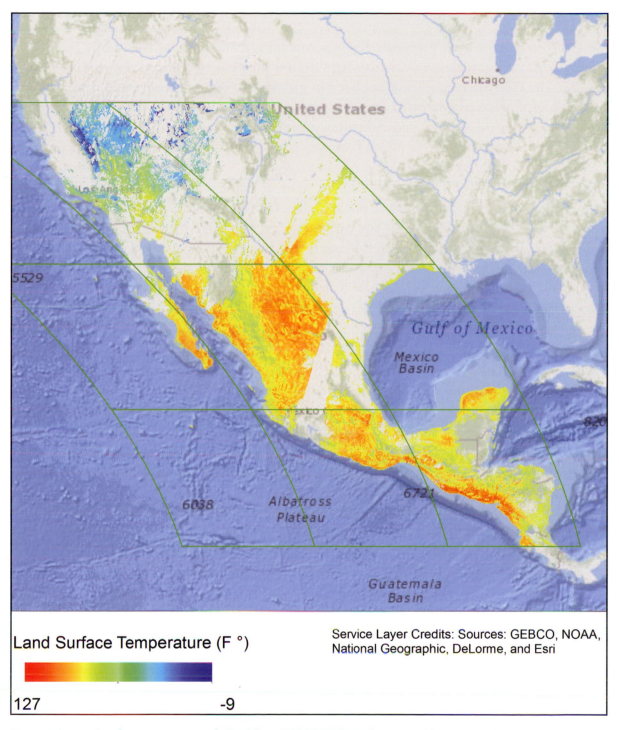

Figure 1.3 Land surface temperature derived from NASA MODIS 11 data stored in a mosaic dataset. | MODIS 11 data product was obtained through the online Data Pool at the NASA Land Processes Distributed Active Archive Center (LP DAAC), US Geological Survey/Earth Resources Observation and Science (EROS) Center, Sioux Falls, South Dakota (https://lpdaac.U.S. Geological Survey.gov/data_access). Ocean basemap sources: Esri, GEBCO, NOAA, National Geographic, DeLorme, HERE, Geonames.org, and other contributors.

GRIB

The GRIB format is used primarily for meteorological data and was created by the World Meteorological Organization (WMO). The GRIB format has two specifications: GRIB1 and GRIB2. The GRIB1 specification has been in use since 1985. As the size and complexity of meteorological datasets increased over the years, weaknesses in the GRIB1 format became apparent. Specifically, GRIB1 had difficulties storing multidimensional and ensemble data. To overcome these weaknesses, the WMO released GRIB2 in 2001. An important data resource available in the GRIB2 format is the National Weather Service's (NWS) National Digital Forecast Database (NDFD). The NDFD is a series of gridded forecasts of weather elements such as cloud cover, temperature, and precipitation. GRIB data are supported in ArcGIS with the same workflows as HDF data. You can use the Extract Subdataset geoprocessing tool to convert the GRIB file to a common GIS raster format, or you can populate a mosaic dataset using the Add Rasters To Mosaic Dataset tool.

The forecasts produced by the NWS in GRIB format are necessarily transient. Users need to reacquire the data when a new forecast is issued. To meet this need, the National Oceanic and Atmospheric Administration (NOAA) created the NOAA Operational Model Archive and Distribution System (NOMADS). NOMADS provides real-time access to the NDFD forecast data through its web service. This web service supports OPeNDAP (described in the next section), which enables direct access of the NDFD data using the OPeNDAP to NetCDF geoprocessing tool.

OPeNDAP

Scientific data have become increasingly abundant and distributed, thus making locating and acquiring current, well-documented, and authoritative sources of data an important component of the scientific process. Even when quality data can be located, they may be in an incompatible format or require extensive time to convert. GRIB1, GRIB2, netCDF, HDF5, NEXRAD, NIDS, DORADE, GINI . . . the list of file formats seems to grow with each new data provider. Coupled with the problem of disparate file formats, atmospheric data are inherently temporal, with model runs or forecasts being generated hourly or daily. The disparate formats, distributed nature, and time-sensitive nature of atmospheric scientific data make traditional data distribution methods untenable. Fortunately, there is an alternative way to acquire data—OPeNDAP. OPeNDAP makes data stored on a remote server accessible to you locally, in the format you need it, regardless of its format on the remote server. Many authoritative data providers, such as NOAA and NASA, provide their data products through OPeNDAP data servers. A large list of OPeNDAP servers and datasets can be found on the OPeNDAP Dataset List web page, http://docs.opendap.org/index.php/Dataset_List. A thematic list of OPeNDAP-enabled datasets is available through NASA's Global Change Master Directory, http://gcmd.gsfc.nasa.gov/KeywordSearch/Home.do?Portal=dods&MetadataType=0.

OPeNDAP is based on a client-server computing model. Software packages that support OPeNDAP make a request for data from the server. The server processes the request and reads the data in its native format and then sends a DAP (Data Access Protocol) representation of the data back to the OPeNDAP-aware client (figure 1.4). It is the client's responsibility to interpret the DAP representation and either display it or convert it to another format. Datasets can be very large, even global, with long time series, so a key value of the OPeNDAP approach is the ability to pull subsets of data from the server, to only get the data you really need.

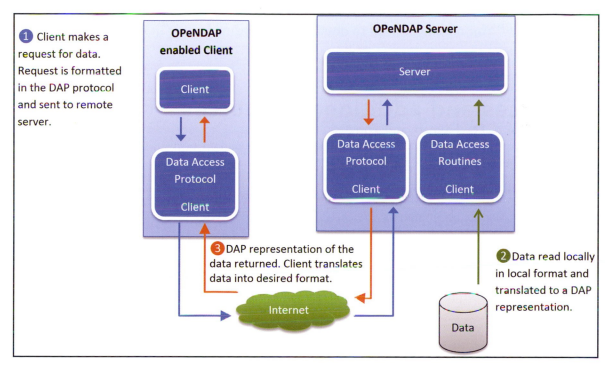

Figure 1.4 Conceptual diagram of OPeNDAP data access.

ArcGIS provides support for OPeNDAP through two geoprocessing tools available in the Multidimension Supplemental toolbox. This toolbox is available for download from the ArcGIS Resources website, http://resources.arcgis.com. The first tool, Describe Multidimensional Dataset, is used to explore the metadata contained within a scientific dataset. Multidimensional datasets are often self-describing, meaning that descriptions of the data, such as measurement units and the data range, are contained in the same file as the data. This tool examines a multidimensional file and displays information about the dimensions and variables the file contains. The file can be a local file on disk or a remote file located on an OPeNDAP server. The tool displays the metadata on the screen and optionally writes it to a text file. Having access to the metadata is crucial to working with scientific datasets stored in a multidimensional format. For example, examining the metadata output from the Describe Multidimensional Dataset tool when run against a dataset from the National Centers for Environmental Prediction Reanalysis project shows that the air temperature variable was modeled at sigma level 995 and recorded on the Kelvin temperature scale.

The second OPeNDAP-enabled tool in ArcGIS is OPeNDAP to NetCDF. This tool will create a subset of the data and download it from web-based servers that support OPeNDAP and save it locally as a netCDF file. You can constrain the data downloaded by specifying specific variables, a spatial extent, and starting and ending values of the dimensions that define a variable. This tool allows you to access data stored on a remote server as part of a geoprocessing workflow. You no longer need to download the entire dataset in order to work with a small subset.

References and additional resources

"CF Metadata. NetCDF Climate and Forecast (CF) Metadata Conventions." Accessed August 13, 2013. http://cf-pcmdi.llnl.gov/documents/cf-conventions/1.6/cf-conventions.html.

Huddart, David, and Tim Stott. 2010. *Earth Environments: Past, Present, and Future.* Chichester, West Sussex: John Wiley & Sons.

OPeNDAP. "What Is OPeNDAP?" Accessed August 13, 2013. http://www.opendap.org.

The HDF Group. "What Is HDF5?" Accessed August 13, 2013. http://www.hdfgroup.org/HDF5/whatishdf5.html.

Unidata. "Network Common Data Form (NetCDF)." Accessed August 13, 2013. http://www.unidata.ucar.edu/software/netcdf/.

CHAPTER 2

Meteorological data in a geodatabase

Jennifer Boehnert and Olga Wilhelmi

With the release of ArcGIS 9.2 software in 2006, Esri included support for Network Common Data Form (netCDF), a common atmospheric and true multidimensional data format, to better support the use of atmospheric and other earth-systems data in a geographic information system (GIS). One can think of multidimensional data as being stored as a data cube (3D, or time varying) or hypercube (4D, or time and altitude varying). In the atmospheric sciences most parameters vary along space and time axes as well as along the traditional x and y axes. Climate model output and weather model results are just two examples of data normally stored in netCDF. Prior to the release of ArcGIS 9, the integration of atmospheric data and GIS data required stand-alone converters, because atmospheric data formats were incompatible with GIS applications.

In 2003, prior to ArcGIS's ability to read netCDF, the GIS Program at the National Center for Atmospheric Research (NCAR) conducted a pilot project to develop a meteorological data model that could serve as features and tables in an Esri geodatabase. Observational meteorological data collected during the International H2O Project (IHOP) field campaign, which took place over the southern Great Plains of the United States in the spring of 2002, was used as a use case for this pilot project. Data were collected from a number of instruments, stored in numerous data formats, and contained many parameters. Most of the data types were 4D, as they varied in x (longitude), y (latitude), t (time), and z (height or pressure level). One of the project outcomes was a data model that organized the data into related sets of tables and features. This data model is called the *IHOP Data Model*.

Database design

Put simply, a data model is a diagram that describes how data can be used and represented effectively. Creating a data model is the first step in database design. Data modeling helps to identify the end user and the system requirements of the database (Goodchild 1992). Each step of developing a data model moves from the more generalized, abstract view of the database to a more detailed data model. This process is not a linear but an iterative process. At any point during the process you can go back and add objects and relationships that become apparent (Date 1995).

Conceptual data model

The first step in building a data model is the development of a *conceptual data model*. A conceptual data model describes the primary objects and their relationships to one another in the database. The conceptual data model is sometimes called the *domain data model* because it is a very high-level identification of domain-specific data structures. It is an important first step because it ensures that all objects are identified. During this phase of data modeling domain-specific terminology is also considered. For example, in the IHOP Data Model the model is a template of future observational meteorological campaigns to follow if you want to load your data into a geodatabase. It was important to identify all aspects of these campaigns and use terminology that was understandable for meteorologists and nonmeteorologists alike.

Logical data model

The *logical data model* is based on the conceptual data model. Each object and relationship is more fully developed in the logical data model without consideration of how it will be implemented in the database. This model should be easily read and understood by domain experts and nonexperts. All attributes are identified, and keys to link objects to one another are specified in this phase of the data model. At this point, it is more important that the data model represents all aspects of the data and the interactions between the data and less important how it looks in the database.

Physical data model

The *physical data model* is derived from the logical data model and describes how the data will be represented in the database. In this phase of data modeling, abbreviations and codes that meet database standards for object and field names are used. Normalization of the objects may occur to better meet the user's requirements. Normalizing a data model refers to the process of organizing tables and fields in order to reduce redundancy. Relationships between objects are well developed using primary and foreign keys. The physical data model will be the database design's implementation, so it must meet all user requirements and database rules.

UML components

Data models are commonly communicated using UML (Unified Modeling Language). UML is a graphical notation used to describe database objects and relationships. The use of design tools, such as Rational Rose and Microsoft Visio, allows for convenient coupling of the UML design language with the underlying data representation. Thus, changes to the UML data model can be easily propagated to the affected data structures, for example, RDBMS (relational database management system) tables or Java classes. Microsoft Visio (Enterprise Edition) was the first component of the CASE (Computer Aided Software Engineering) tool used for developing the IHOP Data Model. Esri provides an extension to Microsoft Visio that makes it possible to design not only a database, but an Esri geodatabase. This extension provides core Esri objects such as Esri Class: Feature, which becomes a feature class in a geodatabase, and Esri Class: Object, which becomes a nonspatial table in a geodatabase (figure 2.1). In order to implement the completed UML physical data model as a geodatabase, Esri developed a Visio add-on called *Esri XMI Export*. This add-on exports the UML data model to an XMI (XML Metadata Interchange) file, which can then be loaded into a geodatabase using the Geodatabase Schema Wizard tool found in the ArcGIS ArcCatalog application.

A *class* is the core element in the data model. It is represented as a rectangle in UML notation. The top compartment of the class is the *class name*, and the middle part of the class is where the attributes are defined. Two types of classes are used in the IHOP Data Model: an abstract class and a concrete class. An abstract class will not become an object in the database. Its purpose is to hold common attributes that multiple classes will share. A concrete class becomes a nonspatial table or a feature class in the geodatabase.

Inheritance and *association* are two important concepts in UML models. Inheritance refers to the ability of one class to inherit the identical attributes and functionalities from a parent class. Parent classes can be abstract classes or concrete classes. Associations represent the relationship between classes and become relationship classes in a geodatabase. This relationship class has a direction and multiplicity value at both ends of the association.

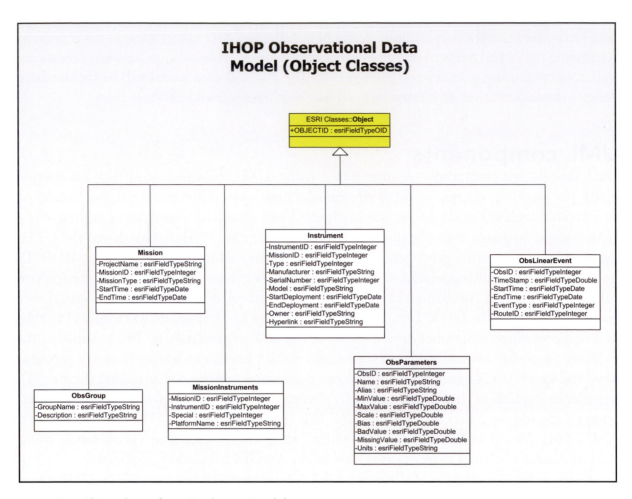

Figure 2.1   Object classes for IHOP observational data.

IHOP Data Model

The IHOP 2002 datasets included upper air observations (radiosondes and dropsondes), surface observations from Integrated Surface Flux Facility (ISFF) stations, aircraft observations from the Wyoming King Air and Lear, and radar reflectivity mosaics. The IHOP Data Model that was developed categorized the previously described datasets into standard geodatabase objects such as feature classes (e.g., points, lines, polygons), rasters, and nonspatial tables. All of the features inherit from the standard class that comes with the Esri add-on to Visio, Esri Class: FEATURE. This class ensures that all the feature classes have a Shape field, which defines their geometry type.

All of the geodatabase feature classes are shown in figure 2.2.

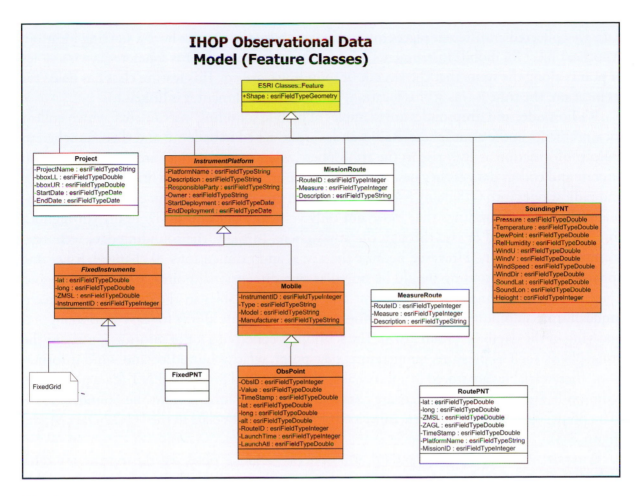

Figure 2.2 IHOP Observational Data Model.

Feature points

The feature points were categorized into two distinct groups: fixed instruments (data point) and mobile instruments (data point). Fixed instruments are observations that do not move over time. Mobile instruments are instruments that move vertically or horizontally over time as they collect data.

Mobile instruments

InstrumentPlatform is an abstract class that models fields about the instrument name, the responsible party, and the owner of the instrument. All mobile and fixed instruments inherit from this class. The Mobile abstract class models fields to describe the type of mobile instrument, the instrument's manufacturer, and the model number of the instrument. The Mobile abstract class inherits its fields from InstrumentPlatform. ObsPoint is an abstract class that holds field definitions about when the instrument was launched. Even though the mobile data are collected at different places in space, all mobile instruments have a starting location. Another object for mobile instruments is RoutePNT (data point). This concrete class is a series of points along the route that the aircraft or sounding traveled. This feature class has fields for its location, the time it was at this location, and which instrument it is linked to.

Radiosondes and dropsondes are examples of mobile sounding instruments, which collect measurements in the atmosphere. Radiosondes are attached to balloons and then launched to collect information as they rise in the atmosphere, whereas dropsondes are dropped from an aircraft and collect data as they descend through the atmosphere. When bringing dropsondes and radiosondes into GIS many issues arise, but perhaps the most fundamental is how to represent data from soundings that move not only vertically but also horizontally throughout time as they descend or rise through the atmosphere. Initially, the sounding data were represented as line events. However, because the x, y, z, and t dimensions all changed, it became apparent that the sounding should be stored as two-dimensional points, where latitude and longitude are the dimensions and height and time are variables in the database. This technique of time-stamping objects and storing time as an attribute allows for easy spatiotemporal querying of the database (Yuan 2013). The soundings collected a lot of information about the atmosphere, such as pressure, temperature, dew point, relative humidity, and wind information. These variables are stored in another abstract class called SoundingPNT (data point). All radiosonde and dropsonde objects are concrete classes that inherit from the SoundingPNT (data point) object, which, in turn, inherits from the ObsPoint class in the IHOP Data Model (figure 2.3).

Aircraft observations are standard atmospheric variables observed during the aircraft's flight. The data received have information such as latitude, longitude, height, time, and variable values. The data could be represented as a continuous line (linear event) or as a series of points. In the IHOP Data Model, the aircraft observations were represented as a series of points, with time, height, latitude, and longitude as variables. Height was added as a variable, but was not used as a means of querying the data. Therefore, only latitude, longitude, and time were used to query and render the data. The aircraft flights, such as Lear (data point) and King Air (data point) are concrete classes that became feature classes in the IHOP geodatabase. These classes inherit fields from ObsPoint (figure 2.4) for the launch information and inherit atmospheric fields such as NDV, H20MX, and Heiman_Raw from an abstract class called Aircraft.

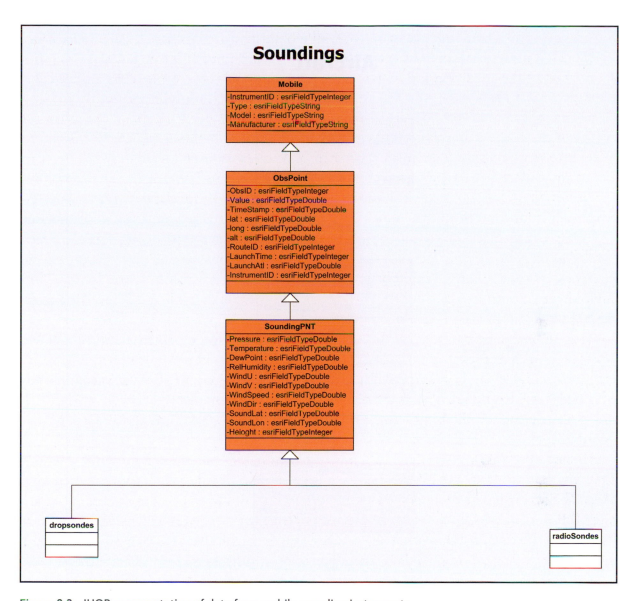

Figure 2.3 IHOP representation of data from mobile sounding instruments.

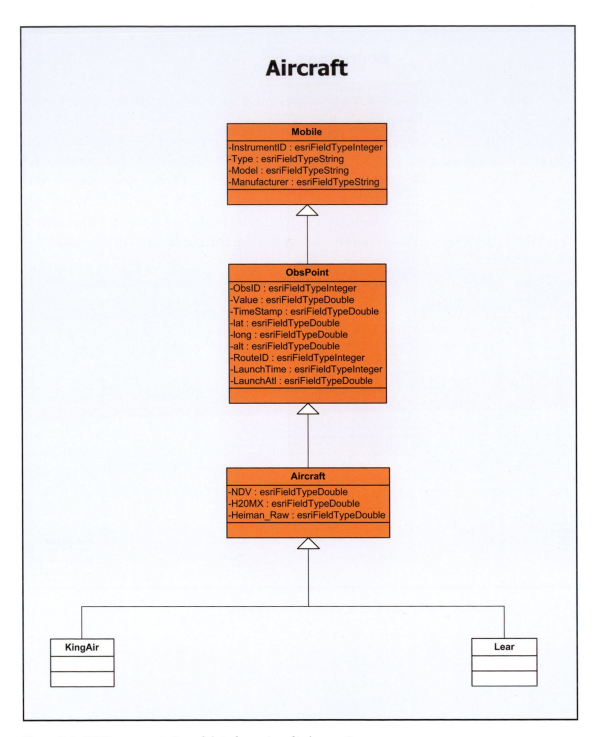

Figure 2.4   IHOP representation of data from aircraft observations.

Fixed instruments

ISFF is designed to study processes between the atmosphere and the earth's surface. The ISFF stations collect information such as fluxes, sensible and latent heat, and standard atmospheric variables. ISFF data were a little easier to represent in GIS because they do not move vertically or horizontally over time. ISFF observations were represented in the IHOP Data Model as point feature fixed instruments (figure 2.5). There are seven ISFF stations, all collecting the same information located at different fixed sites. ISFF is also an abstract class that holds the attributes of time, temperature, and precipitation flux. All seven ISFF instruments inherit these three attributes. The ISFF abstract class inherits from FixedInstrument to get the fields for the location of the instrument, which inherits fields from InstrumentPlatform. ISFF1 through ISFF7 are concrete classes that become point feature classes in the geodatabase.

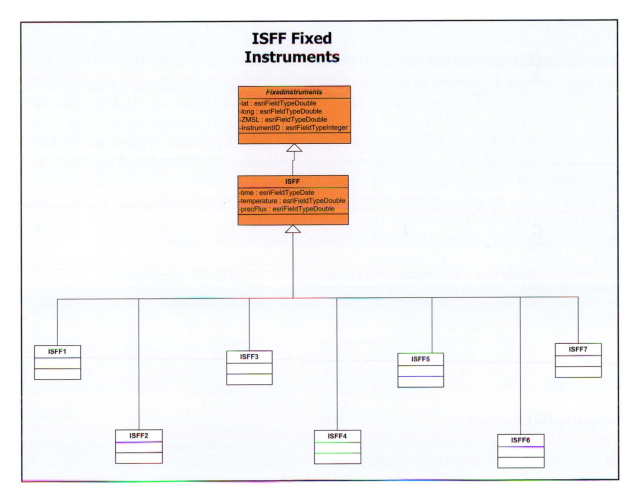

Figure 2.5   IHOP representation of data from fixed instruments.

Feature lines

Two line feature classes that are modeled in the IHOP Data Model are MissionRoute and MeasureRoute. MissionRoute is the original route plan for the aircraft before it takes off. MeasureRoute (line event) is the route the aircraft actually took based on weather. The MeasureRoute (line event) feature class would follow the classes KingAir and Lear exactly. These lines do not hold any information about the observations collected. Both of these feature classes have fields for the length of the route and a description of the route.

Feature polygons

The Project feature class is our only polygon class. This class holds bounding box information about the project domain. This class is used mostly to orient oneself in the project domain.

Rasters

Radar reflectivity mosaics were brought into GIS as gridded data. The radar mosaics are continuous data collections over the surface. These data were represented in the IHOP Data Model as a raster catalog. By storing all the radars in a raster catalog, the radars were able to take on many of the aspects of a time series for query, rendering, and animating the data. This technique is known as the *snapshot model*, where every layer shows the state of the object at a given time (Yuan 2013). Esri's UML data modeling design does not provide support for modeling raster data. Therefore, we put a placeholder in the UML model as a note called FixedGrid and manually added the raster catalog to the geodatabase.

Table 2.1 is a summary of the different data types, how they were represented, and their dimensions. This table demonstrates that, at the time of this project, point feature classes were the easiest and most effective data type for working with multidimensional data.

Table 2.1   Example data types stored in the IHOP data model

Data types	Representations	Dimensions
Radar mosaic	Gridded data (BSQ)	X : Y
Upper air (radiosondes and dropsondes)	Point feature class in a geodatabase	X : Y : TIME : HEIGHT
Aircraft observations	Point feature class in a geodatabase	X : Y : TIME
ISFF stations	Point feature class in a geodatabase	X : Y : TIME

Nonspatial tables

All nonspatial tables inherit from Esri Class: Object. This standard class provides the attribute ObjectID, which is essential for an object class in a geodatabase. We have six object classes in the IHOP Data Model. ObsGroup is an object that holds information about the group name and a description of the group. Every project can have one or more groups participating in the project. The Mission object class has information about the mission and when it started and ended. During a project, many missions collect data, such as an aircraft flight or a dropsonde launch. MissionInstrument is a class that describes which instruments were involved with the particular mission. Instrument is a class that describes the instruments in detail. For a particular dropsonde, information about its serial number, model, type, owner, and when it was deployed is stored. All of this information is important when linking the instrument to the data it collects. ObsParameters is a class that holds the information that summarizes each mission. For example, it has fields to hold information about the minimum and maximum values, scale, bias, bad values, and missing values for all missions.

Relationships

Relationships are called *associations* in UML notation. These associations represent connectivity between objects and become relationship classes in the geodatabase. All associations are linked through a common field. Figure 2.6 contains all the associations in the IHOP Data Model. For example, we can see that a project will have one or more missions, and the two classes are linked through the field ProjectName. Every mission will have many instruments involved, and these two classes are linked through the field InstrumentID. Every mission will also have many RoutePNT measurements, and they are linked through the field MissionID. Every instrument is also associated with all FixedInstruments and all ObsPoint values. This relationship ensures that all data collected can be linked back to the instrument that collected it.

Another set of associations occurs among ObsPoint and ObsLinearEvent with ObsParameter and MeasureRoute. A MeasureRoute will have many ObsPoint and ObsLinearEvent relationships. Every MeasureRoute is the path of a mobile instrument. Each route will be made up of one or more ObsLinearEvents (line events) and one or more ObsPoints (data points). These three tables are linked through the common field of RouteID. Also, ObsParameters will have many ObsLinearEvents and ObsPoint relationships. Because the ObsParameter class holds information about the summary of the data collected, such as minimum and maximum values, bad values, and mission data, every ObsPoint (data point) collected and ObsLinearEvent (line event) will be associated with an ObsParameter. These three tables are linked through the common field of ObsID.

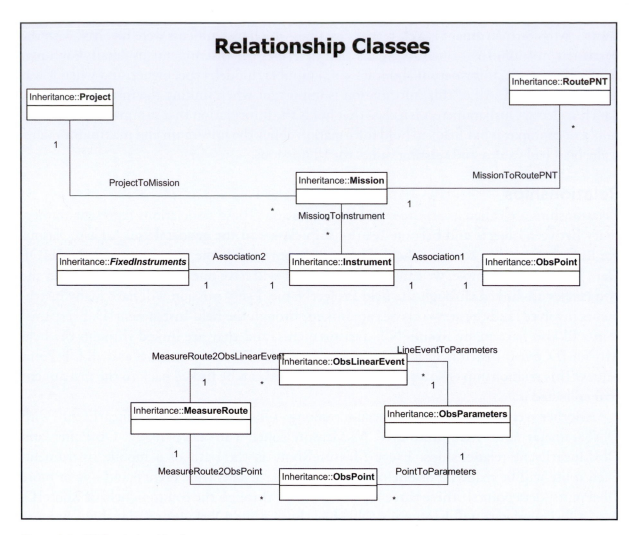

Figure 2.6   IHOP relationship classes.

Conclusion

In the years since this pilot project was conducted much progress has been made in the integration of atmospheric science data types and GIS. The ability of ArcGIS to read netCDF files has greatly facilitated interdisciplinary work across the domains. This pilot project, however, took a different approach to interoperability. Because many of these meteorological data formats were not netCDF, stand-alone converters are still needed to integrate these data types into ArcGIS. The IHOP Data Model is an instrument in the communication and understanding of the data across disciplines. Projects such as Community and Capacity Building (http://gis.ucar.edu/projects) give us a better understanding of the differences and similarities among the data types used in the atmospheric sciences and offer solutions on how to store multidimensional data in a geodatabase.

References and additional resources

Date, C. J. 1995. *An Introduction to Database Systems*. 6th ed. Reading, PA: Addison-Wesley Publishing.

Goodchild, Michael. 1992. "Geographical Data Modeling." *Computers & Geosciences* 18 (4): 401–8.

Henson, Bob. 2002. "Where's the Water Vapor? IHOP2002 Is on a Mission to Find Out." *UCAR Quarterly* Spring. Accessed August 14, 2013. http://www.ucar.edu/communications/quarterly/spring02/ihop.html.

Yuan, May. 2013. "Temporal GIS and Spatio-Temporal Modeling." National Center for Geographic Information and Analysis. Accessed August 14, 2013. http://www.ncgia.ucsb.edu/conf/SANTA_FE_CD-ROM/sf_papers/yuan_may/may.html.

CHAPTER 3

The shape of the earth: Spatial referencing in weather and climate models

Jennifer Boehnert, Andrew Monaghan, and Olga Wilhelmi

The use of weather and climate models for local-scale, high-resolution research and geographic information system (GIS) applications is increasing. These high-resolution modeling efforts rely on inputs from terrestrial and meteorological datasets, which often use different spatial reference systems. In this chapter, we introduce the concepts behind coordinate systems in terrestrial and atmospheric datasets and show GIS users how to work with inputs to and outputs from atmospheric models.

Coordinate systems and datums

Spatial data identify the geographic location of the features on the earth and can be stored digitally. Features such as roads, city boundaries, and land-use types are all examples of spatial data. Spatial data can be mapped because they are based on a coordinate system, which is a reference system for identifying and representing the locations of geographic features.

Many different coordinate systems exist, and all of them are based on an assumed shape of the earth. In reality, the earth is not a true sphere, although for simplicity it is often treated as one. Rather, the earth is an ellipsoid, which is a sphere that has been flattened, causing the equator to bulge outwards (Kennedy 1999). If the assumed shape of the earth is an ellipsoid, specifically a spheroid, the equatorial and the polar radius will be slightly different. If the assumed shape of the earth is a sphere, the equatorial and the polar radius will be equal. Figure 3.1 illustrates the difference between a spheroid and a sphere.

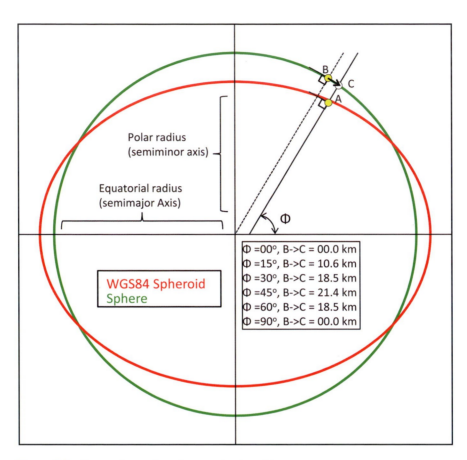

Figure 3.1 Comparison of a sphere and spheroid.

In GIS terminology, the term *datum* refers to how the spheroid is positioned relative to the center of the earth (Kennedy 1999). The shape of the earth acts as a reference for calculating geographic locations of the features on the earth's surface. Commonly used datums include North American Datum 1983 (NAD83) and World Geodetic System of 1984 (WGS84), each providing a slightly different spatial reference to the shape of the earth. Different reference points result in different angles, and ultimately different estimations of latitude and longitude.

The reference shape of the earth is important because coordinate values (i.e., positional locations) are measurements in degrees of latitude and longitude calculated from the center of the earth. These measurements vary for a given feature, such as a building or mountain, based on the assumed shape. Lines of latitude run from east to west. The equator is the line of latitude at the middle of the earth that is of equal distance from the North Pole and the South Pole. The equator is given the value of 0 degrees latitude and is the starting point from which all other lines of latitude are measured (Kennedy 1999). Lines of longitude run from north to south and are called meridians. The prime meridian runs through Greenwich, England, and is given the value of 0 degrees longitude. All other lines of longitude are angular distances that run east or west from the prime meridian. Figure 3.2 illustrates the lines of latitude and longitude on the earth's surface.

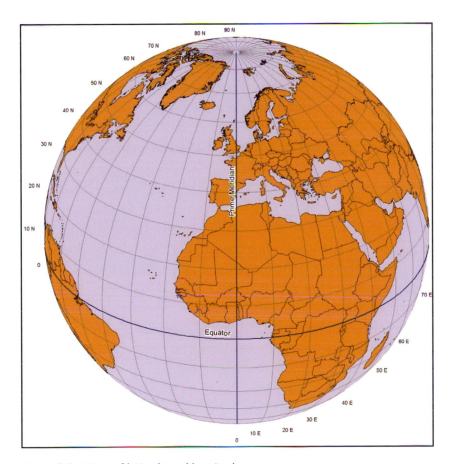

Figure 3.2   Lines of latitude and longitude.

The geographic coordinate system (GCS) and the projected coordinate system (PCS) are two common types of coordinate systems. In a GCS, features are positioned using latitude and longitude locations based on a particular mathematical three-dimensional model of the earth's shape (datum). By contrast, a PCS is a flat, two-dimensional surface on which features are located. The advantage of a PCS is that, depending on the projection, at least one aspect—shape, area, distance, or direction—is consistent across the surface. This is not the case with a GCS. All PCSs are based on a GCS and its underlying datum (reference shape).

How weather and climate models treat the shape of the earth

Atmospheric models that simulate meteorological processes on a variety of time and space scales, such as numerical weather prediction models and global climate models, assume the earth to be a perfect sphere; however, most spatial data used in GIS tools assume the earth to be a spheroid. This difference in the assumed shape of the earth may be imperceptible to GIS users who employ relatively coarse-resolution atmospheric model data in their applications, such as output from global models; however, it may affect GIS users who employ fine-resolution atmospheric model data, such as limited-area atmospheric models (LAMs), in their work. Over the past decade, LAM simulations have been moving toward finer spatial resolution (e.g., Im et al. 2010; Rasmussen et al. 2011; Monaghan et al. 2012), and 1–10 km resolution is currently common. To enhance the fidelity of simulations, users input spatial data representing land cover and elevation (e.g., Chen et al. 2011) and point weather observations from meteorological stations (Hahmann et al. 2010) into LAMs. These datasets can be regional or global and use a number of different coordinate systems in order to preserve properties such as area, shape, distance, and direction (Bugayevskiy and Snyder 1995). Although many of these datasets are based on spheroidal earth models, most LAMs assume the earth's surface is a perfect sphere in order to simplify calculations. Model users should be aware of possible discrepancies resulting from these different assumptions about the earth's surface in LAMs and geographic data. If users do not account for these differences by transforming the data from spheroidal to spherical coordinates, the positional accuracy may be affected, with positional errors of up to 21 km at midlatitudes. In the past, when computational limitations necessitated LAM simulations with coarser spatial resolution (e.g., greater than 25 km), earth model differences among input geographic data to LAMs could often be neglected, and were, because the impact on simulations was assumed to be minor compared to other sources of uncertainty, such as physical parameterizations. At the 1–10 km spatial scales, now typical of LAM simulations, neglecting these differences may lead to significant geolocation discrepancies among input datasets that affect the fidelity of simulations, users who require accurately mapped LAM output to drive other geophysical models, or those using the datasets in GIS applications.

The effect of earth-shape assumptions on LAM simulations

Monaghan et al. (2013) at the National Center for Atmospheric Research (NCAR) conducted a modeling experiment that demonstrates the effect of differences in assumed earth shape on positional accuracy. The experiment explored the effect of using geographic data based on a spheroidal earth shape in a LAM simulation using a spherical earth shape without the necessary transformation. Sensitivity analysis was performed to estimate positional error. The LAM simulations were performed with version 3.3 of the Advanced Research Weather Research and Forecasting (WRF) model (Skamarock and Klemp 2008) and the accompanying WRF Preprocessing System (WPS) (WRF Development Team 2011). The WPS software contains programs that prepare terrestrial data, such as topography and land use, and meteorological data for input to WRF. Of particular interest is how the input geographic data are defined and interpolated to the model domains.

The model simulations were performed for a 1 km spatial resolution model domain over a mountainous region in central Colorado (figure 3.3). This region was chosen for its large elevation gradients and diverse land-use patterns, both being integral to the model experiments. LAMs first require an accurate estimate of the weather conditions at the beginning of each simulation, which is obtained from the output of other atmospheric models that were run previously on coarser resolution, larger domains. For this experiment, the initial weather conditions for WRF were derived from the 32 km North American Regional Reanalysis (NARR; Mesinger et al. 2006). The NARR simulations were performed on a spherical earth; however, the input geographic data, such as topography and land use, in NARR are based on a spheroidal earth, the WGS84 ellipsoid in particular. The experiments described here, performed for a 12-hour daytime period from 1200 UTC 04 July 2009 through 0000 UTC 05 July 2009, were chosen because topography and land use play an important role in determining the summer daytime weather (e.g., Lu et al. 2012), thereby facilitating a comparison of topographic and land-use effects on simulations.

The WPS program that prepares input datasets for use in WRF currently recognizes geographic coordinate systems (i.e., latitude-longitude), as well as three projected coordinate systems for input terrestrial datasets: Lambert conformal, Mercator, and polar stereographic. When an input geographic dataset (e.g., topography, land use) is projected from its native coordinate system to the chosen WRF coordinate system, the program assumes that all coordinates lie on a perfect sphere. Therefore, a reprojection is done, but no earth-shape translation is performed. For the simulations described herein, all input datasets were based on WGS84 datum, and the WRF domain onto which they were projected and interpolated was a Lambert conformal projection.

Three experiments were performed, each only differing by the type and mapping assumptions used for the input geographic data (i.e., topography and land use). The first simulation ("CONTROL") employed the default 30-arc second (~1 km) US Geological Survey (USGS) topography (GTOPO30; Gesch and Greenlee 1996) and land-use categories (24 types; Anderson et al. 1976) that are standard when using WRF. These data are based on the WGS84 GCS, whose spheroidal earth model has a semimajor (equatorial) axis radius of 6,378,137 m; however, WRF assumes that they use a spherical earth model with a radius of 6,370,000 m. The second simulation ("NEW") employed two geographic datasets not available in WPS

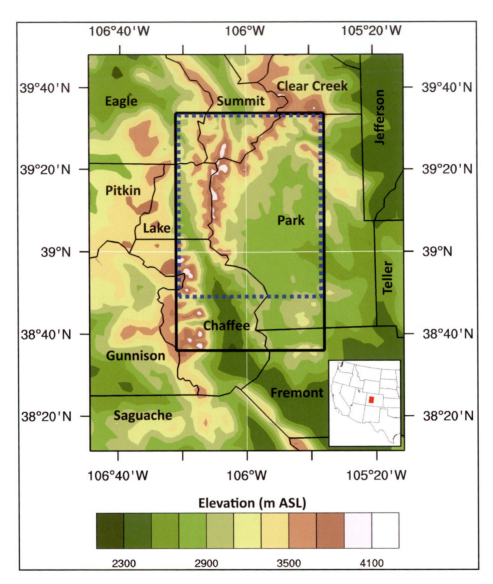

Figure 3.3 **Study area for the impact assessment of earth-shape assumptions on LAM simulations.** | Data courtesy of the National Centers for Environmental Prediction (NCEP).

version 3.3: the 3-arc second (~90 m) National Geospatial-Intelligence Agency (NGA)/ National Aeronautics and Space Administration (NASA) Shuttle Radar Topography Mission (SRTM) version 2.1 dataset (Farr et al. 2007, http://dds.cr.usgs.gov/srtm/) for topography, and the 3-arc second USGS National Land Cover Database (NLCD) 2006 dataset (Fry et al. 2011, http://www.mrlc.gov/nlcd06_data.php) for land use. The NLCD categories (33 total) were recategorized to the USGS 24-category system for consistency with the land-use categories in the CONTROL simulation. No translation from WGS84 to a sphere was performed on the SRTM and NLCD. The third simulation ("NEW_SHIFT") was the same as the NEW simulation, except that a transformation (following Hedgley 1976) from the WGS84 spheroid to the default WRF sphere was applied to the SRTM and NLCD before projecting them in WRF. This transformation effectively validates the assumption of a spherical GCS, so that the latitudinal data for NEW_SHIFT were subsequently mapped "correctly" onto the spherical earth in the model.

Figures 3.4 and 3.5 present the topographic and land-use fields, and their differences, for the three cases. The geolocation of the topography and land use are the same for the CONTROL and NEW cases because the native data for both used the WGS84 spheroid as their earth model, but it was assumed the data were based on a sphere when they were ingested and remapped to the WRF domain. Differences between the CONTROL and NEW datasets (figures 3.4d and 3.5d) are due to variation among their source datasets. Although the differences in topography tend to be subtle (less than +/− 25 m over most of the domain), the differences among the land-use datasets are noticeable. Urban areas are better defined in the NLCD land-use data employed for the NEW case, as are the treeless mountainous areas lying above ~3,700 m: these are correctly categorized as "barren/sparsely vegetated" in NEW, versus "mixed forest" in CONTROL.

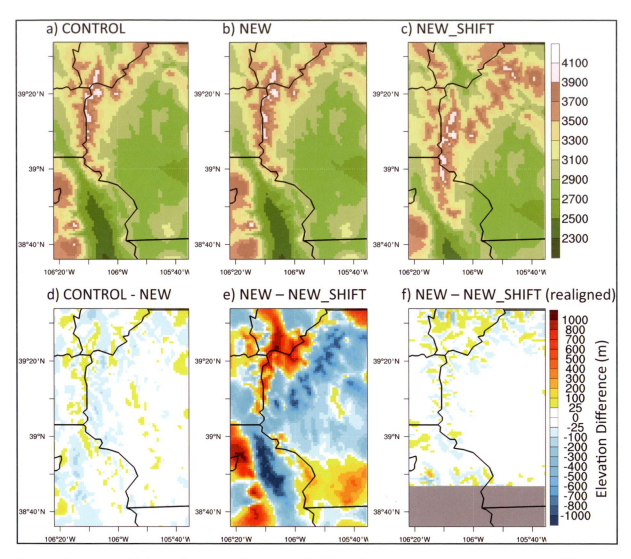

Figure 3.4   Topographic inputs for the CONTROL (a), NEW (b), and NEW_SHIFT (c) simulations and their differences (d–f). | Data courtesy of NASA and US Geological Survey.

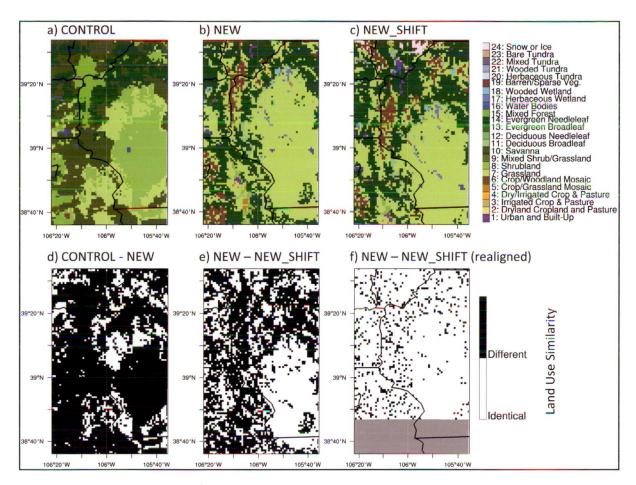

Figure 3.5 Land use inputs for the CONTROL (a), NEW (b), and NEW_SHIFT (c) simulations and their differences (d–f). | Data courtesy of US Geological Survey.

The topography and land use for the NEW_SHIFT case (figures 3.4c and 3.5c) are located about 20 km to the south compared to CONTROL and NEW because the data were transformed from WGS84 to the sphere *before* they were ingested and remapped to the WRF domains. As expected from the ~20 km shift, the differences between the topography and land use in NEW versus NEW_SHIFT are large (figures 3.4e and 3.5e). Note that interpolation techniques led to subtle differences between the NEW and NEW_SHIFT topography and land-use fields when mapped onto the WRF domain, despite being from the same input dataset, because the earth model shift (20.88 km at 39° N) was not exactly proportional to the 1.00 km WRF grid spacing. These subtle interpolation differences are apparent in figures 3.4f and 3.5f, in which the difference between the topography and land use in NEW and NEW_SHIFT is shown *after* realigning NEW_SHIFT 20 grid boxes (i.e., 20 km) to the north, which is the grid increment for which NEW and NEW_SHIFT best correspond when realigned. The "realigned" NEW_SHIFT data facilitates interpreting the causality for differences among the simulations, as discussed in the following.

Figure 3.6 presents the results for 2 m temperature 10 hours into the simulations, at 2200 UTC 04 July 2009 (1600 local standard time [LST]). The differences between CONTROL and NEW (figure 3.6d) are generally within +/– 1°C, suggesting a modest impact on simulations due to differences between the source datasets. The differences between NEW and NEW_SHIFT (figure 3.6e) are substantially larger due to the ~20 km shift in topography, indicating that the manner in which the earth models of geographic input data are treated has first-order impacts on high-resolution simulations. If the NEW_SHIFT data are realigned to correspond with the NEW data (figure 3.6f), the differences due to shifting the topography by 20 km (figure 3.6e) are largely removed, isolating the other shift-related differences among the simulations caused by (1) the differential positioning of topographic/land-use fields with respect to the NARR boundary conditions (which do not shift), (2) subtle topographic/land-use interpolation differences (figures 3.4f and 3.5f), and (3) latitude-dependent physics (i.e., the Coriolis forcing and map factors that appear in the LAM's momentum equations; this effect is likely comparatively minor). The collective impact of these influences is comparable to that of using different terrestrial input datasets (figure 3.6d). These results are robust across other model fields (e.g., humidity, wind speed) (Monaghan et al. 2013). Therefore, even if LAM output is "correctly" remapped during post-processing, important localized impacts on the simulations due to the three factors previously noted still exist and cannot be rectified.

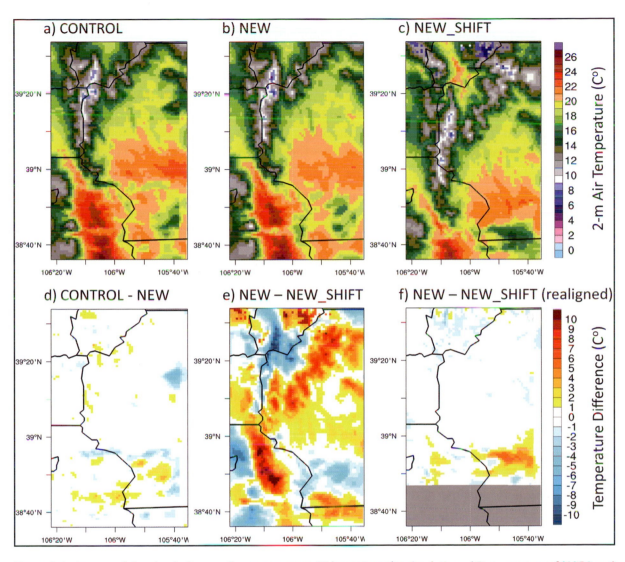

Figure 3.6 Impact of the simulations on 2 m temperature 10 hours into the simulations. | Data courtesy of NASA and US Geological Survey.

Summary and recommendations

The way earth models are treated when mapping geographic datasets to high-resolution atmospheric model domains has important effects on simulated meteorological fields. Even if atmospheric model output is "corrected" during post-processing, as it usually is, residual differences of shifting versus not shifting the coordinates are similar to those due to implementing an alternative geographic dataset. These results suggest that atmospheric modelers should minimally ensure that geographic and meteorological input data are *consistently* mapped before running their simulations (i.e., that all input data have the same earth model). The results also suggest that the atmospheric modeling community should work toward a long-term solution by ensuring that input datasets are *correctly* mapped in future versions of atmospheric models, given that simulations are now using higher resolution spatial data and can be greatly affected by geolocation discrepancies.

What do these results mean for GIS users? When working with atmospheric model input or output, particularly that for or from high-resolution models such as LAMs, GIS users should be careful in the following two situations.

Input: If atmospheric modelers ask GIS users to provide specialized land-use or other datasets, the GIS user should discuss the shape of the earth model of both the atmospheric model and the input data with the atmospheric modeler beforehand. What type of earth model does the atmospheric model assume when ingesting and projecting input geographic data? Does the atmospheric model perform transformations to spheroidal-based input data before projecting it to the (likely sphere-based) model domain? If so, the GIS user will not need to perform any coordinate transformation before passing the spatial data to the atmospheric modeler, and need only provide relevant information (datum, etc.) about the GCS or PCS on which the geographic input data are mapped. If not (this is the more likely case), the GIS user should ask the modeler which GCS or PCS he or she would like the data to be on. Given that the overwhelming majority of input geographic datasets for atmospheric models are mapped on WGS84 spheroids, a safe assumption is to provide the data to the atmospheric modeler in a GCS based on a WGS84 spheroid. This will likely ensure that all of the input datasets are consistently mapped; that is, even if they are geolocated incorrectly to the sphere, all features will at least be located consistently with respect to each other.

Output: If GIS users are employing high-resolution atmospheric model output for their applications (e.g., simulated temperature or humidity fields for assessing heat stress within a city), they should ask the data provider about the mapping assumptions used by the atmospheric model. In particular, is the output on a PCS or GCS (both are common), and, if so, what earth shape (spheroidal or spherical) was assumed? GIS users should be able to easily determine by browsing the data whether they are on a PCS or GCS; however, it may be difficult to ascertain information about the earth shape that was assumed. In this case, given that the input geographic data used in the atmospheric model were likely based on a WGS84 spheroid, and also likely were never transformed before use in the atmospheric model, the safe bet is to assume the atmospheric model output is based on a WGS84 spheroid. This assumption is supported because common visualization programs used by atmospheric modelers (e.g., NCAR Command Language [NCL], Interactive Data Language [IDL], and the Grid Analysis and Display System [GrADS]) all assume the data are based on the WGS84 spheroid, whether on a PCS or GCS. Finally, once GIS users ensure that the atmospheric model output is correctly mapped as a layer in their GIS software, they should also interpret the results with caution, keeping in mind the previous discussion about errors in simulations that arise from improper mapping, some of which cannot be corrected. Atmospheric model output is not perfect.

References

Anderson, J. R., E. E. Hardy, J. T. Roach, and R. E. Witmer. 1976. "A Land Use and Land Cover Classification System for Use with Remote Sensor Data." Geological Survey Professional Paper 964. US Government Printing Office.

Bugayevskiy, L. M., and J. P. Snyder. 1995. *Map Projections: A Reference Manual.* London; Bristol, PA: Taylor & Francis Inc.

Chen, F., K. W. Manning, M. Tewari, A. A. Wyszogrodzki, H. Kusaka, R. Bornstein, J. Ching, C. S. B. Grimmond, T. Loridan, S. Grossman-Clarke, A. Martilli, F. P. Salamanca, S. Miao, C. Zhang, D. Sailor, H. Taha, X. Wang. 2011. "The Integrated WRF/Urban Modelling System: Development, Evaluation, and Applications to Urban Environmental Problems." *International Journal of Climatology* 31: 273–88. doi:10.1002/joc.2158.

Farr, T. G., P. A. Rosen, E. Caro, R. Crippen, R. Duren, S. Hensley, M. Kobrick, M. Paller, E. Rodriguez, L. Roth, D. Seal, S. Shaffer, J. Shimada, J. Umland, M. Werner, M. Oskin, D. Burbank, and D. Alsdorf. 2007. "The Shuttle Radar Topography Mission." *Reviews of Geophysics* 45: RG2004. doi:10.1029/2005RG000183.

Fry, J. A., J. A. Dewitz, C. G. Homer, G. Xian, S. Jin, L. Yang, C. A. Barnes, N. D. Herold, and J. D. Wickham. 2011. "Completion of the 2006 National Land Cover Database for the Conterminous United States." *Photogrammetric Engineering and Remote Sensing* 77: 858–64.

Gesch, D., and S. Greenlee. 1996. GTOPO30 Documentation. http://webgis.wr.usgs.gov/globalgis/gtopo30/gtopo30.htm.

Hahmann, A. N., D. Rostkier-Edelstein, T. T. Warner, F. Vandenberghe, Y. Liu, R. Babarsky, and S. P. Swerdlin. 2010. "A Reanalysis System for the Generation of Mesoscale Climatographies." *Journal of Applied Meteorology and Climatology* 49 (5): 954–72. doi:10.1175/2009JAMC2351.1.

Hedgley, D. R. 1976. "An Exact Transformation from Geocentric to Geodetic Coordinates for Nonzero Altitudes." NASA-TR-458.

Im, U., K. Markakis, A. Unal, T. Kindap, A. Poupkou, S. Incecik, O. Yenigun, D. Melas, C. Theodosi, and N. Mihalopoulos. 2010. "Study of a Winter PM Episode in Istanbul Using the High Resolution WRF/CMAQ Modeling System." *Atmospheric Environment* 44 (26): 3085–94.

Kennedy, M. 1999. *Understanding Map Projections.* Redlands, CA: Environmental Systems Research Institute, Inc.

Lu, W., S. Zhong, J. J. Charney, X. Bian, and S. Liu. 2012. "WRF Simulation over Complex Terrain during a Southern California Wildfire Event." *Journal of Geophysical Research* 117: D05125. doi:10.1029/2011JD017004.

Mesinger, F., G. DiMego, E. Kalnay, K. Mitchell, P. C. Shafran, W. Ebisuzaki, D. Jovic, J. Woollen, E. Rogers, E. Berbery, M. B. Ek, Y. Fan, R. Grumbine, W. Higgins, H. Li, Y. Lin, G. Manikin, D. Parrish, and W. Shi. 2006. "North American Regional Reanalysis." *Bulletin American Meteorological Society* 87: 343–60.

Monaghan, A. J., K. MacMillan, S. M. Moore, P. S. Mead, M. H. Hayden, and R. J. Eisen. 2012. "A Regional Climatography of West Nile, Uganda, to Support Human Plague Modeling." *Journal of Applied Meteorology and Climatology* 51 (7): 1201–21.

Monaghan, A. J., M. Barlage, J. Boehnert, C. L. Phillips, and O. V. Wilhelmi. 2013. "Overlapping Interests: The Impact of Geographic Coordinate Assumptions on Limited-Area Atmospheric Model Simulations." *Monthly Weather Review* 141: 2120–27.

Rasmussen, R., C. Liu, K. Ikeda, D. Gochis, and D. Yates. 2011. "High-Resolution Coupled Climate Runoff Simulations of Seasonal Snowfall over Colorado: A Process Study of Current and Warmer Climate." *Journal of Climate* 24 (12): 3015–48.

Skamarock, W. C., and J. B. Klemp. 2008. "A Time-Split Nonhydrostatic Atmospheric Model for Research and Forecasting Applications." *Journal of Computational Physics* 227: 3465–85.

WRF Development Team. 2011. "User's Guide for the Advanced Research WRF (ARW) Modeling System Version 3.3." National Center for Atmospheric Research. http://www.mmm.ucar.edu/wrf/users/docs/user_guide_V3.3/ARWUsersGuideV3.pdf.

PART 2

Observations

Atmospheric data are collected at regular and irregular intervals. These samples are known as *observations*. Atmospheric observations are a necessity, because they serve as the initial ingredients (or *initial conditions*) for numerical weather/climate prediction (NWP) models.

Before observational data can be used, quality-control techniques must be performed to ensure that they are accurate. In terms of atmospheric modeling, the old adage "garbage in, garbage out" certainly applies. The "cleaner" and more pristine a modeler can make the initial conditions, the more likely a model is able to apply the laws of physics to resolve and evolve atmospheric features into a simulated future. The better the simulation, the more likely the results will accurately forecast conditions. Like a pair of eyeglasses, the dirtier the lens, the less clearly we can see ahead.

Chapters 4 through 7 discuss some commonly collected atmospheric observational data, and some of the nuances of how such data are stored and accessed for ease of use within a geographic information system (GIS) framework.

Chapter 4 discusses how GIS facilitates the use of weather radar data to model spatially and temporally distributed rainfall. The MIKE URBAN modeling system is introduced as a tool to create urban runoff simulation models.

Chapter 5 provides an overview of atmospheric data products derived from observations made by sensors aboard satellites and discusses options to integrate them into a GIS. Background on atmospheric data products and their format is given, as well as the challenges faced when integrating them with a GIS.

Chapter 6 helps to clarify the scope of data archived and serviced at the National Climatic Data Center. The chapter lists the different types of data, explains how to access them, and describes how they are useful to decision makers.

Chapter 7 discusses how social media contribute data about our surroundings and can fill gaps where there are no sensors or existing sample sites to provide information. It describes how these types of data can be harvested and stored in a database, visualized in a mapping application, and shared via web map services.

CHAPTER 4

Weather radar: Urban application

Niels Einar Jensen and Anders Peter Sloth Møller

Radar data are widely used in geographic information system (GIS) mapping because two- and three-dimensional radar data are very suitable for GIS presentations. Recent advances have been made in GIS and radar interoperability. GIS tools facilitate radar operation and the use of radar data in simulation models. Since 2003, the Iowa Environmental Mesonet (IEM) has been providing composites of National Weather Service radar data in formats that are compatible with GIS. Tools have been developed to compare weather radar precipitation data with rain gauge data (Gad and Tsanis 2003) and for operational use of weather information (Next-Generation Radar, or NEXRAD) in decision-support systems (Sznaider 2005).

Another recent advancement in radar technology is the Local Area Weather Radar (LAWR). LAWRs are typically based on marine radar and are used to estimate precipitation at a very high temporal (down to 1 minute) and spatial (100 × 100 m) scale. In El Salvador, a countrywide network of eight LAWRs provides data for real-time presentation of rainfall on the Internet. In Quito, Ecuador, a network of three radars is being installed to monitor rainfall over the city. In La Paz, Bolivia, and in Singapore, LAWRs are used to monitor approaching rainfall to mitigate the risk of flash floods. All these LAWRs have been installed since 2010. In Denmark, six LAWRs have been in operation for several years, the first being installed at Søsterhøj in 1999 (Jensen 2002).

Another advancement in the use of radar technology is the MIKE URBAN modeling system created by DHI (a Danish consulting company). MIKE URBAN is one of the first systems that can directly import radar rainfall data into urban runoff simulation models.

Why use weather radar data? Runoff modeling shows the relationship between rainfall estimates of one or two rain gauges in catchments of 10 km². As these models improved, it became evident that a few point measurements (rain gauges) were not sufficient for a detailed temporal and spatial description of the rainfall. Weather radars provide information on the spatial and temporal distribution of rainfall; however, their accuracy at point level may be less than that of rain gauges. By specifying the position and resolution of the weather radar, distributed precipitation boundaries for urban sewer runoff simulation models can be generated.

Recent increases in rainfall intensity as a result of global warming have made the use of radar rainfall measurement useful, especially in urban areas. Instead of increasing the diameters of existing sewer pipes, which is expensive and time-consuming, real-time controlled systems of retention basins and pumping facilities mitigate excess water flow into cities.

The runoff models discussed here are spatially detailed (figure 4.1). Runoff in urban areas is affected by local conditions, so it is important to know whether rain is falling on one street or on the neighboring street.

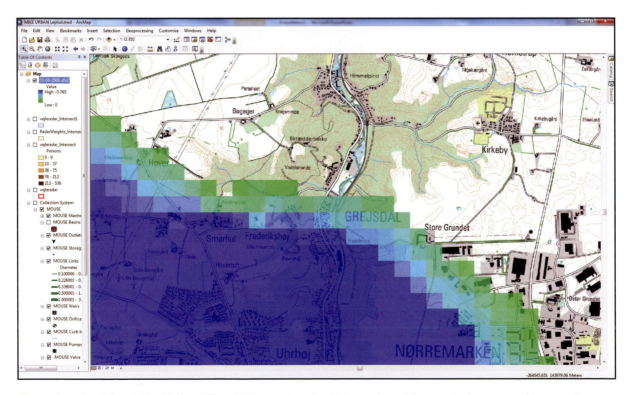

Figure 4.1   2 × 2 km, 500 × 500 m, 250 × 250 m, and 100 × 100 m radar grid presented over an urban area. | Contains data from the Danish Geodata Agency (September 2013), http://eng.gst.dk/media/gst/2364686/Conditionsforuseofopenpublicgeographicdata.pdf.

Local Area Weather Radar

A LAWR provides precipitation information every 1–5 minutes for an area of up to 30 km from the radar. Data are available immediately after scanning as a matrix of radar reflectivities (dBZs [decibels relative to Z]) in polar or Cartesian coordinates that can be converted to rainfall intensities.

When using LAWR data, keep the following in mind: First, the intensities must be connected to the appropriate catchment in the runoff simulation model. Second, because of the physical properties of the radar, the data represent measurements in a plane that is tangent to the surface of the earth, meaning it touches the earth at a single point—the location of the radar (figure 4.2). Finally, the projection that best approximates LAWR data is a planar projection. Placing the measured data in a square grid in a planar projection will ensure that the data are projected correctly onto the earth's surface.

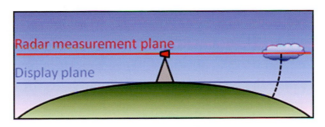

Figure 4.2 A radar measurement plane does not follow the curvature of the earth's surface. | Contains data from the Danish Geodata Agency (September 2013), http://eng. gst.dk/media/gst/2364686/Conditionsforuseofopenpublicgeo graphicdata.pdf.

MIKE URBAN Weather Radar Tool

MIKE URBAN is an urban water modeling software created by DHI. It allows users to simulate most flow conditions in cities, including sewers (combined systems, separate systems, or any combination of the two) and storm water drainage systems with two-dimensional overland flow. MIKE URBAN is a complete integration of GIS and water modeling and is used worldwide.

The MIKE URBAN Weather Radar Tool allows the user to apply radar data from a DHI LAWR or radar data in a similar format as boundaries for a MOUSE (a fully dynamic urban sewer model) runoff simulation. The tool is freely available to owners of LAWRs, and because it can be used with other radars, it also can be procured as an add-on to the MIKE URBAN package. The software can only be used with the Microsoft Windows operating system.

In the MIKE URBAN runoff model, the modeling area is divided into a number of subcatchments. Each of these subcatchments is defined as an individual polygon.

Based on LAWR radar data, the tool can transform reflectivity data to the intensity of the area covered by the radar. From the resulting two-dimensional gridded intensity, a time series of area-weighted rainfall intensity over each catchment in a MIKE URBAN model will be generated. After extraction, the tool can generate MOUSE boundary items connecting each extracted rainfall time series to the proper catchment.

Each pixel in the radar grid describes the measured rainfall in that small area. The catchment can span several pixels in the radar grid. In order to determine the rainfall over a catchment, an area-weighted average of the pixels that cover the catchment must be calculated. In order to prepare for the calculation of the area-weighted precipitation time series for each catchment, a list of pixel weights must be produced.

The radar tool uses a GIS to transform the user-defined coordinate system for the radar layers to the coordinate system used by the runoff model.

Creation of the radar grid (a fishnet) is done by cloning a polygon shaped as a square (figure 4.3). The square is constructed from four points that have been added to a PointCollection. The polygon is cast to IClone, and ITransform2D is used to move the clone to the correct position. The fishnet is built by repeating the clone-and-move procedure. The main reason not to use the built-in fishnet functionality is that it uses a corner coordinate as input. Because the radar needs to be precisely in the middle of the grid, the fishnet functionality cannot be used.

```
IPointCollection pointC = new PolygonClass();
IPoint pnt1 = new PointClass();
IPoint pnt2 = new PointClass();
IPoint pnt3 = new PointClass();
IPoint pnt4 = new PointClass();
```

Define coordinates of each of the four points, and then create the polygon and clone it:

```
IPolygon theSquare = pointC as IPolygon;
theSquare.Close();
IClone polyClone = theSquare as IClone;
ITransform2D trans;
tmpPoly = polyClone.Clone() as IPolygon;
trans = tmpPoly as ITransform2D;
trans.Move(deltaX, deltaY);
```

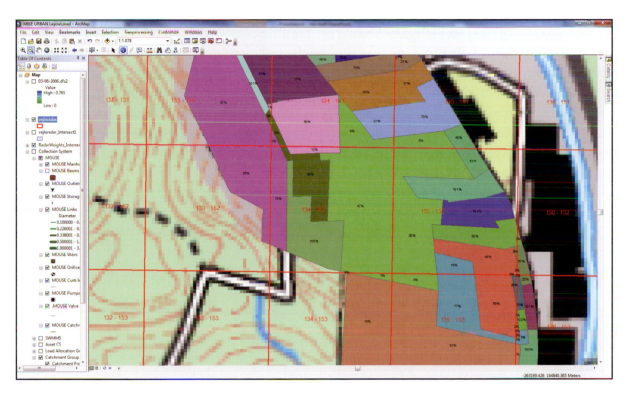

Figure 4.3 The catchment weights layer in MIKE URBAN. The catchment pixel intersect polygons are labeled with their fraction of the total catchment area they are a part of. | Contains data from the Danish Geodata Agency (September 2013), http://eng.gst.dk/media/gst/2364686/Conditionsforuseofopenpublicgeographicdata.pdf.

Once the radar grid is defined, the complex work of calculating the contribution that each runoff catchment receives from the gridded radar data begins. The weight computation procedure consists of two operations: (1) intersection and (2) computation of a weight dataset.

The intersection is done using the GeoProcessor command. The result of the GeoProcessor execute command is stored as an IGeoProcessorResult, and this is used in the code to determine the success of the process as well as to inform the user of the result in the graphical user interface (GUI).

```
Geoprocessor GP = new Geoprocessor();
GP.SetEnvironmentValue("Workspace", path);
string firstLayer = radarNetLayer.FeatureClass.AliasName;
string secondLayer = catchmentLayer.FeatureClass.AliasName;
Intersect ISectTool = new Intersect();
ISectTool.in _ features = firstLayer + ";" + secondLayer;
ISectTool.out _ feature _ class = DataSetName;
IGeoProcessorResult pResult = (IGeoProcessorResult) GP.Execute
(ISectTool, null);
```

Calculation of the pixel weights is based on a summation of all "pieces" of a catchment that are in the actual pixel. This means that the weight calculation will work even for irregularly shaped catchments. The weight computation traverses the intersect feature class using a feature cursor and uses this to build a dataset with catchment name, pixel column, pixel row, and weight. The weight is computed as the intersect feature area divided by the catchment area. Before new weights are added to the dataset, a check is made to determine if features belonging to the same pixel and catchment have already been added. If this is the case, the weights of the two features are combined.

Once the weights are found, the corresponding rainfall intensities can be found using:

$$TS_{Catchment} = TS_{Pixel\_1} \cdot Weight_{Pixel\_1} + \ldots + TS_{Pixel\_n} \cdot Weight_{Pixel\_n}$$

where

$TS_{catchment}$: Resulting area-weighted precipitation time series for the actual catchment

TS_{Pixel_n}: Precipitation time series for the nth pixel

$Weight_{Pixel\_n}$: Relative area of the pixel compared to the total catchment area

If a catchment is covered by a single pixel, the following simple relation applies:

$$TS_{Catchment} = TS_{Pixel}$$

Visualization

Figures 4.3, 4.4, and 4.5 show the results of the various steps previously described. In figure 4.3, the highlighted purple catchment is covered by two pixels. After the intersection, each pixel holds information on the ratio each pixel is covering in the catchment. The weight for a pixel is now calculated as the summed area of the catchment in the pixel divided by the total area of the catchment. Figure 4.4 shows the radar grid, and figure 4.5 shows the area from where boundary data can be extracted.

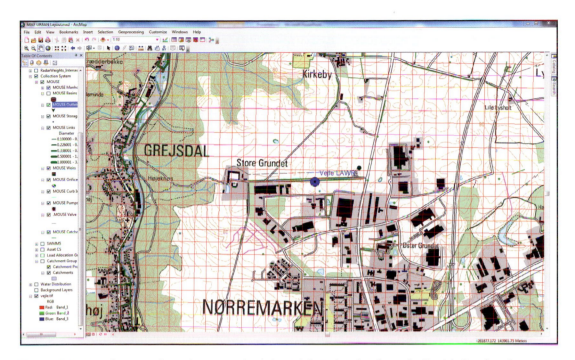

Figure 4.4   **Visualization of a radar site and pixel net.** | Contains data from the Danish Geodata Agency (September 2013), http://eng.gst.dk/media/gst/2364686/Conditionsforuseofopenpublicgeographicdata.pdf.

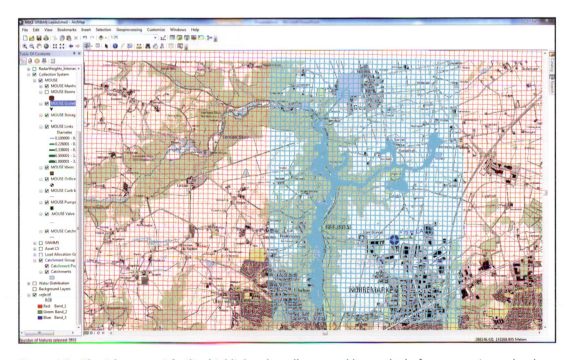

Figure 4.5   **The "show area" facility highlights the cells covered by results before extracting radar data to the boundary file.** | Contains data from the Danish Geodata Agency (September 2013), http://eng.gst.dk/media/gst/2364686/Conditionsforuseofopenpublicgeographicdata.pdf.

Performance

Using radar data implies using a large amount of data. A short time step combined with a large extraction area and a longer period will generate very large files. One month of data with 1-minute resolution covering the maximum extent will produce an intermediate file of approximately 5 gigabytes. Each subcatchment will end up with its own boundary file. Because of the large number of boundary files, the runoff simulation will take a longer time than usual.

Conclusions

The extraction of radar data input for a MIKE URBAN model requires assessment of the validity and limitations of the data. Usually the data used in a model are measured by rain gauges or generated as a synthetic rain from a formula. These methods have advantages and limitations, which are recognized and, in most cases, considered reasonable. The limitations of the radar are not as widely known. It is important to know how the runoff model handles distributed data. These models normally acquire their rainfall information from one or a few rain gauges inside or in the vicinity of the model area, thus the delineation of subcatchment boundaries inside the model area has not been very crucial because the same "mean area precipitation" has been applied to the entire model area. Applying distributed rainfall information (figure 4.6) will in such cases have little or no effect if the subcatchments do not have a spatial resolution similar to the radar rainfall data. In Pedersen et al. (2005) an experiment using relocated radar rainfall on a small urban area indicated a significant dependency on the rainfall resolution. When applying rainfall data measured by weather radar, some of the temporal resolution is lost because the intensity over 5 minutes is averaged, but the loss is offset by the timely knowledge of spatial distribution of rainfall.

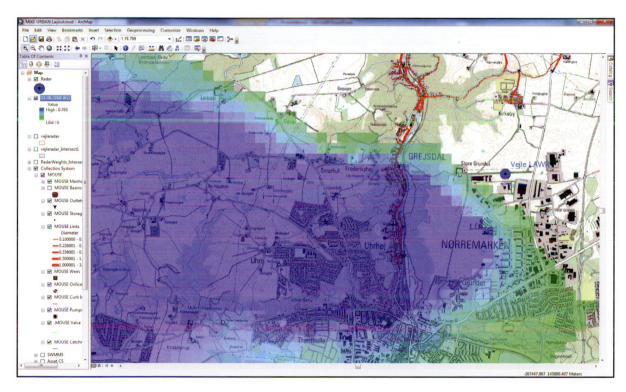

Figure 4.6   Variability in rainfall (100 × 100 m resolution). | Contains data from the Danish Geodata Agency (September 2013), http://eng.gst.dk/media/gst/2364686/Conditionsforuseofopenpublicgeographicdata.pdf.

References and additional resources

Borup, M., J. J. Linde, M. Grum, and P. S. Mikkelsen. 2009. "Application of High Resolution X-Band Radar Data for Urban Runoff Modelling: Constant vs. Dynamic Calibration." Eighth International Workshop on Precipitation in Urban Areas. December 10–13, 2009. St. Moritz, Switzerland.

Gad, M. A., and I. K. Tsanis. 2003. "A GIS Methodology for the Analysis of Weather Radar Precipitation Data." *Journal of Hydroinformatics* 5 (2): 113–26.

Goormans, T., and P. Willems. 2008. "Taking Rain Gauge Errors into Account in the Calibration of a Short Range X-Band Weather Radar." Poster presented at WRaH 2008, International Symposium Weather Radar and Hydrology. March 10–12, 2008. Grenoble, France.

Jensen, N. E. 2002. "X-Band Local Area Weather Radar—Preliminary Calibration Results." *Water Science Technology* 45 (2): 135–38.

Jensen, N. E., and L. Pedersen. 2004. "Radar Rainfall Required for Simulation of Urban Runoff." Third European Conference on Radar in Meteorology and Hydrology (ERAD04). September 6–10, 2004. Visby, Sweden.

_____. 2005. "High Resolution Rainfall—Information in Urban Runoff Simulation." International Stormwater and Urban Water Systems Modeling Conference and SWMM/PCSWMM workshops. February 24–25, 2005. Toronto, Ontario, Canada.

Nielsen, C., F. Dugelay, L. K. Seng, S. Osman, and N. E. Jensen. 2006. "Preliminary Assessment of LAWR Performance in Tropical Regions with High Intensity Convective Rainfall." DHI User Conference. Shanghai, China.

Pedersen, L., N. E. Jensen, M. Rasmussen, and M. G. Nicolajsen. 2005. "Urban Runoff Volumes Dependency on Rainfall Measurement Method—Scaling Properties of Precipitation within a 2 × 2 km Radar Pixel." Tenth International Conference on Urban Drainage. August 21–26, 2005. Copenhagen, Denmark.

Pedersen, L., A. Sloth, and N. E. Jensen. 2010. "MIKE URBAN Radar Tool—A Straightforward Solution for Integrating High Resolution Radar Data." Presentation at the 2010 International MIKE by DHI Conference. Copenhagen, Denmark.

Rollenbeck, R., and J. Bendix. 2006. "Experimental Calibration of a Cost-Effective X-Band Weather Radar for Climate Ecological Studies in Southern Ecuador." *Atmospheric Research* 79: 296–316.

Sznaider, R. 2005. "Operational Uses of Weather Information in GIS-Based Decision Support Systems." IDS Emergency Management sector paper. http://www.idsemergencymanagement. com/emergency_management/corporate/_Ronald_J__Sznaider/90/paper_information. html.

CHAPTER 5

Atmospheric satellite observations and GIS

Amit Sinha

Earth's environment is experiencing dramatic changes, including rising sea levels, global warming, ozone depletion, acid rain, biodiversity loss, and deforestation. These changes profoundly affect humans; therefore, it is critical to develop a scientific understanding of Earth's interrelated systems and its response to natural and anthropogenic changes (Goddard Space Flight Center, National Aeronautics and Space Administration 2012). In addition, observations about Earth are also needed to support the formation of authoritative scientific evidence, establish baselines, monitor compliance with treaties and agreements, assess progress, improve predictions, and manage and mitigate impacts of weather and natural disasters (Rio+20 2012). Artificial satellites orbiting Earth are the key mechanism to remotely observe Earth's environment. These satellites carry a multitude of sensors that provide continuous measurements of Earth's environment that are used to derive atmospheric data products that have many practical applications. Integration of these atmospheric data products with information about people and property in a geographic information system (GIS) can aid in making decisions that can save lives, promote national security, and boost the economy. However, integrating atmospheric data products with GIS remains a challenge because of their incompatible formats, multiple dimensions, and prohibitive size. This chapter presents an overview of atmospheric data products derived from observations made by sensors aboard satellites and discusses options to integrate them into a GIS.

Satellite missions

A host of nations fly satellite missions that provide measurements on Earth's environment that are used in myriad applications. The World Weather Watch (part of the World Meteorological Organization) is an international agency that provides a collaborative network of satellite-borne sensors and ground-based sensors to nations around the world. These satellites' observations are used in environmental monitoring, meteorology, and mapping. An estimated 114 different operational Earth observation satellite missions exist. Information about major satellite missions can be obtained from the "Catalog of Satellites" published in the *Earth Observations Handbook* (Ward 2012).

Among these missions, the satellite missions operated by the National Aeronautics and Space Administration (NASA) and National Oceanic and Atmospheric Administration (NOAA) are the most advanced, and their atmospheric data products are the focus of this section. NASA satellite data are primarily used for earth science research; most of this data is distributed for free by NASA's Earth Observing System Data and Information System (EOSDIS). NOAA satellite data are primarily used for operational activities, such as NOAA numerical weather forecasting models; most NOAA data are also distributed for free by NOAA's National Environmental Satellite, Data, and Information Service (NESDIS). For nations that do not operate their own satellite programs, data products from these satellite missions are the primary source of remote sensing information. The following sections present major NASA and NOAA satellite missions, sensors measuring atmospheric parameters, and data products derived from them.

NASA satellite observations and data products

Earth observation satellites are satellites designed to observe Earth from orbit. NASA operates a series of polar-orbiting and low-inclination satellites as part of its Earth Observing System (EOS) that provides long-term global observations about Earth's atmosphere, biosphere, land, and oceans that are used by scientists to study global change. Figure 5.1 shows all missions operated by NASA's EOS missions and its partners. To predict and understand Earth's environment, it is important to collect data on it over a long period of time to assess the changes taking place. Before the EOS missions, such a comprehensive and continuous dataset on Earth's environment did not exist. To fill the gap, the EOS was initiated to gather a long-term set of data that scientists could use to study changes in atmospheric, oceanic, and land processes over a longer period of time.

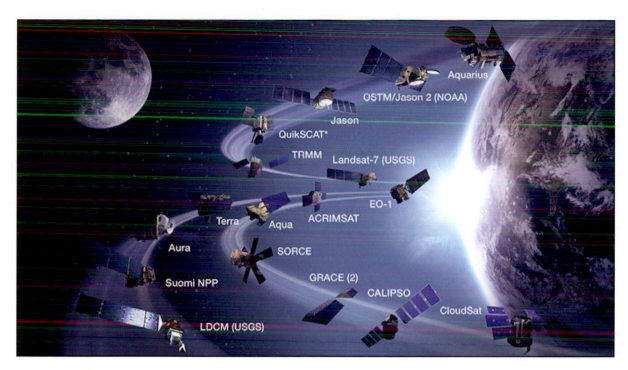

Figure 5.1 NASA's satellite missions. | Courtesy of NASA; image by Jenny Mottar, NASA Headquarters. Contains data from the Danish Geodata Agency (November 13), Cadastral Map, and WMS.

Terra, Aqua, and Aura are the major satellite series of the EOS. The Terra satellite helps in studying the interactions within Earth's atmosphere. The Aqua satellite measures water vapor in the atmosphere. The Aura satellite helps in understanding the atmosphere's chemistry and dynamics. These satellites operate in a polar sun-synchronous orbit at an elevation of about 700 km and provide a complete coverage of Earth in about 16 days. EOS satellites carry sensors that make observations at visible, infrared, radio wave, and microwave wavelengths (Goddard Space Flight Center, NASA 2012). Table 5.1 presents a list of sensors onboard EOS satellites that measure atmospheric parameters, observations and atmospheric data products, and data formats. From the table, it is clear that Hierarchical Data Format (HDF; The HDF Group 2010) and Network Common Data Form (netCDF; Shea 2007) are prevalent formats. Both are discussed later in this chapter. Figure 5.2 presents an atmospheric data product derived from observations taken by the AMSR-E sensor aboard the Aqua satellite.

Table 5.1 NASA's EOS sensors measuring atmospheric parameters

Sensor	Observation and resolution	Data format
Advanced Microwave Scanning Radiometer-Earth Observing System (AMSR-E) on Aqua	Brightness, temperature, water vapor, cloud liquid water, sea surface temperature, and rain. Global coverage at spatial resolutions of 12 km, 5.4 km, 21 km, 25 km, 38 km, 56 km, and 0.25 degree.	HDF-EOS
Atmospheric Infrared Sounder (AIRS/AMSU-A/HSB) on Aqua	Air temperature, humidity, clouds, and surface temperature. Global coverage at spatial resolution of 13.5 km in the IR band and ~2.3 km in the visible band. Swath products are available at 50 km resolution.	HDF-EOS
Aura High Resolution Dynamics Limb Sounder (HIRDLS)	Temperature; concentrations of O_3, H_2O, CH_4, N_2O, NO_2, HNO_3, N_2O_5, CFC_{11}, CFC_{12}, and aerosols; polar stratospheric clouds. Global coverage at vertical 1 km and horizontal 10 km × 300 km resolution.	HDF-EOS
Aura Microwave Limb Sounder (MLS)	Ozone, water vapor, OH, HO_2, CO, HCN, N_2O, HNO_3, HCl, HOCl, ClO, BrO, and SO_2, temperature, cirrus ice, relative humidity. Coverage between 82° N to 82° S at 3 km vertical × 165 km along track.	HDF-EOS
Aura Ozone Mapping Instrument (OMI)	Solar backscatter radiation, ozone, NO_2, SO_2, BrO, HCHO, OClO, and ozone profiles, UVB radiation, aerosol and cloud properties. Global coverage at resolutions 13 × 24 km to 13 × 12 km.	HDF-EOS
Cloud-Aerosol Lidar and Infrared Pathfinder Satellite Observations (CALIPSO)	Cloud and aerosol. 64 km swath and 1 km resolution data available. Global coverage at resolution of 125 m, 333 m, 1 km, and 5 km.	HDF

(Continued)

Table 5.1   NASA's EOS sensors measuring atmospheric parameters   (*continued*)

Sensor	Observation and resolution	Data format
Clouds and the Earth's Radiant Energy System (CERES)	Top atmospheric layer radiation, aerosols, UVA/UVB, photosynthetically active radiation, cloud properties. Global coverage with 1° swath and 2.5° zonal data.	HDF and NetCDF
International Satellite Cloud Climatology Project (ISCCP)	Radiances, sea ice, snow cover, ice cover, cloud properties, ozone, percepitable water profiles. Global coverage with equal area grid.	Raw and HDF
Lightning Imaging Sensor/Optical Transient (LIS/OTD) Detector	Global coverage of lightning and thunderstorm climatology.	HDF
LIS and OTD Science Data	Space-based lightning sensors capable of detecting and locating lightning events during day and night. LIS, 35° N to 35° S; OTD, 70° N to 70° S, and LIS, 4 km; OTD, 70 km	HDF
Measurements of Pollution In The Troposphere (MOPITT)	Atmospheric profiles of CO mixing ratio and CO total column values. Global data at 22 horizontally and 4 km vertically.	HDF
Moderate Resolution Imaging Spectroradiometer (MODIS) Atmosphere Products	Aerosols, cloud properties, atmospheric temperature and moisture profiles, water vapor, ozone. Global coverage at 1 km, 5 km, 10 km, and 1° resolution.	HDF-EOS
Multi-angle Imaging Spectro Radiometer (MISR)	Cloud, aerosol, radiance, land surface, albedo. Global coverage at 250 m to 70.4 km and 0.5° × 0.5° or 1° × 1°.	HDF and netCDF
Tropical Rainfall Measuring Mission (TRMM)	Precipitation, ice, cloud liquid water, and both convective and stratiform rain rate. Coverage is 50° N to 50° S at 0.25° × 0.25°, 1° × 1°, 2.2° × 2.2°, 4° × 4°, 5° × 5°.	HDF and netCDF
MSFC SSM/I Brightness Temperature Data Sets	Integrated water vapor, cloud, liquid water, and oceanic wind speed. Global coverage at 12.5 km at 85 GHz and 25 km for others.	HDF-EOS

(*Continued*)

Sensor	Observation and resolution	Data format
Stratospheric Aerosol and Gas Experiment (SAGE) I, II, and III	Ozone, water vapor, and nitrogen dioxide, nitrogen trioxide, chlorine dioxide, clouds, temperature, and pressure.	SAGE I, II and III: HDF, Binary
Total Ozone Mapping Spectrometer (TOMS)	Ozone amounts and UV reflectivity. Global coverage at 1° × 1.25°.	ASCII
Tropospheric Emission Spectrometer (TES)	Water vapor, ozone, carbon monoxide, atmospheric temperature, methane, nitric acid, carbon dioxide, ammonia, and heavy water. Global coverage at 0.5 × 5 km (nadir) and 2.3 × 23 km (limb) resolution.	Level 1: HDF; Level 2 and 3: HDF-EOS
Upper Atmosphere Research Satellite (UARS)	Upper atmospheric chemical constituents, winds, solar irradiance, and energetic particle input. Coverage from 80° N to 80° S at 4° resolution.	Various and dataset dependent

Courtesy of NASA. Data from Earth System Science Data Resources (2012), https://earthdata.nasa.gov/library/earth-system-science-data-resources.

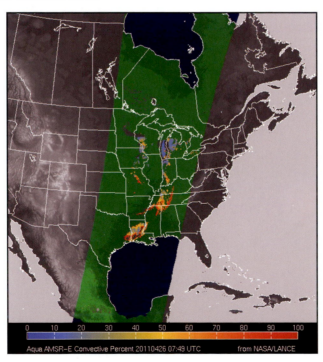

Figure 5.2   Image derived from AMSR-E sensor aboard the Aqua satellite to estimate the convective percent of storms. | Courtesy of ESSDR (2012), NASA, https://earthdata.nasa.gov/library/earth-system-science-data-resources.

NASA's EOSDIS is responsible for processing, archiving, and distributing satellite data products. EOSDIS operates data centers across the United States that are focused on serving the data product needs of a particular earth science community. Table 5.2 provides a list of data centers operated by EOSDIS.

Table 5.2   Satellite data centers

NASA Earth Observing System Data Information System (EOSDIS)	
1	Alaska Satellite Facility Synthetic Aperture RADAR (SAR) Data Center (ASF SDC)
2	GSFC Earth Sciences Data and Information Services Center (GES DISC)
3	Global Hydrology and Resource Center DAAC (GHRC DAAC)
4	Langley Research Center (LaRC) Atmospheric Science Data Center (ASDC)
5	Land Processes DAAC (LP DAAC)
6	MODAPS Level 1 Atmosphere Archive and Distribution System (MODAPS LAADS)
7	National Snow and Ice Data Center DAAC (NSIDC DAAC)
8	Oak Ridge National Laboratory DAAC (ORNL DAAC)
9	Physical Oceanography DAAC (PO-DAAC)
10	Socioeconomic Data and Applications Center (SEDAC)
NOAA National Environmental Satellite, Data, and Information Service (NESDIS)	
1	National Oceanographic Data Center (NODC)
2	National Geophysical Data Center (NGDC)
3	National Climatic Data Center (NCDC)

Courtesy of NASA. Data from Earth System Science Data Resources (2012), https://earthdata.nasa.gov/library/earth-system-science-data-resources.

NOAA satellite observations and data products

NOAA, in collaboration with NASA, maintains two primary series of environmental satellites in polar and geosynchronous orbits. The satellite series operated by NOAA in the geosynchronous orbit is called Geostationary Operational Environmental Satellites (GOES), and the satellite series in the polar orbit is called Polar orbiting Operational Environmental Satellites (POES). Figure 5.3 shows the GOES and POES satellites orbiting Earth (Goddard Space Flight Center, NASA 2012).

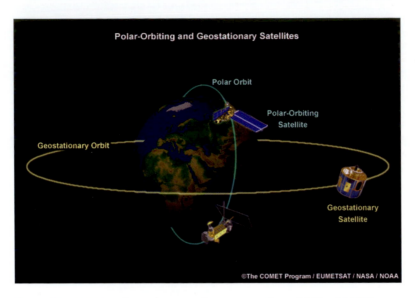

Figure 5.3 NOAA polar and geosynchronous satellites. | ©The COMET Program/EUMETSAT/NASA/NOAA. Courtesy of NESDIS.

GOES spacecraft operate as a two-satellite constellation, GOES-East and GOES-West, in geosynchronous orbit above the equator and observe 60 percent of Earth. They measure Earth's atmosphere, its surface, cloud cover, and the solar and geosynchronous space environment. GOES satellites provide short-term forecasts for monitoring and predicting weather and environmental events such as dust storms, tornadoes, hurricanes, forest fires, and flash floods. GOES data are used in weather forecasting numerical models. The GOES satellites continuously observe the western hemisphere and provide a full image of Earth every 30 minutes, with 5-minute lead times planned in the future. POES satellites consist of two sun-synchronous satellites known as Advanced Television Infrared Observation Satellite (TIROS) that orbit Earth close to both poles. These satellites support long-term forecasts, with lead times that range from 2 to 10 days. These satellites carry advanced sensors for measuring weather and climate data in Earth's environment and provide full coverage of Earth twice a day. POES satellites measure many parameters, including precipitation, sea surface temperatures, atmospheric temperatures, humidity, and vegetation. They also help in search and rescue missions. Table 5.3 provides a list of sensors measuring atmospheric parameters on board POES and GOES satellites, observations, and their data formats (National Geophysical Data Center, National Oceanic and Atmospheric Administration 2013). Figures 5.4 and 5.5 show a visual representation of data products from these satellite series.

Table 5.3   Sensors onboard NOAA's POES and GOES series of satellites

Sensors	Observation and resolution	Data format
GOES I-M Imager	Radiant energy and reflected solar energy from Earth's surface and atmosphere, GOES Aerosol Smoke Product, GOES Biomass Burning Emissions Product, Automated Biomass Burning Algorithm (ABBA), Fire Product Archive, Hazard Mapping System (HMS) Fire and Smoke Analysis, Rainfall Hydro Estimator, Volcanic Ash Advisories, Volcano Imagery, High Density Infrared and Visible Cloud Drift Winds, High Density Water Vapor Cloud Drift Winds. Coverage from 80° N to 80° S at 1 km (visible) to 4 km (infrared) resolution.	Raw files, netCDF, images (e.g., PNG, JPEG, GeoTIFF)
GOES Sounder	Vertical temperature and moisture profile of the atmosphere, surface and cloud top temperatures, and ozone distribution, Sounder Cloud Top Pressure, Satellite Cloud Product (SCP), Derived Product Imagery (DPI), Skew-T Profiles of Temperature and Moisture Soundings, High Density Water Vapor Cloud Drift Winds. Coverage from −64° E to −178° W and 53° N to 6 °S at 8 km resolution.	Raw files, netCDF, imagery (e.g., PNG, JPEG, GeoTIFF)
POES Advanced Very High Resolution Radiometer (AVHRR/3)	Cloud cover and the upper atmosphere surface temperature, Aerosol Optical Thickness, Cloud Classification CLAVR-x, Fire Id, Mapping and Monitoring Algorithm (FIMMA), Fire Product Archive, Hazard Mapping System (HMS) Fire and Smoke Analysis, Precipitable Water Index, Absorbed Solar Energy, Available Solar Energy, Outgoing Longwave Radiation, Skew-T Profiles of Temperature and Moisture Soundings, Advanced TIROS Operational Vertical Sounder (ATOVS). Global coverage at 1–4 km resolution.	Access through CLASS protocol, netCDF
POES Advanced Microwave Sounding Unit-A (AMSU-A)	Precipitable water, cloud liquid water, surface temperature, snow cover, rain rate, ice water path, Cloud Liquid Water (CLW), Ensemble Tropical Rainfall Potential (eTRaP), Total Precipitable Water (MSPPS). Global coverage at 40 km resolution.	Raw, HDF-EOS, BUFR

(Continued)

Sensors	Observation and resolution	Data format
POES Microwave Humidity Sounder (MHS)	Humidity profile, surface temperature and emissivity, Microwave Rain Rate (MSPPS). Global coverage at 15 km resolution.	Raw, BUFR, HDF5
POES High Resolution Infrared Radiation Sounder (HIRS/4)	Upper tropospheric humidity, this channel provides information on the distribution and transport of water vapor in the atmosphere, Total Precipitable Water (ATOVS), Outgoing Longwave Radiation. Global coverage with 20 km (visible) and 18.9 km (infrared) resolution.	Raw, BUFR, HDF5
Solar Backscatter Ultraviolet Version 2 (SBUV/2)	Ultraviolet rays, ozone, 1B Capture product, Product Master File, Total Ozone Analysis from SBUV and TOVS (TOAST). Global coverage at 170 km resolution.	Raw, BUFR

Courtesy of NASA.

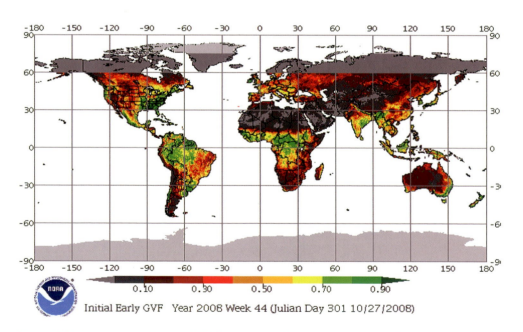

Initial Early GVF   Year 2008 Week 44 (Julian Day 301 10/27/2008)

Figure 5.4   Image derived from AVHRR (Advanced Very High Resolution Radiometer) sensor data showing active green vegetation used in numerical weather forecast models. | Courtesy of ESSDR, NASA, and NOAA.

Figure 5.5 Imagery from GOES satellite showing Hurricane Sandy. | Courtesy of NOAA/ NASA.

NOAA's NESDIS is responsible for distribution of NOAA's satellite data products to users. NESDIS provides global environmental data from GOES and POES series satellites to a variety of users that help in protecting lives and properties from severe weather events; they are also used by businesses to build enhanced weather products. These satellites also provide real-time and near-real-time observations to US military users that help them protect their assets on land, air, and sea worldwide. NESDIS operates three data centers that deal with oceanographic, geophysical, and climate data. The National Climatic Data Center (NCDC) is responsible for providing satellite-based weather, climate, and other atmospheric data products. These data can be accessed by dataset or sensor type at the NCDC's website. The following sections discuss options to get these satellite data products into ArcGIS software for geospatial analysis.

ArcGIS and satellite data formats

Tables 5.1 and 5.3 show the data formats in which atmospheric data products are available from satellite missions operated by NASA and NOAA. These data are processed at multiple levels. Level 0 products are the raw data from sensors at full resolution. Higher levels of data products reflect further processing for quality and usability. Major data formats of atmospheric data products are presented in the following sections.

HDF

The HDF is a data model, library, and file format designed for efficient archival and access of complex data in high volume. HDF has two data formats: HDF4 and HDF5. HDF-EOS (Hierarchical Data Format-Earth Observing System) is a special type of format that deals with NASA's EOS satellite data and is NASA's primary format to manage satellite data. Table 5.1 shows that most of NASA's atmospheric data products are available in the HDF-EOS format. HDF-EOS data are geolocated with additional conventions and data types. The two versions of HDF-EOS are HDF-EOS2, based on HDF4, and HDF-EOS5, based on HDF5. Both data formats support point, swath, and grid geospatial data types. HDF-EOS5 also supports a Zonal Average data type, which is like swath data without geolocation information.

The Geospatial Data Abstraction Library (GDAL) is a data translation library for raster data formats. It provides an abstraction layer that can map any HDF data format to the GDAL data format. ArcGIS integrates the GDAL library, and thus can read HDFs that are supported by GDAL. However, HDF data products could be generated by many providers, and GDAL integrated with ArcGIS may not read all of them.

NetCDF

NetCDF is a machine-independent, self-describing, and scalable data format created for managing high-volume multidimensional scientific data (Rew, Davis, and Emmerson 1993). Esri created a series of geoprocessing tools that translate the multidimensional format of Climate and Forecast–compliant netCDF into the more common two-dimensional GIS format. These tools are available in the Multidimension Toolbox in the ArcGIS Spatial Analyst extension. The tools do not convert the data but provide translation of data on demand. Translating is faster than converting and does not require the creation of another copy of the data. These geoprocessing tools enable the direct use of netCDF data in desktop and server geoprocessing workflows. For further discussions on ArcGIS tools for netCDF, refer to part 6.

Other formats: Esri shapefiles, KML, and images

Sometime atmospheric data products are created by third parties for commercial purposes and may be available as Esri shapefiles or as image formats such as TIFF, PNG, or JPEG. These data can be directly used in ArcGIS. For example, some government agencies provide some weather data as shapefiles (National Weather Service 2013). Shapefiles are native to ArcGIS.

The image files previously listed can be imported as rasters into ArcGIS. Another satellite data product format is the Open Geospatial Consortium (OGC)-compliant KML (Keyhole Markup Language). KML is natively supported by ArcGIS, and there are geoprocessing tools available to convert KML files into feature layers.

OPeNDAP and other data formats

Another way to get satellite data products could be through the Open-source Project for a Network Data Access Protocol, also known as OPeNDAP (Cornillon, Gallagher, and Sgouros 2003). OPeNDAP works on a client-server model and provides a programming API (application programming interface) for access and publishing. OPeNDAP clients can read data stored on remote OPeNDAP servers in a transparent manner regardless of the data format on the server. This implies that data formats such as HDF, GRIB (Gridded Binary Form), or other formats published on OPeNDAP servers can be imported into OPeNDAP clients for further analysis. ArcGIS is an OPeNDAP client, and it provides support for OPeNDAP through two geoprocessing tools available in the Multidimension Supplemental toolbox. This toolbox is available for download from the ArcGIS Resources website, http://resources.arcgis.com. For further discussion on the tool, refer to chapter 20.

ArcGIS supports a variety of tools that can be used to integrate atmospheric data products created from satellite observations for advanced geospatial analysis.

Conclusion

Observing Earth is necessary to understand and predict its environment. NASA and NOAA operate an array of satellites carrying a multitude of sensors to measure Earth's environment. These sensors make observations at various wavelengths and use soundings to produce atmospheric data products. Capturing satellite data at this scale generates very high volumes of data (Shea 1996) at various spatial and temporal resolutions that need to be archived, processed, and managed. NASA operates the EOSDIS service and NOAA operates the NESDIS service to provide satellite data products to users in various data formats. Integrating satellite data with GIS can provide valuable information that can aid decision making, but this remains a challenge because of incompatible formats, multiple dimensions, and the inherently large size of the datasets. ArcGIS provides tools that make it possible to import, with some limitations, satellite data for advanced geospatial analysis to study changes in Earth's environment.

References

Cornillon, P., J. Gallagher, and T. Sgouros. 2003. "OPeNDAP, Accessing Data in a Distributed, Heterogeneous Environment." *Data Science Journal* 2 (October): 159.

Goddard Space Flight Center, National Aeronautics and Space Administration. 2012. "Earth System Science Data Resources (ESSDR)." https://earthdata.nasa.gov/library/earth-system-science-data-resources.

National Geophysical Data Center, National Oceanic and Atmospheric Administration. 2013. "Comprehensive Large Array Data Stewardship System (CLASS)." http://www.class.ngdc.noaa.gov/saa/products/search?sub_id=0&datatype_family=GVAR_SND&submit.x=24&submit.y=12.

National Weather Service. 2013. "National Weather Service (NWS) GIS—AWIPS Shapefile Database." Accessed June 2013. http://www.nws.noaa.gov/geodata/.

Rew, R. K., G. P. Davis, and S. Emmerson. 1993. "NetCDF User's Guide, An Interface for Data Access, Version 2.3." http://www.unidata.ucar.edu/software/netcdf/docs/user_guide.html.

Rio+20. 2012. "Report of the United Nations Conference on Sustainable Development." United Nations. June 20–22, 2012. Rio de Janeiro, Brazil. http://www.uncsd2012.org/content/documents/814UNCSD%20REPORT%20final%20revs.pdf.

Shea, D. J., S. J. Worley, I. A. Stern, and T. J. Hoar. 1996 (updated 2007). "An Introduction to Atmospheric and Oceanographic Data." NCAR/TN-404+IA.

The HDF Group. 2010. "Hierarchical Data Format, Version 5, 2000–2010." Accessed June 2013. http://www.hdfgroup.org/HDF5.

Ward, S. 2012. *The Earth Observation Handbook*. European Space Agency. http://www.eohandbook.com.

CHAPTER 6

Climatological products

Rich Baldwin

One motivating factor in the National Oceanic and Atmospheric Administration's (NOAA) efforts to create a climate services portal is to provide access to a host of climate products produced across the agency. The intent of the portal is to provide access to data, scientific and anecdotal discussions, and educational resources to further public and industry understanding of the climate and its societal impacts.

Identifying climate products begins with using collection-level metadata records in FGDC (Federal Geographic Data Committee) or ISO (International Organization for Standardization) format to describe adequate documentation and attribution. US agencies follow a mandate to provide collection-level metadata, which allows references to standardized web services and access systems to be included in data searches. This service-oriented approach is enhanced by OGC (Open Geospatial Consortium) standards, which unite search and discovery systems using CSW (Catalog Service for the Web), product image integration using WMS (Web Map Service), desktop analysis with WFS (Web Feature Service), and Google Map integration using KML (Keyhole Markup Language).

Many climate products can be used with geographic information systems (GIS). This chapter discusses some, but not all, GIS-related climate products. The climate products in this chapter are distinguished by surface and remote observations (in situ, radar, and satellite), models, and summarizations.

Search and discovery

Leveraging CSW services and the indexing capabilities of the Apache Solr platform, the NOAA climate portal provides search and discovery function for over 300 climate products. Figure 6.1 shows the climate portal user interface for the Data and Services tab, which has two functions. First, web mapping applications either tell a story or provide data access. Their second function is product search and discovery, where collection-level metadata describe these products in either ISO or FGDC formats. An application profile, which exists as part of both formats, has recently been introduced to provide better product and service labeling (figure 6.2). The idea of maintaining service links in collection metadata has some appeal until one considers the long-term implications. Ideally, these should be managed in a web service of services. See NOAA's Climate.gov website for more information: http://www.climate.gov.

Figure 6.1   Climate portal user interface for data and services. | Courtesy of NOAA. Data from CDR.

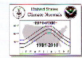

U.S. Hourly Climate Normals (1981-2010)

The U.S. Hourly Climate *Normals* for 1981 to 2010 are 30-year averages of meteorological parameters for thousands of U.S. stations located across the 50 states, as well as U.S. territories, commonwealths, the Compact of Free Association nations, and one station in Canada. NOAA Climate *Normals*... stations that have a Weather Bureau Army-Navy (WBAN) station identification number, including stations from the Climate Reference Network (CRN). The comprehensive U.S. Climate *Normals* dataset includes various derived products including daily air temperature *normals* (including maximum and minimum

Information   Download   KML   Map Search   Data Search   Metadata
http://www.ncdc.noaa.gov/oa/climate/normals/usnormals.html

U.S. Daily Climate Normals (1981-2010)

The U.S. Daily Climate *Normals* for 1981 to 2010 are 30-year averages of meteorological parameters for thousands of U.S. stations located across the 50 states, as well as U.S. territories, commonwealths, the Compact of Free Association nations, and one station in Canada. NOAA Climate *Normals*... stations that have a Weather Bureau Army-Navy (WBAN) station identification number, including stations from the Climate Reference Network (CRN). The comprehensive U.S. Climate *Normals* dataset includes various derived products including daily air temperature *normals* (including maximum and minimum

Information   Download   KML   Map Search   Data Search   Metadata
http://www.ncdc.noaa.gov/oa/climate/normals/usnormals.html

Figure 6.2   The application profile helps define many different services for each climate product. | Courtesy of NOAA.

Surface and remote observations

The scope of data archived and maintained at NOAA's National Climatic Data Center (NCDC) includes not only products related to global in situ station data, but also balloon, radar, satellite, and model data. Its goal is to provide users a consistent approach to data discovery across all of these data networks.

Surface observations

Dozens of US and global surface observation networks exist that feed into various climate products or datasets. To fully explain the instrumentation, observed variables, computed variables, recording periods, quality control, and so on for all of these networks is beyond the scope of this chapter. Many products have been developed around the data provided by these networks, and, as a result, inconsistencies exist (e.g., no recorded observations, varying observation accuracy, etc.). These issues are addressed through standards established by the World Meteorological Organization. As station metadata and other documentation improve, the products will improve and reflect the observation period (hourly/subhourly, daily, monthly, annual), the observation type (temperature, precipitation, 30-year normal, etc.), and platform (land or marine) with greater consistency. Land-based networks include data from the following sources: National Weather Service (NWS), Automated Surface Observing System (ASOS), Automated Weather Observing System (AWOS), Community Collaborative Rain, Hail & Snow (CoCoRAS), and the World Meteorological Organization (WMO). Data products derived from in situ stations include Integrated Surface (hourly), Global Historical Climatological Network (daily), Global Historical Climatological Network (monthly), and Quality Controlled Local Climatological Data. Marine data include observations from ships at sea as well as buoys, both fixed and free floating. Data products derived from these measurements are ICOADS (International Comprehensive Ocean-Atmospheric Data Set project) Global Buoy Data and VOSClim (Voluntary Observing Ship Climate project). Many products available through the NCDC's Climate Data Online (CDO) system reflect the transition from network-based to period-, observation-, and platform-based products. See NCDC's CDO website for more information: http://www.ncdc.noaa.gov/cdo-web/.

Access to climate data at NOAA's NCDC has changed significantly in recent months as old datasets and products have been retired and new ones have been made available. CDO version 2.0 was released in December 2011 with three primary entry points for data acquisition (data search, dynamic maps, and web services). All three of these methods have an integrated underlying data model that allows a consistent user interface to be developed, providing access to all products and services through a single system. Over the coming months, datasets and systems will continue to transition from old to new.

The data search functionality allows users to search by common station name, station identifier, ZIP Code, country, county, state, or hydrologic unit. The search results can be categorized by either a single station or by location (a group of stations). For example, a search on "Charlotte, NC" will return results showing stations and locations that match the search term. Results can be filtered or sorted to meet user needs. Selection of stations or locations, data types, and a time range of interest allows the user to order CSV (comma-separated value), ASCII (American Standard Code for Information Interchange) text, and PDF (Portable Document Format) output forms.

Dynamic mapping applications allow users to visually discover NCDC data through a GIS. As a starting point, maps display the station distribution of the various data networks archived at NCDC. Users can display these stations by the frequency of collection or summarization (hourly/subhourly, daily, monthly, or annually) or by climate theme (temperature, precipitation, drought, snowfall, etc.). A number of tools allow users to select stations by location (country, state, county, ZIP Code, hydrologic unit), by freehand (rectangle, polygon), by proximity from a point, or by gazetteer (geographic name search). The data from the resulting station search can be ordered.

CDO web services are constructed in a "RESTful" (representational state transfer) style, allowing users to write their own client software to access NCDC datasets. Users who have limited and well-defined data requirements will benefit from this type of access. These services are not meant as a replacement for bulk data download, which is available through file transfer protocol (FTP). See NCDC's CDO website on web services for more information: http://www.ncdc.noaa.gov/cdo-web/webservices.

Other stand-alone systems provide access to products describing weather and climate events such as summaries, statistics, and descriptive information. Weather and climate events include extreme events such as hurricanes, tornadoes, floods, and severe thunderstorms.

Remote observations

As technology continues to advance, our ability to make observations from remote platforms also improves. The following sections will give a brief overview of balloon data, radar data, and satellite data, highlighting some of the resulting products currently available.

Balloon data (upper air)

Balloon data include temperature, relative humidity, atmospheric pressure, and wind direction and speed above the earth's surface. Products derived from these measurements are accessible from NOAA's NCDC website: http://www.ncdc.noaa.gov. The two primary datasets are the Integrated Global Radiosonde Archive (IGRA) and the Radiosonde Atmospheric Temperature Products for Assessing Climate (RATPAC).

Radar data

Observations from Doppler radar stations are available throughout the United States and select overseas locations. Level II data are the three meteorological base data quantities: reflectivity, mean radial velocity, and spectrum width. From these quantities, computer processing generates numerous products known as Level III data. Products with dual-polarization enhancements will continue to become available for select stations.

Figure 6.3 shows an OGC WMS composite image from Iowa State University for the contiguous United States displayed by a dynamic mapping application used to access radar data. See NOAA's NCDC mapping application for more information: http://gis.ncdc.noaa.gov/map/viewer/.

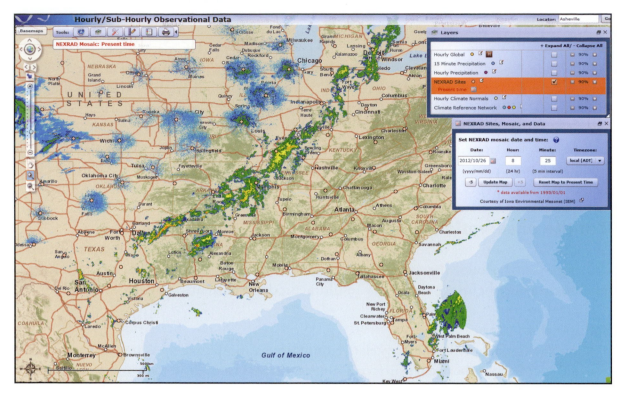

Figure 6.3 A display of Doppler radar observing stations with a WMS composite image of reflectivity for the United States. Note: Image portrayed was collected a few days before the landfall of Hurricane Sandy. | Courtesy of NOAA and Iowa Environmental Mesonet.

Satellite observations (climate data record)

NOAA's NCDC recently initiated a satellite Climate Data Record (CDR) program to continuously provide objective climate information derived from weather satellite data that NOAA has collected for more than 30 years. These data comprise the longest record of global satellite mapping measurements in the world and are complemented by data from other sources, including NASA and Department of Defense satellites and foreign satellites. The mission of NOAA's CDR program is to develop and implement a robust, sustainable, and scientifically defensible approach to producing and preserving climate records from satellite data.

The National Research Council (NRC) defines a climate data record as a time series of measurements of sufficient length, consistency, and continuity to determine climate variability and change (National Research Council 2004).

For the first time, NOAA is applying modern data analysis methods, which have advanced significantly in the last decade, to these historical global satellite data. This process will unravel the underlying climate trend and variability information and return new economic and scientific value from the records. In parallel, NCDC will maintain and extend these climate data records by applying the same methods to present-day and future satellite measurements. Access to these data is being provided through a dynamic mapping application. This application uses the WMS and subsetting services in THREDDS (Thematic Real-time Environmental Distributed Data Services) to display historical imagery, provide netCDF (Network Common Data Form) clip-n-ship data download functionality, and enable time-series plotting (figure 6.4).

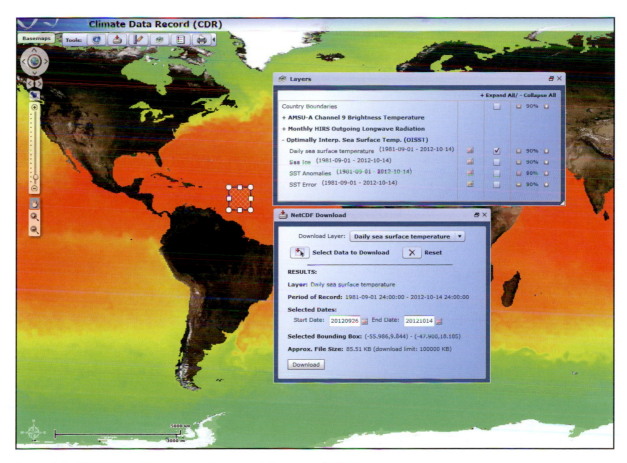

Figure 6.4 **CDR sea-surface temperature map.** | Courtesy of NOAA.

Model

To address the growing need for remote access to high-volume numerical weather prediction and global climate models and data, NCDC, the National Centers for Environmental Prediction (NCEP), and the Geophysical Fluid Dynamics Laboratory (GFDL) initiated the NOAA Operational Model Archive and Distribution System (NOMADS) project. NOMADS is a repository of weather model output datasets, model input datasets (assimilation), and a limited subset of climate model datasets generated by NOAA. NCDC provides near-real-time access to these weather model forecast data, in addition to historical model data.

Looking into the past, present, and future, three broad categories of modeled data are available through NOMADS: reanalysis, numerical weather prediction, and climate prediction. To assist users in the analysis of multidisciplinary datasets and promote interoperable data analysis, NOMADS also services derived/other model data, including sea surface temperatures (SST), paleoclimate (tree ring and ice core) data, observational information, and derived observational datasets. Figure 6.5 shows the live-access server display of an air temperature model. This is one of many access avenues available for model data held on THREDDS data servers. See NOAA's NOMADS website for more information: http://nomads.ncdc. noaa.gov.

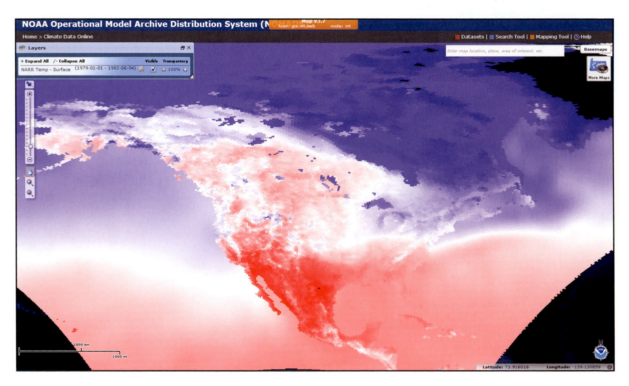

Figure 6.5 NOMADS live-access server, one of many model data access points. | Courtesy of NOAA.

Summaries and statistics

Many climate products provide summaries or statistics that monitor and assess the state of Earth's climate in near real time, providing decision makers at all levels of the public and private sectors with data and information on climate trends and variability, including perspectives on how the climate of today compares to the past. The National Drought Information Data System (NIDIS) portal provides a specialized suite of products used by local, state, and regional decision makers (figure 6.6). Global climate station summaries provide statistical analyses of a dozen observation types for user-defined time periods, as shown in figure 6.7. Climate indices are statistical indicators of climate stability or variability through time. Figure 6.8 shows a dynamic mapping application that displays indices for temperature, precipitation, drought, and degree days. Analysis of snowfall data is presented in a dynamic map shown in figure 6.9. Here, daily snowfall totals, monthly summaries, monthly departures from normal, and a snowstorm index are available for users.

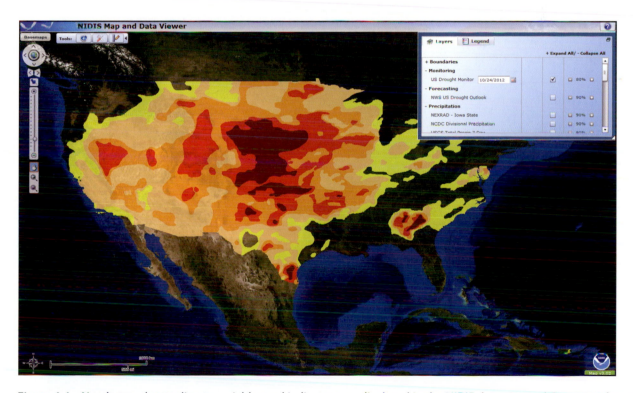

Figure 6.6 Nearly two dozen climate variables and indicators are displayed in the NIDIS data viewer. | Courtesy of NOAA.

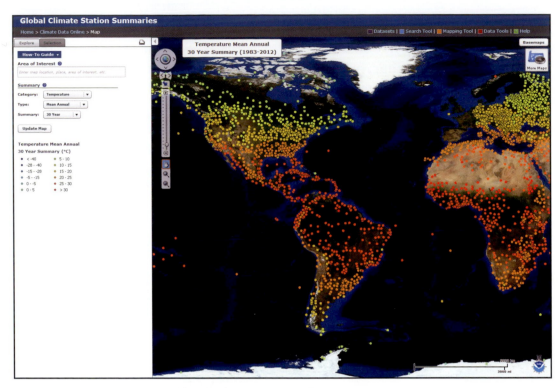

Figure 6.7   Summaries of global hourly data. | Courtesy of NOAA/NCDC.

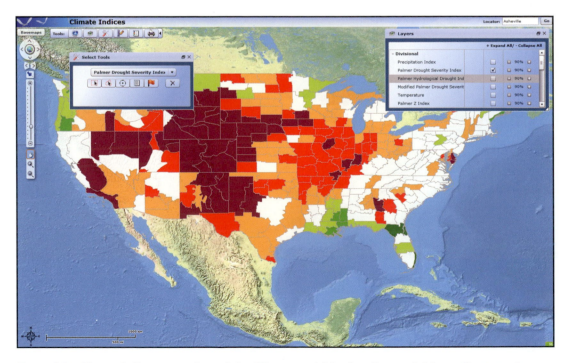

Figure 6.8   Climate indices maps show eight different variables for climate divisions, climate regions, states, and the contiguous United States. | Courtesy of NOAA.

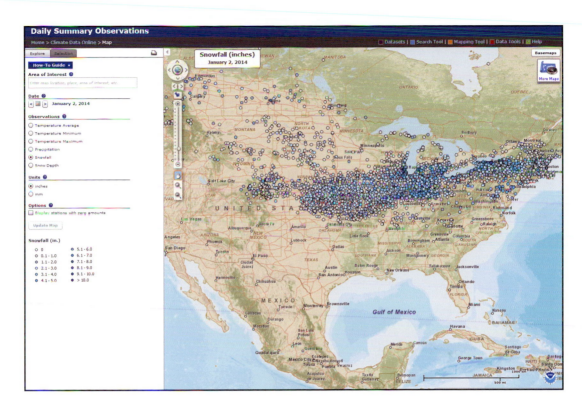

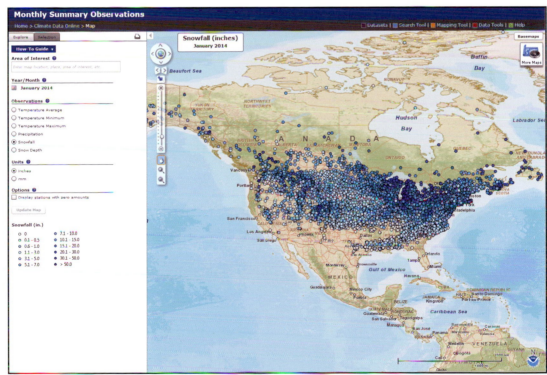

Figure 6.9 Dynamic snowfall maps provide access to and analysis of daily and monthly snowfall data and the Northeast Snowfall Impact Scale (NESIS) snowstorm index. | Courtesy of NOAA.

Conclusion

Many organizations use GIS mapping systems and OGC standard services to provide quality climate products to industry, educators, and governments. As technology and data management practices improve, these products will also evolve, provide greater value and novel presentation, and be used ubiquitously by the public.

Reference

National Research Council. 2004. *Climate Data Records from Environmental Satellites: Interim Report.* Washington, DC: The National Academies Press.

CHAPTER 7

Social media

Nazila Merati

The public is becoming a network of sensors, reporting locations of the best taco trucks, the weather, and even our moods through social networks and mobile monitoring applications. We consume data about our surroundings, and at times add value to these data through our responses and comments on social platforms. Marketers and companies have historically used this rich information to create successful product launches and to direct advertising efforts. Dozens of mobile applications exist to help us create and locate these data points: location-based social networking applications, social photo-sharing applications, online diaries, and active social networks. Commercially available social media dashboards and mapping software APIs (application programming interfaces) can consume this passively produced location information. Data mining protocols can further analyze the impact of these data by showing how this information is disseminated throughout our social networks. This indirect approach to collecting and analyzing consumer information can also be used to gather scientific observations from social media streams of chatter. This data stream can further scientific and humanitarian efforts by filling in gaps where there are no sensors or existing sample sites.

Directed collection of information occurs when users download purpose-built applications for data collection. The number of environmental and weather monitoring applications available for download to mobile devices increases every week. As of early 2014, 4,200 weather-related apps exist in the iPhone marketplace alone, and nearly the same amount exists for the Android platform (Pocket Gamer.biz 2014). These applications allow citizens to engage with their surroundings and contribute to community data collection efforts on topics such as flower bud break or bird sightings marking the start of spring or marine debris reporting (Sully 2011). Although these platforms empower citizens to make contributions to science, the information provided on these platforms also fills in gaps in existing environmental observing networks. This approach is known as a *direct* or *volunteered* method of collecting observations and has been shown to be very useful for citizen engagement and data validation (Connors et al. 2011). Information generated from the directed applications can be shared via social networks and can encourage others to join in the same efforts (Menninger 2013).

Both direct and indirect observations are helpful for research projects where resources are scarce or reporting networks have not been fully developed. These direct and indirect approaches complement each other. The ability to use geolocated tweets, location-based check-ins, and tagged or georeferenced rich media assist researchers in searching large streams of data for key words, phrases, and sentiment associated with events such as marine mammal strandings, coastal flooding, or oil spill reporting. This incident reporting via text, video, or image can act as a data point to test for spatial overlap between observations and predicted model outcomes. In addition, socioeconomic information can also be overlaid on these results to determine the societal impacts of environmental hazards and community resilience. Sentiment analysis uses natural language processing to extract information from text (e.g., tweets, blog comments, and hashtags) to determine users' attitudes about an issue based on the words or phrases they use. This analysis is common in commercially available social marketing mining tools and dashboards (e.g., Radian 6) and can be used to quantify the social impact of phenomena, especially when they affect places of leisure or scenic beauty. For example, public perception of posted beach closures because of debris wash up or harmful algal blooms may be reported as negative by social mentions that proclaim disappointment because of a shortened vacation or a sudden change in plans.

This chapter describes how direct and indirect methods of data harvesting are used for model forecast validation and climate observation. The chapter discusses data, analysis techniques, tools, and the possible uses for each method through case studies. The chapter also describes issues and implications of using social media information for weather and environmental reporting.

Tsunami marine debris tracking and the 2011 Honshu earthquake

Lucky beachcombers find glass floats from fishing nets or rubber ducks and single athletic shoes that have washed onshore from shipping containers lost at sea. Traditionally, printed newsletters and electronic message boards have been used to link beachcombers reporting these kinds of finds and have served to match paired objects, such as shoes found by beachcombers. Object sightings have proven useful to physical oceanographers who rely on floating object sightings (landings) to track and validate ocean current models and serve as a proxy for float cards for ocean current modeling (National Oceanic and Atmospheric Administration [NOAA], Southwest Fisheries Science Center 2014). Satellite imagery and more complex modeling techniques are used to predict circulation regimes, but floating objects are still useful for checking and verifying model output.

Maritime experts, emergency managers, and oceanographers are concerned with the tons of debris that resulted from the March 2011 Honshu earthquake and tsunami. The impact of the tsunami on the east coast of Japan led to the destruction of entire communities. The debris included boats, cars, docks, and building materials that were washed out to sea. Concerns about radiation exposure have been raised by many, but experts believe that the debris field washed out before the release of radioactive material (NOAA 2014). To date, oceanographers have tracked debris as it moves with the ocean currents using satellite imagery (for the larger patches) and through incident reports from ships of opportunity (International Pacific Research Center [IPRC] 2014). The majority of the debris was expected to impact the Hawaiian Islands and the west coast of the United States by February 2012, but debris will continue to drift in the Pacific for years. A drifting bottle released by Woods Hole scientists in 1956 was just found on a beach in Nova Scotia (Associated Press 2014).

Researchers worry that the lingering debris field may continue to affect shipping routes, posing navigation hazards in the open water. On shore, debris may endanger marine mammal habitat or land on well-used public beaches. These landings may negatively affect coastal tourism if they occur during a peak tourist season and if the removal of the debris is difficult. Public officials have been proactive by informing visitors about current beach conditions and how to report debris sightings via social media feeds (e.g., Facebook pages), website updates, Twitter status updates, or through print media. This may reassure visitors that the coastline is safe and open for tourism and encourage them to help in the debris tracking efforts. In any case, social media users are having conversations about aspects of debris, and this information is useful to scientists and modelers if the appropriate questions are framed and analysis is conducted.

Researchers also "mine" social media, extracting information from metadata, to locate debris. As demonstrated in a study of oil spill response (Aulov and Halem 2011), imagery and text can be mined for location and sentiment using social network content. Researchers extract debris wash up locations from geolocated images. Researches and planners also use the video or text descriptors that tag photos to verify debris tracking models. In this case, results are useful for both validating debris transport model accuracy and providing information to concerned beachgoers (Aulov and Halem 2011; also see the NOAA Marine Debris Program, http://marinedebris.noaa.gov/disaster-debris). Figure 7.1 shows a map of debris sightings reported to NOAA displayed in the Environmental Response Management Application (ERMA) disaster response tool.

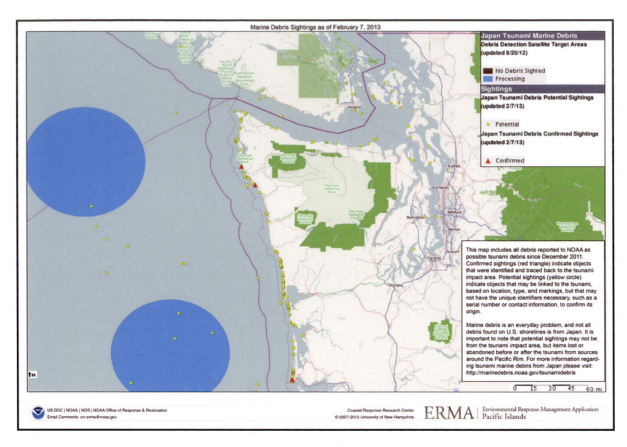

Figure 7.1 ERMA map of Washington State tsunami debris sightings from March 2013. | Courtesy of NOAA, http://marinedebris.noaa.gov/tsunamidebris/faqs.html.

Text mining techniques are based on the frequency and use of keywords and what weight analysts assign to the phrases in terms of their significance. This analysis can be somewhat subjective. Before heading into a large analysis effort, it is a good idea to determine a baseline of words to use for monitoring. Sentiment can vary widely depending on the portrayal of an event in the media and the level of buzz that surrounds a particular event. In the case of manmade disasters, most of the sentiment is likely to be negative, with a few positive mentions focusing on recovery efforts. The type of sentiment that is seen after an event can help steer and focus recovery events and public outreach. For example, the tsunami debris sightings reported on the Pacific Northwest beaches can be used to build awareness about community and governmental efforts to report and recover debris through press releases and official social media channels. Information that is retweeted or that acknowledges the source of the report can validate the citizen reporter and encourage others to do the same (figure 7.2).

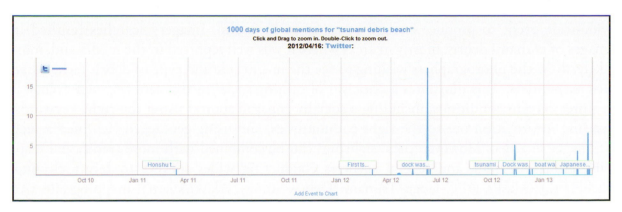

Figure 7.2 PeopleBrowsr analytics showing spikes in tsunami debris mentions after each sighting of grounded debris.

Researchers can easily monitor social channels, such as Twitter, Facebook, and social photo- and video-sharing sites, for conversations about and sightings of tsunami debris. The APIs of many of these sites are available for developers and researchers to perform advanced searches using different constraints. Social monitoring tools such as Hootsuite, Salesforce Marketing Cloud, Tweetdeck, and RavenTools can also generate reports and analyses of mentions and sentiment of keywords for different events. In events where people are less likely to report their findings or experiences via social media, text mining of news article comments and blog comments can yield some information for researchers (Barone 2007). Researchers using this technique may find information from people whose views cannot be voiced in fewer than 144 characters.

Data mined from social media can be displayed within a map and overlaid with debris field and oil spill tracks to determine the extent and precision of model results if there is good coverage within the debris or spill area of effort. This study monitored press accounts, Twitter, and Flickr for mentions of tsunami debris wash up on the Pacific Coast. Figure 7.2 shows the results of monitoring Twitter; PeopleBrowsr, a social monitoring platform; and Flickr for keywords such as "tsunami," "debris," "tsunami debris," "Oregon," "Washington," "Haida Gwaii," "ghost ship," "floating," and "dock." Due to the amount and complexity of Twitter data, the search parameters were limited. Lower volume data sources allowed larger search ranges (e.g., the search range for Flickr was approximately one year).

Although the hope was that sightings would be broadcast via social media, it appears most mentions are news stories and articles about debris wash up that are reported and retweeted by social media. To gather more original data, using something like a directed collection effort described in the next section might be more useful. These spontaneous efforts used for social data mining (Facebook mentions and Twitter) may require a large, wide-scale event to produce enough postings to be useful. Imagery searches resulted in images of tsunami debris, mostly in areas where it was well reported in the media and, most likely, drew the photographers wishing to see the magnitude and type of debris rather than first responders. This illustrates a criticism of mining social media data for such events: it requires certain conditions, including a socially engaged spotter using the right keywords, sending information out to the right communities, and using geotagged rich media such as images or video. However, these sightings can be combined with more traditional mapping efforts by state and federal agencies conducting wider surveys to target cleanup, such as the Alaska DEC Japan Tsunami Debris Survey, Alaska's aerial mapping effort to survey its vast coastline for debris impacts: http://www.arcgis.com/home/webmap/viewer. html?webmap=8ac40a055c5349b19e20cf84fdbeacf0.

Development of citizen science–reporting applications and debris-specific applications such as NOAA's Marine Debris Application (http://www.noaa.gov/features/02_monitoring/marinedebris.html) allow users to share their discoveries with other like-minded coastal enthusiasts and encourage others to participate via social-sharing options embedded within the application. Much like using programs that map jogging routes or describe exercise regimes or photo-sharing applications that link to existing social networks, contributors can broadcast their image and location to their network. Links to the applications and information about cleanup programs can also be viewed and serve as a call to others to visit their sites and join in efforts. Viral marketing efforts that ask customers to share greatly increase the exposure of untapped populations to environmental cleanup efforts (New York Times Consumer Insights Group 2013).

The NOAA marine debris application and other environmental monitoring applications allow *registered* users to log debris found on beaches, locate the finding through the device's GPS (Global Positioning System), and make notes about the condition and surroundings and upload data. The information is automatically located on a map application, and the data are available for download. Data can be logged when the device is out of network range and uploaded at a later time, which works well for those working in remote locations. The weakness of this application is that the user cannot upload a picture of the debris for visual verification. For example, if a user is uncertain that an item is tsunami debris, but the debris is labeled with Japanese script, having a picture would let researchers identify its provenance. The tracker is a great start, but researchers must conduct quality assurance to remove anomalous points of information; for example, sightings found a certain distance inland from the shoreline should be excluded from results. Developing interactive guides, wikis, and mobile catalogs of debris types will improve the quality of debris sightings by helping to train users. In places or situations where weather or recovery events are likely to reoccur, training classes and workshops will also improve the quality of observer-reported information.

Bering Sea storms: Gathering community baseline data for coastal storm impacts

In November 2011, the Bering Sea storms that affected western Alaska garnered global media coverage (Alaska Dispatch News 2011). Emphasis was placed on setting up response and information centers ahead of the event to improve communication and quality of information communicated (figure 7.3) and on the use of citizen accounts to record the magnitude and impact of the storm in near real time. Prior to the storm, Humanity Road (http://www.humanityroad.org) listed points of contact, information portals, event hashtags, and mapping applications to monitor the storm. Although procedures were in place to monitor and mitigate the effects of the storm through the dissemination of information, the storm area was sparsely populated and resulted in few real-time reports.

Figure 7.3   Archived version of Humanity Road's summary page of resources and outreach conducted during the 2011 Alaska storm event. | Courtesy of Humanity Road, http://www.humanityroad.org. Cached version at http://webcache.googleusercontent.com/search?q=cache:b4nKsr2MaoMJ:humanityroadinc01.businesscatalyst.com/situation-report/akstorm+&cd=5&hl=en&ct=clnk&gl=us, accessed 4/17/14.

The same level of planning would greatly improve data collection rates and relief efforts in more populated areas. For more recent super storms, such as Hurricane Sandy, where the impact was felt along the US Eastern Seaboard, the level of effort and reporting was greater. Official channels of information such as the National Weather Service or local emergency management officials provided prestorm information about watch areas and preparedness suggestions using the same hashtags for the event, which reinforced the use of the hashtag. Organizations including Humanity Road provided a one-stop information kiosk for relief information, social streams, and information based on categories such as hospital evacuations, traffic conditions, and map results. This planning was also done quite effectively by FEMA (Federal Emergency Management Agency) and other organizations prior to Hurricane Sandy's landfall, making it easier to find useful information in the millions of pieces of information created during the event.

Establishing protocols to monitor event conversations begins by developing and testing keyword searches, creating hashtags specific to the event (e.g., #Sandy), and identifying and informing active users of social media and influencers before the event. These steps may remove levels of ambiguity and uncertainty when analyzing output from social media search results by encouraging people to use consistent tags and locations for incident reporting. The influencers may be a community of emergency managers, local weather offices, local weather celebrities, elected officials, or popular newscasters with large followings of local users. The crisis mapping community has been effective in developing and launching procedures prior to events. SocialFlow provides a good summary of social media mapping related to Hurricane Sandy (http://giladlotan.com/2012/11/sandy-social-media-mapping/) that discusses the spread, and subsequent correction, of misinformation via social channels.

Conclusions

Directed reporting is useful in developing and maintaining long-term monitoring programs to assess a variety of events such as oil spills, marine debris landings, coastal flooding, erosion or accretion of coastal dunes, and shoreline changes. Using existing mobile data collection platforms used by citizen science groups to record the impacts after an event is useful for event analysis. Long-term citizen science projects using applications to collect data on stream water quality, invasive species, and biodiversity have proven to be robust and sustaining.

Direct observations can be captured using an open-source data toolkit developed by Extreme Citizen Science (ExCiteS, http://www.ucl.ac.uk/excites/) or by developing customizable applications using Esri's software development kits for field reporting on smartphones. In both cases, data can be uploaded to a web application when the user arrives at a location with web connectivity. Captured information is downloaded, stored in a database, and visualized in a desktop mapping application or shared with others via a web map service. The data can then be reviewed, edited, and annotated by the contributor to add extra information or make corrections. This technique allows the citizens to directly document their own landscapes and the impacts of storms on their beaches, including changes to wildlife habitat and ecology, by creating baseline images and videos and then documenting changes after an event. This feedback keeps contributors engaged and, by validating their own data additions, adds a level of reliability.

In parallel, information about a coastal storm's impacts from individual or group postings of information can be harvested from public-facing social sites or comments posted to Facebook pages of weather- and news-related outlets reporting on the event. For example, a regional weather office can serve as an information clearinghouse for storm-threatened communities to disseminate information prior to the storm event and later to post citizen storm experiences. Information collected from these indirect sources can be mapped and served to the public using ArcGIS Online, especially if the content has geographical features associated with the content (e.g., Esri US Severe Weather Map). Additionally, others can annotate the maps and make suggestions for other keywords or areas to study to look for additional impacts. Real-time accounts of ground conditions can be used to help revise and verify forecasts, engage local residents, and educate citizens about coastal storms.

These methods give the community, researchers, and social scientists a way to tap into social networks and conversations about how these events impact communities and assist in directing response. By gathering photography, video submissions, and user input into an observation application, we can get an idea of landscape processes before, and changes during, average storm and seasonal occurrences. At the same time, researchers can conduct baseline monitoring of social media conversations focused on the weather, climate, and coastal environment. This allows them to determine keywords, phrases, and sentiment to use for semantic searches, such as "storm," "coastal," "ice pack," "cold," "wind," "debris," "run up," "surge," "destruction," "movement," and "wave," that may peak during severe storm events. The key word searches, coupled with geolocated video or image validation, can provide the regional Weather Forecast Offices (WFO) verification of their storm forecasts by providing more accurate levels of measurement in areas where no sensors exist. These data can be overlaid on a map with warning polygons to determine the accuracy of storm reporting. Esri disaster maps are examples of online collaborative mapping tools (figure 7.4).

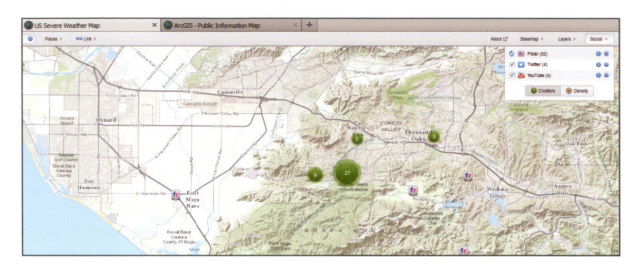

Figure 7.4 Esri disaster map showing geolocated social networking information relating to the May 2013 Southern California wildfires. | © 2013 Esri; Accuweather, Inc., Environment Canada. Basemap data from Esri, DeLorme, FAO, NOAA, and EPA.

The projects discussed here show how public agencies can collect, use, and manage social data to fill information gaps. Employing user-generated content during weather events and for crisis response has great potential, but it is also a new use of technology. These projects, although relatively small in scope, can help in developing best practices for accessing and managing this data. A long-term approach of collecting baseline information, which includes opportunities for citizen engagement through training and outreach, can provide robust data products because citizens are engaged at the early part of the data collection (e.g., weather spotters or CoCoRaHS). Younger residents are typically more comfortable with smart devices and can provide training and help for older members of their networks. As residents become more familiar with the techniques and see their data added to a map or visualized as part of a network, they are more likely to engage and contribute to data collection. Data collection applications that incorporate user feedback will also keep users engaged.

Indirect data sources such as data mining add value as well. For example, researchers can use commercially available tools to monitor social media streams for keywords and to measure sentiment about the storm impacts. Although the ideal case would have a large stream of geolocated information, researchers can infer location based on IP addresses to get general geographic location for analysis purposes. Social media channels worth exploring are ever-changing but include Twitter, public Facebook posts, Flickr, YouTube, Integra, Facebook pages about area-specific storm information, and local news reports and user comments found using commercially available social media analytical software or services.

These projects, along with others, serve as test beds to determine if data harvesting from social networking channels is a viable and inexpensive method of forecast validation. Initially, it requires studying social conversations to discover which keywords and phrases to monitor; however, once the tools are in place, monitoring is simple and can be done remotely. The information gathered can be easily reported to stakeholders. The data used for monitoring are public and available to everyone. However, there remain issues of data ownership, privacy, and data stewardship with user-generated data.

References and additional resources

Alaska Dispatch News. 2011. "North Pacific 'Super Storm' Makes Its Way toward Western Alaska Coastline." November 8. http://www.adn.com/article/north-pacific-super-storm-makes-its-way-toward-western-alaska-coastline.

Associated Press. 2014. "Bottle Released by Mass. Scientist in 1956 Found." *Boston Herald,* February 7. http://bostonherald.com/news_opinion/local_coverage/2014/02/bottle_released_by_mass_scientist_in_1956_found.

Aulov, O., and M. Halem. 2011. "Human Sensors for Improved Modeling of Natural Disasters." *Proceedings of the IEEE Remote Sensing of Natural Disasters* 100 (10): 2812–23.

Barone, F. 2007. "Current Approaches to Data Mining Blogs, Kent, University of Kent." http://www.academia.edu/185772/Current_Approaches_to_Data_Mining_Blogs.

Community Collaborative Rain, Hail, and Snow Network (CoCoRaHS) website. Accessed May 6, 2013. http://www.cocorahs.org.

Connors, J. P., S. Lei, and M. Kelly. 2011. "Citizen Science in the Age of Neogeography: Utilizing Volunteered Geographic Information for Environmental Monitoring." *Annals of the Association of American Geographers* 102 (6): 1267–89. doi:10.1080/00045608.2011.627058.

Extreme Citizen Science (ExCiteS) website. Accessed March 1, 2012. http://www.ucl.ac.uk/excites/.

International Pacific Research Center. 2014. "Tsunami Debris Models." Accessed July 31, 2014. http://iprc.soest.hawaii.edu/news/marine_and_tsunami_debris/IPRC_tsunami_debris_models.php.

Li, C., and J. Bernoff. 2011. *Groundswell—Winning in a World Transformed by Social Technologies.* Boston, MA: Forrester Research.

McCallum, A. K. 2002. "MALLET: A Machine Learning for Language Toolkit." Accessed March 6, 2012. http://mallet.cs.umass.edu.

Menninger, H. 2013. "Citizen Science Synthesis: Observations from Science Online 2013."PLOS Blogs, February 11. http://blogs.plos.org/citizensci/2013/02/11/citizen-science-synthesis-observations-from-science-online-2013/.

New York Times Consumer Insights Group. 2013. "The Psychology of Sharing—Why People Share Online." http://nytmarketing.whsites.net/mediakit/pos/.

National Oceanic and Atmospheric Administration. 2014. "Japan Tsunami Marine Debris." Last modified July 18. http://marinedebris.noaa.gov/tsunamidebris/.

National Oceanic and Atmospheric Administration, NOAA Southwest Fisheries Science Center. 2014. "OSCURS Model." http://www.pfeg.noaa.gov/products/las/OSCURS.html.

PeopleBrowsr website. Accessed August 22, 2013. http://www.peoplebrowsr.com.

Pocket Gamer.biz. 2014. "App Store Metrics." Accessed February 2014. http://148apps.biz/app-store-metrics/?mpage=catcount.

Sully, P. 2011. "Mobile Apps for Citizen Science." Musematic.net. http://musematic.net/2011/10/12/mobile-apps-for-citizen-science.

Verma, A. 2012. "Skymotion—Introduces Accuracy to Weather Reporting." *Modern Life Blogs,* October 7. http://www.modernlifeblogs.com/2012/10/skymotion-introduces-accuracy-to-weather-reporting/.

Whalley, B. 2011. "How to Evaluate and Compare Social Media Tools." *Hubspot: Inbound Marketing blog,* August 17. http://blog.hubspot.com/blog/tabid/6307/bid/29343/How-to-Evaluate-and-Compare-Social-Media-Tools.aspx.

PART 3

Models

Although atmospheric observations are arguably the most important data collected in the field of atmospheric sciences, a close second is the output data generated from numerical weather/climate prediction (NWP) models.

NWP output is the result of complex physical equations being evaluated on supercomputers, usually at representative grid points. Numerical models generate output with variable spatial domains, time steps, and forecast valid times. On one end of the scale, NWP models can run on global domains with grid spacing on the order of tens of kilometers, with time steps measured in hours, resulting in forecasts that are months to years into the future. On the other end of the scale are models that are run on city scales and are used to attempt to track plumes of trace elements, sometimes of a biochemical nature, within a city environment. Regardless of the settings that a given numerical model uses, the key is that these models produce voluminous output that is ripe for further processing using geographic information system (GIS) tools.

Part 3 will build on prior observations to explain the interdependence between observations and atmospheric models and how both can be handled within a geospatial environment to the benefit of both GIS practitioners and atmospheric scientists.

Chapter 8 discusses how models are used to increase our understanding of climate, to characterize the interactions of climate components, and to quantify its past, present, and future states.

Chapter 9 provides examples and gives recommendations for downsizing climate projections from global climate models.

Chapter 10 shows how the Climate Prediction Center uses GIS in three products: the Drought Monitor, the Global Tropical Hazards Outlook, and the US Hazards Outlook. It also discusses how geospatial technology helps the forecast process.

Chapter 11 discusses how linking models to a GIS creates an application with an intuitive interface, making it easier for new users to explore modeling. It also explains how researchers are able to easily combine model results with in situ measurements to more completely describe a system, perform analysis of model results, visualize and display spatial patterns, and clearly present their findings.

CHAPTER 8

Exploring future climates in a GIS

Olga Wilhelmi, Kevin Sampson, and Jennifer Boehnert

Climate science and modeling

The earth's climate is defined as a long-term average of daily weather in any given geographic location. Both natural and human factors determine the climate of a region or a place through complex interactions within the atmosphere–hydrosphere–land surface–human system. The natural factors include the atmosphere, geosphere, hydrosphere, and biosphere, and the human factors involve use of land and resources. Variations in any of these factors can lead to local, regional, and global changes in the climate. These changes are significant to both human activities and natural processes, which are central motivations for understanding the climate system, characterizing interactions of its components, and quantifying its past, present, and future states.

Scientists have been studying the earth's climate system for centuries. Climatology is the study of atmospheric conditions over periods of time measured in years or longer for a given location. Climatology includes a wide breadth of subdisciplines, such as dynamic, synoptic, and physical climatology, and a variety of analytical approaches and scales, ranging from microclimates to global climate. In its applied sense, climatology is related to geography, especially when the emphasis is on understanding the climate conditions at a particular location on the earth's surface (Oliver and Hidore 2002).

Just as forecasting weather presents one of the main research and operational challenges of meteorology, predicting climate is one of the great challenges in climate science. It is widely recognized that human activities are changing the earth's climate (Intergovernmental Panel on Climate Change 2007). Recent progress in understanding how the climate is changing in space and time has been achieved through improvements in modeling the climate by more realistically representing the interactions between the atmosphere and ocean. This has been accomplished by using a broader geographic coverage area, by better understanding the uncertainties associated with the model, and by using a wider variety of measurements (Washington and Parkinson 2005). These measurements come from thousands of weather stations around the globe, which have been recording weather observations for over one hundred years and providing high-quality climate data to quantify and detect global aspects of climate change (World Meteorological Association 2012). Weather stations record atmospheric variables such as air temperature, barometric pressure, precipitation, wind speed, and direction, to name a few. Weather data are increasingly observed through the use of satellites, aircraft, and shipborne instruments, which have substantially contributed to observations of changes in glaciers, snow cover, sea level, and ice sheets in recent decades.

Weather observations play a critical role in climate science; however, understanding current climate and prediction of future climate requires reconstruction of past climate states, preceding the instrumental and observational record. Reconstruction of climate over time requires the use of proxy data or paleoclimatological archives. Proxies for rainfall patterns, for example, may include the width of tree rings, whereas ice cores help identify temperature patterns or snow accumulation (Oliver and Hidore 2002). Proxies that help reconstruct temperature beyond the instrumental record inform the science of long-term climate change.

For future climate projections, scientists rely on complex computer models of the climate system. Major progress in understanding climate change was made possible through advancements in three-dimensional climate modeling and the number of simulations available from a broader range of models (Washington and Parkinson 2005). Taken together with weather observations and proxy data, these models provide a quantitative basis for estimating possible future climates (Washington and Parkinson 2005). Changes in climate, whether human caused or natural, involve a complex interplay of physical, chemical, and biological processes. Therefore, a climate model is typically constructed of component models that characterize certain parts of the climate system. For example, the National Center for Atmospheric Research (NCAR) Community Earth System Model (CESM) uses five component models: atmosphere, land, ocean, sea ice, and land ice. The component models are coordinated by a coupler that passes information between them (Vertenstein et al. 2013). The CESM produced robust suites of climate simulations for the Intergovernmental Panel on Climate Change (IPCC) fifth assessment report (IPCC 2013). Models such as CESM and its earlier version, Community Climate System Model (CCSM), advance climate science, provide critical information on climate change drivers, and contribute to knowledge of impacts and response strategies for climate change. However, large volumes of climate data have primarily remained within the atmospheric research community and can be overwhelming to nonexperts. Differences in the terminology, scientific data-modeling concepts, and the way research communities use and describe their data present a number of obstacles to the use of climate simulations by different domain experts. This chapter describes how climate modeling experiments are conducted, what climate model output consists of, and how to use the model output in a geographic information system (GIS).

Simulations of future climate

The collective effort of climate modeling focuses on conducting multiple experiments using coupled atmosphere–ocean global circulation models. Each model experiment is an individual trial, attempting to discover what happens to the earth system when perturbations, such as changes in the amount of solar radiation or changes in greenhouse gas concentrations, are introduced (Sanderson and Knutti 2011). The model's ability to simulate the earth system and show good agreement with observations validates the ability of the model to simulate future climate states. Long-term observations and paleoclimate records reveal that carbon dioxide levels in the atmosphere are increasing largely as a result of anthropogenic (i.e., resulting from human activities) emissions (IPCC 2007, 2013). The increase in greenhouse gases (GHGs), such as carbon dioxide, results in a mean warming response of the climate system.

The climate modeling community integrates a set of standard assumptions about future GHG concentrations into global climate models and analyzes the results of each model experiment. To perform a range of experiments, multiple possible future carbon dioxide levels must be determined. The most recent modeling efforts among the world's climate modeling groups use Representative Concentration Pathways (RCPs) as their standards. RCPs start with a future greenhouse gas concentration and build storylines that support that outcome (Moss et al. 2010). Climate simulations produced by modeling groups are analyzed and archived by the Coupled Model Intercomparison Project (CMIP), which provides a standard experimental protocol for studying the output of global climate models (for more information, see the CMIP website: http://pcmdi-cmip.llnl.gov/index.html?submenuheader=0). Contributions of different climate modeling groups, including NCAR's CCSM, encompass the range of time-varying projections of the various simulations defined by the CMIP protocol. For example, the output of CCSM includes averages over a range of time scales of important physical, chemical, and biological values from the atmosphere, ocean, land, and sea ice components of CCSM for multiple RCPs and using multiple ensembles.

Ensembling is a way of dealing with the uncertainty associated with the initial conditions (Tebaldi and Knutti 2007). Before a model is run, it must have a set of initial conditions, including weather conditions across the globe at a given time (e.g., air and surface temperature, wind, and humidity) and a variety of other environmental conditions (e.g., snow depth over ice, land fraction, surface pressure). Models are sensitive to these initial conditions, and the result of two identical models will vary based solely on the initial conditions used to start the model. Thus, for each RCP, the modelers will run the same model multiple times, altering only the initial conditions, in order to create an ensemble.

GIS applications in climate change research

Challenges of earth-system science include not only the integration of complex physical processes into climate models but understanding the interactions among climate, environment, and society. These challenging questions require integration of climate projections with environmental and societal information. Therefore, it is critical that climate model outputs are accessible and can be used by a wide community of researchers, educators, practitioners, and policy makers. Users of climate science need to be able to link projected climate changes with environmental, socioeconomic, and demographic factors to assess local impacts of and responses to climate change (Farber 2007). Due to this need, GIS use in climate science as well as climate change vulnerability, impacts, and adaptation communities has been on the rise.

Although many research and computational challenges still exist at the nexus of geographic information and climate science, a growing number of applications use GIS in climate change research, impacts and vulnerability assessments, and decision-support systems for adaptation planning. Recent studies include analyses of climate impacts on agriculture (e.g., Knox et al. 2010), conservation and biogeography (e.g., Ackerly et al. 2010), and coastal areas (e.g., Weiss, Overpeck, Strauss 2011; Iyalomhe et al. 2013). For example, Knox et al. (2010) conducted an assessment of climate change impacts on sugarcane production in Swaziland. The study integrated GIS with outputs from a climate and crop growth model to assess the spatial and temporal impacts of climate change on sugarcane yields and irrigation needs. Weiss et al. (2011) used GIS data and geoprocessing techniques to identify coastal areas in the United States that might be at risk from sea level rise and coastal flooding. Focusing mainly on coastal biodiversity, Iyalomhe et al. (2013) conducted an inventory of GIS-based decision-support systems that assess and manage climate change impacts on coastal waters and related inland watersheds.

Climate and society are coevolving in a manner that could place more vulnerable populations at risk from climatic hazards (Wilhelmi and Hayden 2010). Hazard risk management in a changing climate is particularly crucial, because climate change is predicted to affect the spatial and temporal distribution of climate hazards and extreme weather events (Morss et al. 2011). Recent advancements in and accessibility of GIS tools and data have increased the potential for mapping and modeling vulnerability to hazards and climate change. In a comprehensive review of spatial vulnerability assessments, Preston et al. (2011) emphasized the diversity of approaches to vulnerability mapping and identified strengths and weaknesses associated with specific applications. As climate change adaptation planning becomes more integrated into natural resource and disaster management plans, use of climate model output in GIS is expected to grow, along with development of new spatially explicit assessment methods. Therefore, knowing how to work with climate model outputs in a GIS is essential to broadening understanding, as well as planning.

Working with climate model outputs in a GIS

The one component that most atmospheric data, including climate model outputs, have in common is their *multidimensionality*. Multidimensional data vary not only in longitude (x) and latitude (y), but also in time (t) and/or a vertical dimension (z). The temporal dimension (t) may vary from seconds to long-term averages over multiple years or decades. The vertical dimension (z) can represent distance above sea level, distance above ground level, and pressure levels. Numerical climate models are commonly visualized and analyzed in three or four dimensions.

Several data formats can store multidimensional data for visualization and analysis. One format that is very common in climate science is the Network Common Data Form (netCDF) (for more information, see Unidata's description of netCDF: http://www.unidata.ucar.edu/software/netcdf/). NetCDF is a self-describing, array-based data format. "Self-describing" means that all netCDF data have a header file that explains the contents of the dataset. No external files are needed to explain the data. NetCDF is very flexible and may be structured in a number of different ways. This flexibility makes netCDF very useful for storing climate model outputs, but it also makes netCDF difficult to use in a GIS. Metadata conventions are essential for sharing and using netCDF data in general, and in GIS in particular. The most common metadata convention for netCDF currently is the Climate and Forecast (CF) metadata convention (for more information, see the CF Conventions and Metadata website: http://cfconventions.org). The CF convention provides a description for what each variable contains and the properties for all dimensions in the data. Data that conform to the CF convention are structured in a similar manner so that software packages know what to expect and how to interpret the information. Esri ArcGIS software includes tools that access, visualize, and query multidimensional netCDF data as "slices" through their dimensions. For more information about multidimensional tools, see chapter 20.

Improving data usability: GIS climate change portal

Despite recent progress in the interoperability between ArcGIS and netCDF, and the availability of the CMIP archives, accessibility of climate model outputs in the formats used and understood by decision makers can be improved. The data complexity associated with the multidimensionality of netCDF formats and the different metadata conventions present a number of challenges for working with netCDF data in a GIS. To address the challenge of data accessibility and complexity, the GIS Program at NCAR developed an online interactive Climate Change Scenarios data portal that distributes CCSM outputs in file formats commonly used by GIS professionals and decision makers, namely shapefiles, text files, and images (for more information, see the Climate Change Scenarios data portal website: http://gisClimateChange.ucar.edu). The Climate Change Scenarios portal was the first of its kind when it was released in 2005 and is one of only a few that offer such services today. This portal serves as a means to access the NCAR CCSM climate change simulations, as well as an educational resource to better understand the climate science behind the data. Users can access their choice of geographic area, time period, climate model variables, and file formats as well as download processed data products such as long-term averages and climate anomalies. These data are available for both present-day climate and for model-simulated future climate to assess changes in temperature, precipitation, and other variables that may be of interest to the users. The future climate projections are based on the RCPs (Moss et al. 2010), with a full ensemble of model experiments. In addition to providing direct access to the model output on a global scale (spatial resolution of current climate models ranges between 100 and 150 km^2), the portal distributes statistically downscaled model outputs for near-surface air temperature and precipitation for the continental United States at 4.5 km spatial resolution. Statistical downscaling of global climate models follows the methodology described in Hoar and Nychka (2008). Examples of climate model data that users can download from the Climate Change Scenarios portal are shown in figure 8.1.

Because the majority of the portal users seek information about climate change or climate anomalies (discussed in the following), providing multiple entry points for the data access increases the usability of climate science and data products. In addition to the NCAR GIS portal, climate anomalies as well as long-term averages of temperature and precipitation can also be accessed through Open Geospatial Consortium (OGC) protocols of Web Map Services (WMS; for more information, see the University Corporation for Atmospheric Research [UCAR] WMS website: http://gis.ucar.edu/data/climate/wms) and Web Coverage Services (WCS; for more information, see the UCAR WCS website: http://gis.ucar.edu/data/climate/wcs) via a THREDDS (Thematic Real-time Environmental Distributed Data Services) Data Server (TDS). WMS and WCS requests are GET-type uniform resource locators (URLs) with key-value parameter lists. Users can write a WMS request for an image that can then be used in documents or presentations. Otherwise, users can write a WCS request and retrieve a GeoTIFF or a netCDF file. These OGC web services can be automated by software developers or used directly by GIS professionals to work with climate model data in ArcMap.

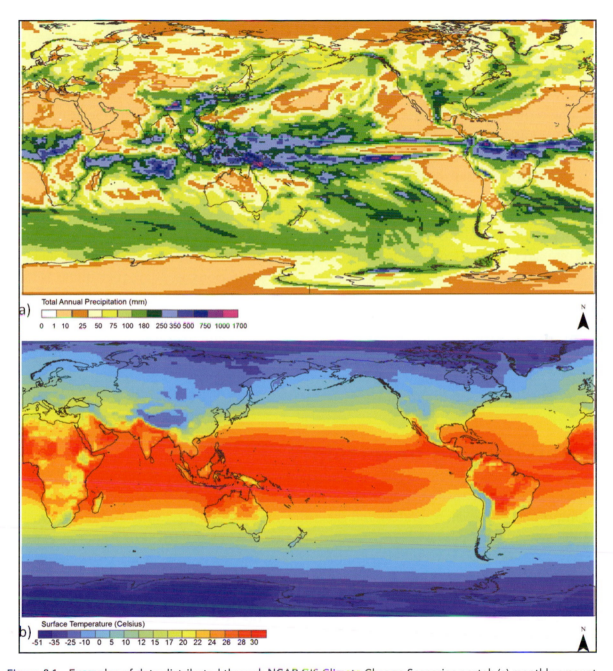

Figure 8.1 Examples of data distributed through NCAR GIS Climate Change Scenarios portal: (a) monthly amount of rainfall for May 2050, as simulated by CCSM4 using the ensemble average of RPC 8.5; (b) 20-year average annual temperature for mid-century (2040–2059) as simulated by CCSM4 using the ensemble average of RPC 8.5. | Courtesy of National Center for Atmospheric Research (NCAR).

Looking for trends with climate anomalies and long-term averages

Climate is naturally variable; no two years are ever exactly alike. Due to this variability, the best way to analyze the "climate signal" is through long-term averages of daily or monthly data. The long-term seasonal averages, for example, are useful for regional-scale temperature analysis, such as answering the question: "Which regions in the northern latitudes may be affected by permafrost melt in the middle of the twenty-first century?" Because climate is defined as a long-term average of daily weather in any given geographic location, climate change is a change in long-term average weather conditions. This change is typically calculated using an anomaly approach: a deviation of a future climate from the present or past climate. This change or anomaly can be calculated for each grid cell in a global climate model. With an anomaly map, one can visualize regions where the most warming may occur or regions where the most drying may occur. For example, according to CCSM projections, in 2050, the annual average temperature in most regions of high latitudes of North America will still remain below freezing. However, if we compare the 2050 average annual temperature to the present-day climate, we can clearly see the overall warming trend, its magnitude, and spatial variability (figure 8.2). When generating anomalies, a model simulation of present climate should be used instead of observed station-based values. Model results are most useful when compared to other model output, which will contain similar biases.

Understanding uncertainty

All climate models contain degrees of uncertainty. Although uncertainty exists, informed decisions may still be made based on the results of climate models (Dessai and Wilby 2011). It is important, however, to understand the different types of uncertainty and how scientists and decision makers deal with the uncertainty that is known. First, uncertainties exist in the physical processes that are being modeled. Many important small-scale processes cannot be represented explicitly in models, and so they must be represented in approximate form. These "parameterizations" are made to simplify complex processes, such as cloud formation, for purposes of computational efficiency (Stensrud 2007, 6). Uncertainties also exist in the magnitude and timing of events, as well as the regional details of particular phenomena. For example, it is impossible to know exactly where rain will fall, or exactly how much. The usefulness of climate model data comes from the ability of the model to represent broad patterns rather than extreme precision.

There is uncertainty as to the future of the earth's climate system. Will increased warming result in more cloudiness and lead to a cooling response? Do aerosols in the atmosphere contribute to or mitigate the greenhouse effect of carbon dioxide? The answers may require additional investigation and depend on the policies regarding future emissions. As previously discussed, a great deal of uncertainty exists about what technologies will be implemented in

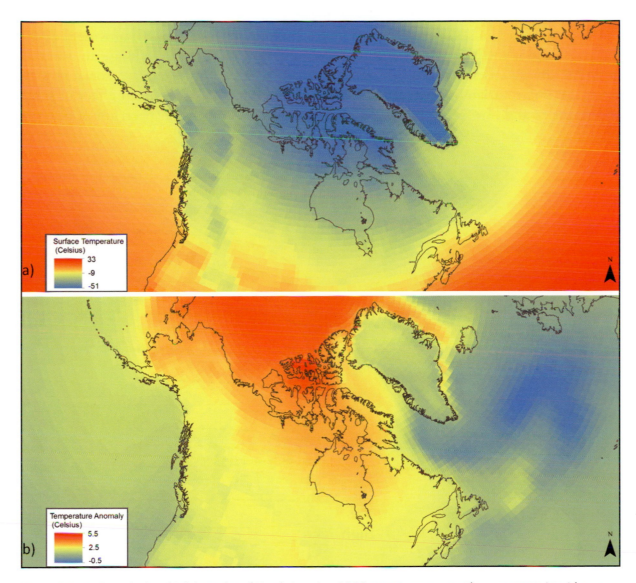

Figure 8.2 A closer look at high latitudes of North America: (a) 20-year average annual temperature in mid-century (2040–2059) as simulated by CCSM4 using ensemble average of RPC 8.5; (b) projected change (anomaly) of average annual temperature for mid-century (2040–2059) compared to the reference period 1986–2005 for the ensemble average of RCP 8.5. | Courtesy of National Center for Atmospheric Research (NCAR).

the future and the capacity of future populations to combat rising greenhouse gas levels (Moss et al. 2010); thus, the RCPs attempt to manage this uncertainty by capturing the spectrum of plausible futures from low to high emissions.

Finally, uncertainty exists among ensemble members. Each ensemble member represents a possible future state, based on a set of initial conditions, but no ensemble member is more "true" than another. Each exhibits variability, which may be used to examine extreme events and short-term responses of the climate system. The ensemble average will provide the general trend and is the best guess about broad-scale climate change in the long run, whereas variation among ensemble members gives an estimate of the uncertainty associated with internal climate variability (IPCC 2007). Figure 8.3 illustrates the mixed effect of some uncertainties and how the combination of uncertainties results in a spectrum of possible outcomes.

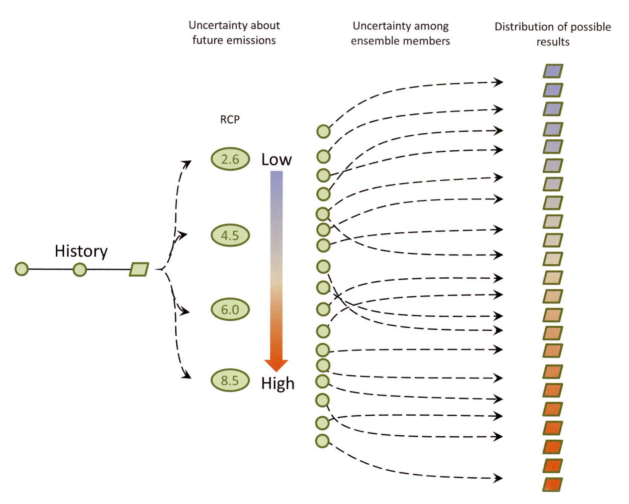

Figure 8.3 Sources of uncertainty in the climate modeling process lead to a range of possible future climate states. | Courtesy of National Center for Atmospheric Research (NCAR).

Summary and best practices

The analysis of climate simulations in a GIS allows decision makers, researchers, and educators to explore complex questions that include certain climatic thresholds, future scenarios, and a number of diverse social and environmental datasets. Using GIS to answer interdisciplinary questions about the impacts of climate change as well as the vulnerabilities of physical and social systems can place the complexity of the problems in the context of local, regional, and global geographies and help formulate potential responses through mitigation and adaptation strategies.

As previously discussed, climate model projections are not weather predictions, and the output of a climate model should not be used in the way a weather forecast is used. Many processes that affect weather are too fine in scale and time to be modeled effectively using a climate model. Further, weather models use precise initial conditions based on observations. Climate models get their initial weather conditions not from observations, but from control experiments in which twentieth-century climate is simulated. Once the model has run to a steady equilibrium state and is able to accurately reproduce the general climate of the historical record, it is run into the future. Thus, the general features of future climate in the model yield a better representation of the future than an instantaneous point in model time. "Best practices" for working with global climate model projections in a GIS are summarized in the following:

- Use a 10- or 20-year average for the variable in question when analyzing climate model output for future time horizons. For example, the 10-year window around the 2050 average temperature will average out interannual variability in the model and provide a best guess for the approximate 2050 temperature.

- Create an anomaly from of the climate model output. Rather than just viewing the precipitation for the future time period, compare it to "current" modeled precipitation (1986–2005, for example) to yield an expected change rather than a precise estimate.

- Use the ensemble average, rather than an individual model run, when trying to determine the model's general estimate of future conditions.

- Use output from different RCPs and multiple climate models to encompass the range of possible future conditions.

- Use climate models at scales that are appropriate for your scale of analysis. A fine scale of analysis may require a downscaled product.

References

Ackerly, D. D., S. R. Loarie, W. K. Cornwell, S. B. Weiss, H. Hamilton, R. Branciforte, and N. J. B. Kraft. 2010. "The Geography of Climate Change: Implications for Conservation Biogeography." *Diversity and Distributions* 16 (3): 476–87.

Farber, D. A. 2007. *Climate Models: A Users Guide.* Berkeley: University of California.

Hoar, T., and D. Nychka. 2008. "Statistical Downscaling of the Community Climate System Model (CCSM) Monthly Temperature and Precipitation Projections." White paper. http://gisclimatechange.ucar.edu/sites/default/files/users/Downscaling.pdf.

Intergovernmental Panel on Climate Change (Nakićenović, N., and R. Swart, eds.). 2000. *Special Report on Emissions Scenarios: A Special Report of Working Group III of the Intergovernmental Panel on Climate Change.* Cambridge, UK: Cambridge University Press.

———. 2007. *Climate Change 2007—The Physical Science Basis, Working Group I Contribution to the Fourth Assessment Report of the IPCC.* Cambridge, UK: Cambridge University Press.

———. 2013. IPCC Activities. http://www.ipcc.ch/activities/activities.shtml#.UZL8ocqDl8E.

Iyalomhe, F., J. Rizzi, S. Torresan, V. Gallina, A. Critto, and A. Marcomini. 2013. "Inventory of GIS-Based Decision Support Systems Addressing Climate Change Impacts on Coastal Waters and Related Inland Watersheds." In *Climate Change: Realities, Impacts over Ice Cap, Sea Level, and Risks,* edited by Bharat Raj Singh. Intech. doi:10.5772/3459.

Knox, J. W., J. A. Rodríguez Díaz, D. J. Nixon, and M. Mkhwanazi. 2010. "A Preliminary Assessment of Climate Change Impacts on Sugarcane in Swaziland." *Agricultural Systems* 103 (2): 63–72.

Moss, R. H., J. A. Edmonds, K. A. Hibbard, M. R. Manning, S. K. Rose, D. P. van Vuuren, T. R. Carter, S. Emori, M. Kainuma, T. Kram, G. A. Meehl, J. F. B. Mitchell, N. Nakicenovic, K. Riahi, S. J. Smith, R. J. Stouffer, A. M. Thomson, J. P. Weyant, and T. J. Wilbanks. 2010. "The Next Generation of Scenarios for Climate Change Research and Assessment." *Nature* 463: 747–56. doi:10.1038/nature08823.

Morss, R. E., O. V. Wilhelmi, G. A. Meehl, and L. Dilling. 2011. "Improving Societal Outcomes of Extreme Weather in a Changing Climate: An Integrated Perspective." *Annual Review of Environment and Resources* 36: 1–25.

Oliver, J. E., and J. J. Hidore. 2002. *Climatology: An Atmospheric Science.* Upper Saddle River, NJ: Prentice Hall.

Preston, B. L., E. J. Yuen, and R. M. Westaway. 2011. "Putting Vulnerability to Climate Change on the Map: A Review of Approaches, Benefits, and Risks." *Sustainability Science* 6 (2): 177–202. doi:10.1007/s11625-011-0129-1.

Sanderson, B., and R. Knutti. 2012. *Encyclopedia of Sustainability Science and Technology,* edited by Robert A. Meyers. New York: Springer.

Stensrud, D. J. 2007. *Paramerization Schemes: Keys to Understanding Numerical Weather Prediction Models.* Cambridge, UK: Cambridge University Press.

Tebaldi, C., and R. Knutti. 2007. "The Use of the Multi-Model Ensemble in Probabilistic Climate Projections." *Philosophical Transactions of the Royal Society A* 365 (1857): 2053–75. doi:10.1098/rsta.2007.2076.

Vertenstein, M., T. Craig, A. Middleton, D. Feddema, and C. Fischer. 2013. *CESM1.0.4 User's Guide.* http://www.cesm.ucar.edu/models/cesm1.0/cesm/cesm_doc_1_0_4/book1.html.

Washington, W. M., and C. L. Parkinson. 2005. *An Introduction to Three-Dimensional Climate Modeling,* 2nd ed. Sausalito, CA: University Science Books.

Weiss, J. L., J. T. Overpeck, and B. Strauss. 2011. "Implications of Recent Sea Level Rise Science for Low-Elevation Areas in Coastal Cities of the Conterminous U.S.A." *Climatic Change* 105: 635–45. doi:10.1007/s10584-011-0024-x.

Wilby, R. L., and S. Dessai. 2010. "Robust Adaptation to Climate Change." *Weather* 65 (7): 180–85.

Wilhelmi, O. V., and M. H. Hayden. 2010. "Connecting People and Place: A New Framework for Reducing Urban Vulnerability to Extreme Heat." *Environmental Research Letters* 5: 014021.

World Meteorological Association. 2012. "World Meteorological Organization, Climate Data and Monitoring." http://www.wmo.int/pages/prog/wcp/wcdmp/index_en.php.

CHAPTER 9

Downscaling of climate models

Henrik Madsen

Climate projections from global climate models (GCMs) have, in general, a too coarse spatial resolution to be used directly for local impact assessment studies. In addition, GCMs may have significant biases when compared to local-scale climate variables. Downscaling is required for obtaining high-resolution and bias-adjusted climate projections at the local scale. Downscaling can be accomplished through statistical adjustments of GCMs directly or by combining statistical downscaling with dynamic downscaling, using higher resolution regional climate modeling (RCM) nested within GCMs.

Global and regional climate models

GCMs are used to project future climate. They simulate climate response to climate forcing scenarios of atmospheric composition of greenhouse gases. It is generally accepted that GCMs provide credible estimates of climate change at continental and larger scales. The confidence in the model projections, however, varies for different climate variables. The confidence is generally higher for temperature than for precipitation (e.g., Randell et al. 2007). The GCMs may have significant errors at smaller scales, but large errors are also present in the simulation of large-scale features and teleconnections. GCM projection data are not, in general, of sufficient resolution and reliability to be used directly for climate change impact assessments at the local scale. Typically, downscaling is needed to obtain more reliable climate projections, either by dynamic downscaling using regional climate models (RCMs) or by statistical downscaling.

An RCM covers a certain geographical area and is nested within a GCM, using GCM projections as boundary conditions for the simulation. State-of-the-art RCMs use a horizontal resolution of about 10–50 km. This allows a better representation of topography and land surface heterogeneities, and thus more realistic simulations of associated processes than GCMs. However, significant errors may still be present. For instance, the RCM inherits the biases and other deficiencies of the driving GCM. Another important source of error in the RCM is the physical parameterizations used to resolve processes at the subgrid scale, such as cloud processes, convection, boundary layer processes, and land surface–atmosphere interactions. As a result, RCMs may have severe biases, and cannot, in general, be used directly in impact studies. Bias correction and statistical downscaling is required prior to using RCM projections in impact modeling.

Traditionally, statistical downscaling has been considered an alternative to dynamic downscaling. However, in recent years the focus has been on developing statistical downscaling methods for RCM projections to optimally combine dynamic and statistical downscaling. Statistical downscaling has two main purposes: (1) to downscale climate model projections from the GCM or RCM grid scale to the local scale of application (spatial downscaling) and (2) to correct biases in the GCM or RCM projections (statistical correction). In general, these two elements cannot be separated, and proposed statistical downscaling procedures address both spatial downscaling and statistical correction simultaneously.

Statistical downscaling

Statistical downscaling relates the climate projections at the larger scale (from GCMs or RCMs) to climate variables at the local scale. A number of different methods have been developed. Recent reviews have been given by Fowler, Blenkinsop, and Tebaldi (2007), who focus on downscaling in relation to hydrologic impact assessments, and Maraun et al. (2010), who provide a comprehensive review of methods for statistical downscaling of precipitation. Maraun et al. (2010) classified statistical downscaling into perfect prognosis (PP) methods, model output statistics methods, and stochastic weather generators.

PP methods are based on statistical relationships between large-scale (synoptic) predictors (e.g., geopotential height, wind components, and humidity at different atmosphere levels) and local-scale climate variables (e.g., precipitation, temperature, and wind speed). PP methods are typically used with GCM projections but can also be combined with RCM projections. The statistical relationship (transfer function) is established by using observed large-scale predictors (typically gridded reanalysis data) and observed local-scale climate variables. For the downscaling, projected large-scale predictors by the GCM are then used to project the local-scale climate variable. The performance of PP methods is highly dependent on the choice of large-scale predictors and the transfer function. Suitable predictors should be simulated well by the GCM and be physically meaningful for describing the local-scale climate variability. The PP methods implicitly assume that the statistical relationship between predictors and local climate is stationary in time; that is, the estimated relationship in the present climate can also be applied in a changed climate. This assumption is questionable and cannot be verified. It is also important to emphasize that PP methods are not as effective in downscaling extreme events because such events are rare and are in the extreme tail of the distribution of the observed climate variable used for estimating the transfer function.

Model output statistics (MOS) methods are based on direct statistical relationships between simulated and observed climate variables (e.g., simulated precipitation by a climate model and observed local-scale precipitation). MOS methods can be applied with both GCM and RCM data. In its simplest form, MOS uses the change in the mean of the climate variable from current to future climate simulated by the GCM or RCM model to provide downscaled local projections. This method is often referred to as the *delta change method* or *perturbation method*. For temperature, an additive change is applied, whereas for precipitation, a relative change is usually applied. The delta change method is a special case of a general class of MOS methods based on a common change factor methodology. The basic concept in change factor methods is that climate model simulations are used to extract changes in different statistical characteristics of climate variables from current to future climate (denoted change factors), and these changes are then superimposed on the statistical characteristics of the climate variable representing the local scale. Typically, change factors are calculated by comparing a 30-year future projection time slice with a 30-year baseline period (usually referred to as control period). The principle of MOS using change factors is illustrated in figure 9.1. An implicit assumption of MOS methods is that the climate model better represents changes in climate variables rather than the absolute values. In other words, climate model biases are assumed constant in a changing climate. This assumption is questionable, and recent research shows that biases may not be time invariant in a warming climate (Christensen et al. 2008).

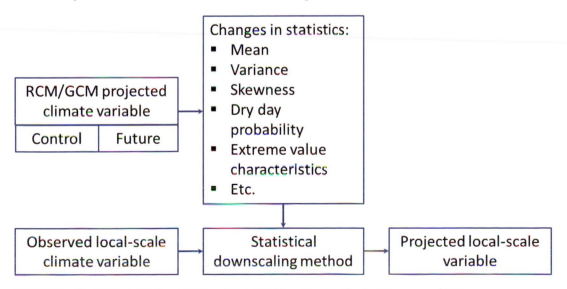

Figure 9.1   Illustration of change factor–based downscaling methods. | Courtesy of DHI.

Stochastic weather generators (WGs) are statistical models that generate random sequences of local-scale weather variables that resemble the statistical properties of the observed variables. Some WGs use climate variables derived directly from RCMs, and hence resemble MOS methods, whereas other WGs also use large-scale predictors, as in PP methods. For statistical downscaling of precipitation, a number of WGs based on a change factor methodology using RCM data have been applied (e.g., Kilsby et al. 2007). In this case, changes in the statistical characteristics used to parameterize the WGs are estimated from the RCM simulations, and these changes are then superimposed on the statistical characteristics estimated from the observed record to obtain WGs for generation of the downscaled variables in the future climate. Compared to the change factor–based MOS methods, WGs utilize changes in different statistics representing both the temporal structure (wet–dry sequences) and the distribution of precipitation intensity. Another advantage of WGs is that they can be used for generation of synthetic time series of arbitrary length. This is especially important when considering changes in extreme events where long time series can be generated by a WG for obtaining robust projections of the extreme value distribution.

Example of GCM downscaling: The MIKE by DHI Climate Change Tool

Global climate projections from 22 GCMs included in the Coupled Model Intercomparison Project (CMIP3; http://www-pcmdi.llnl.gov/ipcc/about_ipcc.php) and reported in the Intergovernmental Panel on Climate Change (IPCC) Fourth Assessment Report have been made available in the MIKE by DHI Climate Change Tool. The tool can be used for larger scale impact studies and for a first screening at the regional or local scale. For downscaling GCM projections, delta change factors for precipitation, temperature, and potential evapotranspiration are available for the 22 GCM models for the three most common SRES emission scenarios: B1, A1B, and A2. For precipitation and potential evapotranspiration relative change factors are supported, whereas absolute changes are given for temperature. For calculation of the change in potential evapotranspiration, a temperature-based method is used, as recommended by Kay and Davies (2008). Monthly change factors are provided that are calculated as averages for three 20-year time slices (2011–2030, 2046–2065, 2080–2099). For some GCM models change factors for the time slice 2180–2199 are also available.

The tool automatically modifies the climate time series of an existing model setup according to specified location (longitude, latitude), GCM model, emission scenario, and projection horizon. Projected climate time series are calculated using the delta change approach (i.e., precipitation time series are multiplied by the precipitation change factors, temperature change factors are added to the temperature time series, and potential evapotranspiration time series are multiplied by the evapotranspiration change factors). Different scenarios (e.g., different GCMs, emission scenarios, and projection horizons) can be defined within the same setup, allowing an easy evaluation and comparison of different climate change scenarios. The tool supports the selection of an ensemble of GCM models for calculation of ensemble average change factors. The Climate Change Tool user interface is shown in figure 9.2.

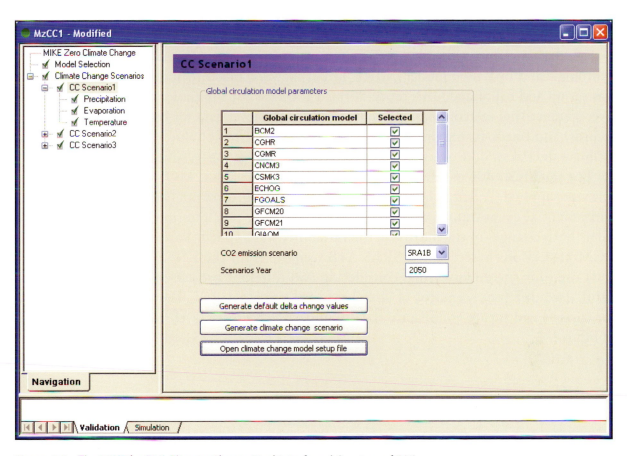

Figure 9.2   The MIKE by DHI Climate Change Tool interface. | Courtesy of DHI.

An example of RCM downscaling and impact assessment: Flood risk analysis

The use of downscaled RCM projections for climate change impact assessment is illustrated for a flood risk analysis study of the Vidaa River catchment, a cross-border catchment in Denmark and northern Germany (Madsen et al. 2013). The Vidaa River discharges into the sea through a tidal sluice. Extreme water levels in the lower part of the river system occur during storm surges where the sluice is closed over a prolonged period, and at the same time increased runoff from the catchment occurs due to heavy precipitation. The low-lying part of the catchment is protected by river dikes.

To assess the impacts of future climate change both changes in the meteorological forcing (precipitation, temperature, and potential evapotranspiration) and changes in seawater level have to be considered. Changes in meteorological forcing data were estimated from regional climate model projections included in the ENSEMBLES data archive (van der Linden and Mitchell 2009). Future seawater levels were estimated from current projections of the mean sea level rise in the area, estimated isostatic changes, and changes in storm surge statistics predicted from a regional hydrodynamic model forced with RCM projections of wind and pressure fields. To estimate the changes in flood risk in the Vidaa River system, an integrated hydrologic and hydraulic model (MIKE 11, http://www.mikebydhi.com/products/mike-11) was set up and calibrated. This model formed the basis for simulation of water levels in the river system using meteorological forcing and seawater-level data for current (using observed records) and future (using projected records) climate. Extreme value analysis was applied to estimate the risk of dike overtopping at different locations.

For statistical downscaling of the RCM climate variables, MOS change factor methods were applied. A delta change approach was applied for temperature (additive change) and potential evapotranspiration (relative change). For precipitation, a method that considers both changes in the mean and the variability was applied (Sunyer et al. 2012). Fifteen RCM projections based on the SRES A1B scenario from the ENSEMBLES data archive were used for the downscaling, considering two different projection horizons, 2050 and 2100. Two different scenarios of global sea level rise were used. The estimated flood risks for current and future conditions in 2100 under the high sea level rise scenario are shown in figure 9.3.

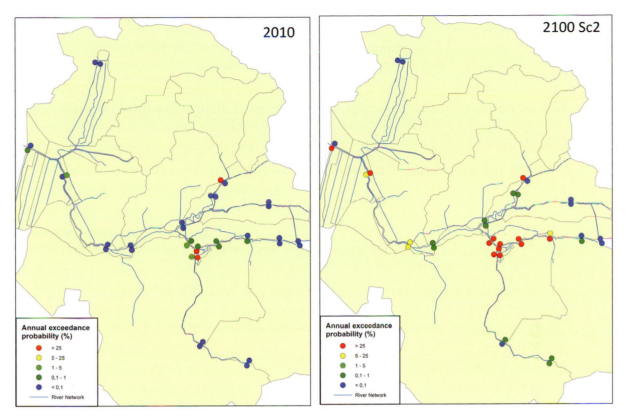

Figure 9.3 Estimated flood risk at selected locations in the Vidaa River system for current (2010) and future (2100 with high mean sea level scenario) climate. For each location, the annual exceedance probabilities for overtopping left and right bank are shown. | Courtesy of DHI.

Conclusion

For climate change impact analysis it is important to identify the climate variables and associated characteristics (e.g., mean value, variability, or extremes) that are most sensitive for the problem at hand and therefore should be accurately downscaled. In this regard one should be aware of the limitations and advantages of the different downscaling methods. In general, choice of statistical downscaling method is less important in the case where the impacts are determined mostly by average conditions on larger scales. However, when the properties of extremes are important for the impact assessment, the choice of statistical downscaling method is crucial. The widely applied delta change method implicitly assumes that the change in the extreme tail is the same as the change in the mean. Thus, this method is not recommended for analyzing changes in extremes. MOS methods that include changes in the variance or changes in the full distribution using quantile mapping or WGs are generally expected to provide a better projection of extremes.

References

Christensen, J., F. Boberg, O. Christensen, and P. Lucas-Picher. 2008. "On the Need for Bias Correction of Regional Climate Change Projections of Temperature and Precipitation." *Geophysical Research Letters* 35 (20): L20, 709.

Fowler, H. J., S. Blenkinsop, and C. Tebaldi. 2007. "Review: Linking Climate Change Modelling to Impacts Studies—Recent Advances in Downscaling Techniques for Hydrological Modelling." *International Journal of Climatology* 27: 1547–78.

Kay, A. L., and H. N. Davies. 2008. "Calculating Potential Evaporation from Climate Model Data: A Source of Uncertainty for Hydrological Climate Change Impacts." *Journal of Hydrology* 358: 221–39.

Kilsby, C. G., P. D. Jones, A. Burton, A. C. Ford, H. J. Fowler, C. Harpham, P. James, A. Smith, and R. L. Wilby. 2007. "A Daily Weather Generator for Use in Climate Change Studies." *Environmental Modelling & Software* 22: 1705–19.

Madsen, H., M. Sunyer, J. Larsen, M. N. Madsen, B. Møller, T. Drückler, M. Matzdorf, and J. Nicolaisen. 2013. "Climate Change Impact Assessment of the Dike Safety and Flood Risk in the Vidaa River System." *Climate Change and Disaster Risk Management, Climate Change Management.* 2013: 583–95.

Maraun, D., F. Wetterhall, A. M. Ireson, R. E. Chandler, E. J. Kendon, M. Widmann, S. Brienen, H. W. Rust, T. Sauter, M. Themeßl, V. K. C. Venema, K. P. Chun, C. M. Goodess, R. G. Jones, C. Onof, M. Vrac, and I. Thiele-Eich. 2010. "Precipitation Downscaling under Climate Change. Recent Developments to Bridge the Gap between Dynamical Models and the End User." *Reviews of Geophysics* 48 (3): RG3003. doi:10.1029/2009RG000314.

Randall, D. A., R. A. Wood, S. Bony, R. Colman, T. Fichefet, J. Fyfe, V. Kattsov, A. Pitman, J. Shukla, J. Srinivasan, R. J. Stouffer, A. Sumi, and K. E. Taylor. 2007. "Climate Models and Their Evaluation." In *Climate Change 2007: The Physical Science Basis. Contribution of Working Group I to the Fourth Assessment Report of the Intergovernmental Panel on Climate Change.* S. Solomon, D. Qin, M. Manning, Z. Chen, M. Marquis, K. B. Averyt, M. Tignor, and H. L. Miller, eds. Cambridge, UK; New York: Cambridge University Press.

Sunyer, M. A., H. Madsen, and P. H. Ang. 2012. "A Comparison of Different Regional Climate Models and Statistical Downscaling Methods for Extreme Rainfall Estimation under Climate Change." *Atmospheric Research* 103: 119–28.

van der Linden, P., and J. F. B. Mitchell, eds. 2009. *ENSEMBLES: Climate Change and Its Impacts. Summary of Research and Results from the ENSEMBLES Project.* Exeter, UK: Met Office Hadley Centre.

CHAPTER 10

Climate applications at the NOAA Climate Prediction Center

Sudhir Raj Shrestha, Matthew Rosencrans, Kenneth Pelman, and Rich Tinker

Since the 1990s, the National Weather Service (NWS) has used an internal hardware/software system known as the Advanced Weather Interactive Processing System (AWIPS). AWIPS shares forecast products and data among all the geographically disparate NWS field offices and National Centers for Environmental Prediction (NCEP) within a secure network. When the World Wide Web increased in popularity in the early 2000s, NWS issued official products via the Internet and AWIPS. For the past 5 to 10 years, awareness and demand for climate and weather geospatial data has increased markedly. To meet the demand of stakeholders and users, the Climate Prediction Center (CPC) started to disseminate the data and products in geospatial formats such as shapefiles and GeoTIFFS. Initially, this distribution method was not possible because of the NWS proprietary software application in the product generation. In addition, some collaborative products were created in Esri's ArcMap application but still needed to be disseminated via AWIPS. This caused duplication of workflow for the CPC scientists because they needed to create the product twice: once for the AWIPS and once to produce shapefiles. To overcome this problem, CPC developed workflows to adapt NWS technologies to the geographic information system (GIS) framework.

Despite getting off to a slow start, CPC was able to incorporate both front- and back-end Esri technology to increase forecaster efficiency while serving more of its products in geospatial formats. This was accomplished while continuing to satisfy NWS dissemination requirements via the web and AWIPS without burdening forecasters. Future goals at CPC include serving its geospatial data and products to the world via a Web Map Service (WMS), hosted on both ArcGIS for Server and an open-source server. In addition, CPC is involved in a number of other projects, such as data access, discovery, and interoperability; metadata development; and improvements that leverage the collective GIS knowledge of its scientists.

This chapter provides a brief background on how CPC incorporated improvements in geospatial technology into its existing workflow while maintaining its existing operation requirements. This chapter shows how CPC uses GIS in drought monitoring, the Global Tropical Hazards Outlook, the US Hazards Outlook, and the Data Access and Interoperability effort with Climate.gov. Each section will describe the history of the product, as well as some of the specifics on how geospatial technology helps the forecast process.

Drought products

At CPC, drought analysis is carried out by various methods and across the different spatial scales. Automated, objective indicators are calculated on fixed spatial scales and grids, which serve as input to the manually drafted products that are created in collaboration with subject matter experts (SMEs).

Drought assessment parameters

To facilitate the monitoring of a wide range of environmental conditions, the United States has been divided into 344 climate divisions, which are regions that have common climatic attributes. A large number of drought assessment parameters are generated for those climate divisions. The drought parameters are objectively generated from observations and measurements and are used to define the spatial extent and amplitude of ongoing dryness. Initially, these parameters were only published in a joint CPC–United States Department of Agriculture (USDA) publication called the *Weekly Weather and Crop Bulletin* (http://www.usda.gov/oce/weather/pubs/Weekly/Wwcb). This weekly publication consists of maps and tables that quantitatively assess the effect of ongoing dryness on the various crops grown in each state. The publication needed to be aesthetically pleasing and intuitive, which was achieved through a considerable amount of effort each week.

With the introduction of ArcGIS into the product workflow, the raw input data could easily be joined to a shapefile of the 344 climate divisions, allowing for quick generation of multiple publication-quality maps. In addition, spatial analysis tools allow for the easy generation of statewide maps and tables by integrating the shapefile of climate divisions for the 50 states. Currently, this product is only available on the web in static format.

Moving forward, the plan is to make these data interactive, potentially allowing users to retrieve any crop condition parameter, current or historic, by clicking a web graphic. Data download options for the user could include those for retrieving data for the entire United

States or a geographic subset that is dynamically identified by the user. Another part of the plan is to provide the raw data, differences between current and historic values, or the value as an anomaly. Making these data available as shapefiles or GeoTIFFs will maximize their potential use, allowing users to display or analyze these data in endless ways.

Drought Monitor

The US Drought Monitor (USDM) is the official federal government depiction of drought over the United States, covering the contiguous United States, Alaska, Hawaii, and Puerto Rico (figure 10.1). The map is a weekly product that depicts different levels of drought on a scale from D0 to D4, with D0 representing abnormal dryness and D4 representing the most intense drought. Each level of drought is associated with certain measurements, such as precipitation, soil moisture, and streamflow levels, as well as impacts such as reservoir levels, crop failures, and waterway navigability (figure 10.2).

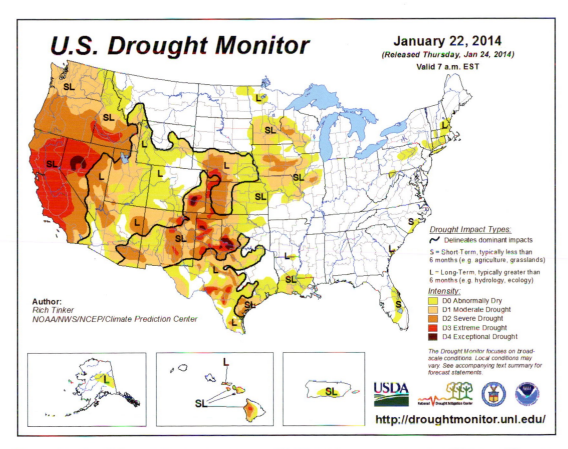

Figure 10.1   The US Drought Monitor (as of January 22, 2014). | NOAA, USDA, NDMC, WRCC. The US Drought Monitor is jointly produced by the National Drought Mitigation Center at the University of Nebraska–Lincoln, the United States Department of Agriculture, and the National Oceanic and Atmospheric Administration. Map courtesy of NDMC-UNL. http://droughtmonitor.unl.edu/AboutUSDM.aspx.

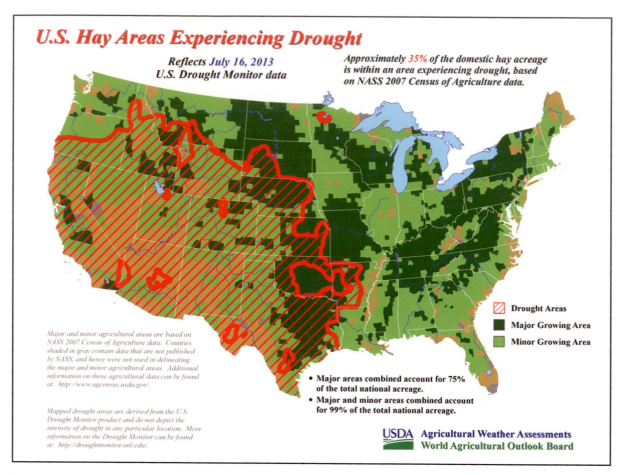

Figure 10.2 Sample product comparing hay growing areas to areas experiencing drought (as of July 2013). | Courtesy of USDA/WAOB. The US Drought Monitor is jointly produced by the National Drought Mitigation Center at the University of Nebraska–Lincoln, the United States Department of Agriculture, and the National Oceanic and Atmospheric Administration. Map courtesy of NDMC-UNL.

CPC runs a collaborative effort with other National Oceanic and Atmospheric Administration (NOAA) line offices, the National Drought Mitigation Center (NDMC), the USDA, and the Western Region Climate Center (WRCC) to produce the USDM. The volume of data and depth of knowledge required to complete the USDM dictates a collaborative process involving many SMEs. Each agency involved in this collaborative program rotates as lead author on a weekly basis, incorporating inputs and data from approximately 350 SMEs.

Since 2003, the originating centers have been using the ArcMap application of ArcGIS to produce the USDM. This allows all the centers to operate in the same geospatial environment; for example, if a new tool is produced in one of the centers, it can be quickly disseminated to the other centers. ArcMap also permits the author to draw the map on top of a mashup of geospatial data.

Geospatial mashups

Multiple, sometimes disparate, data sources are required to produce the comprehensive representation of drought depicted by the USDM. The gathering and quality control of these data sources is accomplished via Python scripts, using standard modules and the Esri ArcPy library. As of February 2014, the USDM authoring process involved approximately 75 different quantitative data layers, in addition to the quantitative inputs and qualitative impacts submitted by nearly 350 participants and the public (for more information, see the NDMC—Drought Impact Reporter website: http://droughtreporter.unl.edu). Among the inputs collected are precipitation measurements from rainfall gauges, multisensor precipitation estimates (Advanced Hydrologic Prediction System, CPC Unified Precipitation Analysis), soil moisture estimates from multiple soil moisture models (CPC, North American Land Data Assimilation System, National Aeronautics and Space Administration-Goddard Space Flight Center), streamflow measurements (US Geological Survey [USGS]), snowfall data (Natural Resources Conservation Service), well-level data (USGS), and others from climate science partners. The data are typically subjected to a quality control process to remove missing values, outdated data, and data outside of the target domain.

To facilitate the combination and comparison of observed data with model-derived outputs, some of the point data are converted to gridded data using the interpolation routines. Use of raster data also increases the speed of display, a major concern for authors faced with strict deadlines. The interpolation is performed using the Python script, which uses the Natural Neighbor Interpolation routine. This routine produced better results when compared with the other available methods. Inverse Distance Weighted (IDW) interpolated output was consistent with the underlying point data, but did not result in a raster with a high correspondence to the physical system represented by the data due to the assumptions made in the IDW routine.

In addition to the download, quality-control, and format conversions, value-added products are constructed that help reduce the dimensionality of the data, either temporally or spatially, and simplify the interpretation. One of the precipitation inputs used is the Standardized Precipitation Index (SPI; McKee, Doeskin, and Kieist 1993). The SPI provides a comparison of the precipitation accumulated over a specific accumulation period with the precipitation accumulated over the same period for all the years included in the historical record and returns the normalized probability of receiving that amount of precipitation. Normalizing precipitation allows for different spatial areas to be compared to each other. SPI values are then combined to produce a value-added product that weighs recent precipitation more heavily than precipitation that fell further in the past (figure 10.3).

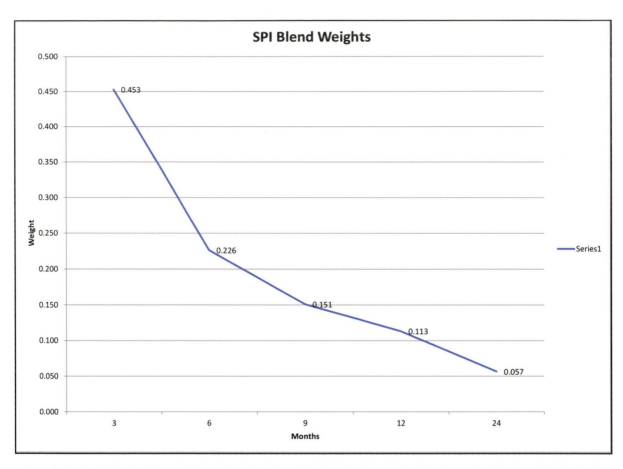

Figure 10.3 Weights (vertical axis) associated with each SPI evaluation period (horizontal axis) as used in the SPI Blend Tool at CPC. | McKee et al., 1993.

The SPI values are weighted according to a normalized portion of the inverse of their contributing period. For example, a 3-month SPI is weighted to 0.453 of the total SPI blend. To calculate the SPI blend weighting factor, do the following:

- Sum the total number of contributing months (CPC runs a 3-, 6-, 9-, 12-, and 24-month SPI, for a total of 54 months).

- Divide the total contributing months by the SPI analysis period (for a 3-month SPI, 54/3 = 18).

- Divide the fractional contribution by the sum of all of the fractional contributions (ensures that total weights always sum to 1.00).

The calculations are done by using ArcGIS Spatial Analyst and Raster Calculator, with the final result being stored as a GeoTIFF and accessible to the authors.

The authors need to interact with the background data to manually draw the USDM. Display of the supporting data is done in ArcGIS for Desktop as a mashup of the various datasets. The polygon shapefiles from the prior USDM serve as the starting point for the current week's analysis. Most of the work is done with only the outlines of the polygons being highlighted. This allows the authors to look "through" the data layer upon which they are working and draw it to match different background layers or dynamic data layers. For the final product, the polygons are symbolized as specified by the USDM's governing documents.

Product delivery

Because the USDM is an official CPC product, it is required to be disseminated via the AWIPS network. Thus, the author had to draw the product twice: once in ArcMap and once for AWIPS. To remove this extra work, Python script was written that uses the ArcPy library to accomplish the following tasks:

- Get the vertex coordinates of each drought polygon shapefile using the ArcPy search record cursor.

- Output the vertex coordinates, as well as attribute information about the contour, into an ASCII (American Standard Code for Information Interchange) file using a specific format.

- Use NCEP proprietary software to convert the ASCII file of latitude/longitude values into an AWIPS-compatible format.

This program has made the operation smooth and efficient, and has ensured that the product matches in AWIPS and ArcMap. This effort at CPC has made it possible to use ArcMap to produce the USDM while satisfying internal NWS requirements.

Global Tropical Hazards Outlook

The Global Tropics Hazards Outlook (figure 10.4) is produced weekly at CPC after receiving input from academic, domestic, and foreign operational weather service partners. Participants include those from the State University of New York–Albany, the Cooperative Institute for Climate and Satellites (CICS), the Australian Government Bureau of Meteorology, the Taiwan Central Weather Bureau, the Naval Postgraduate School, the Joint Typhoon Warning Center, and other NOAA offices, including the National Hurricane Center. The product is constructed in ArcGIS for Desktop and distributed to the web in multiple formats, both static and dynamic.

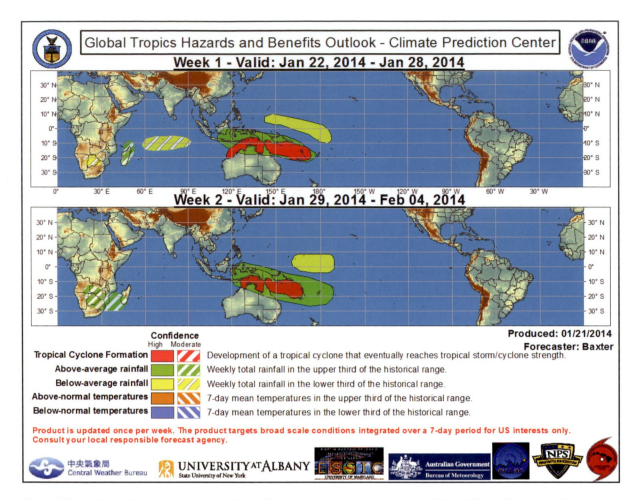

Figure 10.4   Global Tropical Hazards and Benefits Outlook issued January 21, 2014. | NOAA, University of New York–Albany, CICS, Australian Government Bureau of Meteorology, the Taiwan Central Weather Bureau, the Naval Postgraduate School, and the Joint Typhoon Warning Center.

ArcGIS has streamlined the production of the Global Tropics Hazards and Benefits Outlook. Through the use of ArcGIS functions, any feature representing a heightened risk of tropical cyclone formation can be spatially "deconflicted" from landmasses by simply erasing the intersecting portions.

Additionally, the use of high-resolution topography (Shuttle Radar Topography Mission, or SRTM) has allowed CPC to more accurately pinpoint areas where heavy rain would pose a risk to life and property. SRTM elevation data are overlaid with outputs from atmospheric models so that the influences of terrain can be included in the forecasts and in the derivation of impacts to society from forecast conditions. If heavy rain is forecast over mountainous terrain that has been relatively dry until that point, flash flooding is more likely to occur over those coincident areas, pinpointed with the help of the elevation and slope data. Over some regions precipitation follows the contours of the land, so displaying the elevation data allows forecasters to more precisely denote an area of interest for their forecast polygon.

Verification of the forecasts is accomplished by translating the vector shapefiles to raster data, which can be compared to satellite images, satellite sounder data, or the official gridded precipitation analysis from CPC. The files are copied over to the centralized computers and analyzed or used as easily as any other gridded data product. Interoperability was a major factor to consider when undertaking the project to convert the forecasts from shapefiles (vector data) to gridded formats, which had to be compatible with the software and hardware available on the high-performance computing systems used by CPC employees. This is accomplished by the following steps:

1. Feature_to_Raster
   - On 0.5 × 0.5 degree and 1.0 × 1.0 degree (Lat/Lon) grid
     - ☐ Aligns with existing precipitation and satellite data products.
     - ☐ Raster produced needs to be offset by either 0.25 or 0.5 degree (other plotting routines reference grid by the vertices, Esri Grids reference the center point).
   - Raster values are determined by maximum area method—feature values covering more than half of a grid square are assigned to that grid square.
2. Raster_to_ASCII
3. Post-processing
   - Header rows are removed (unimportant to many other plotting routines and can be handled in an external file).

ArcGIS can produce files that are interoperable with many other plotting and analysis routines, as well as being compatible with multiple operating systems and environments. The forecasts are disseminated in KMZ (Keyhole Markup language Zipped) files and shapefiles, as requested by users.

Hazards Outlook

CPC's Hazards Outlook is a daily forecast designed to provide users, including emergency managers, information on potential extreme weather events (e.g., high winds, severe weather, heavy rain, heavy snow, flooding, and drought) that may occur 3 to 14 days in the future.

The Federal Emergency Management Agency (FEMA) asked CPC to provide the Hazards Outlook in industry-standard geospatial formats, which improves ingest workflow into their situational awareness tools. To meet this request, CPC reformulated its production and dissemination workflow. Initially, forecasters had to draw their maps, as with all official products, using NWS proprietary software so that they could be transmitted to AWIPS. In addition, the forecasters had to meticulously redraw forecast information coming from other centers and from the USDM. This process was time- and labor-intensive because it forced forecasters to duplicate information.

Forecast preparation and dissemination process

To address FEMA's request and also improve the efficiency of the forecast process, CPC used Esri's ArcMap and Python ArcPy library for the forecast processes. Each day, the forecasters begin their shift by executing a Python script that captures a number of forecasts from different centers. This script does the following:

- Downloads precipitation forecasts from the Weather Prediction Center, severe weather and wildfire forecasts from the Storm Prediction Center, and the latest Drought Monitor from the Drought Mitigation Center.

- Creates empty shapefiles and adds relevant attributes, such as forecast date, valid date, and a text label describing the hazard.

- Copies the relevant data from the external center shapefiles into process-specific shapefiles.

- Performs logic to separate multiple-day forecasts into individual records in one shapefile with an appropriate forecast and valid dates.

These shapefiles are then displayed in an ArcGIS MXD file as an automatic first-guess map (figure 10.5). The forecasters can use this file to make any suitable changes. This process allows the forecasters to finish their forecasts earlier because they do not need to spend time re-creating features now downloaded automatically. Once forecasters finish their forecast, they execute another Python script that does the following:

- Exports the ArcGIS MXD files to PNG files for the web.

- Generates KML files and zips the five subfiles associated with the shapefiles.

- Acquires the latitude/longitude coordinates of the shapes, outputs them to ASCII files, and sends them to a Linux server to be converted into AWIPS-compatible files, exactly like what is done for the USDM.

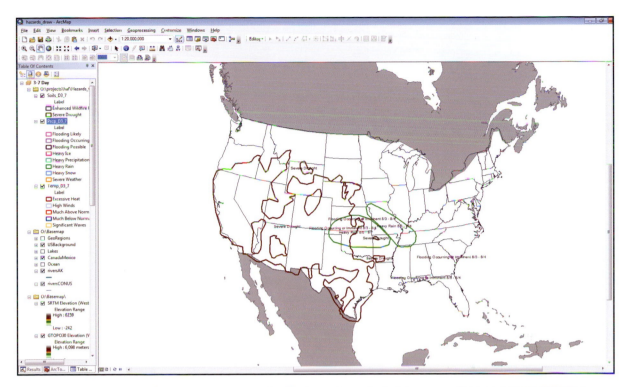

Figure 10.5 Screenshot of the drawing session for the Hazards Outlook. | Courtesy of NOAA/NWS/NCEP/CPC.

FEMA is able to ingest KML and shapefiles of the Hazards Outlook into its situational awareness tools. Its daily reports, including the Hazards Outlook, which go to the US president, can be generated more efficiently. FEMA also uses CPC's new web-based application (figure 10.6).

Improving data access and interoperability between Climate.gov and CPC

The NOAA Climate.gov team, in collaboration with CPC, is enhancing users' ability to locate, preview, interact with, and access and acquire climate data and products in the most commonly used data formats through a seamless and simple Climate.gov Maps and Data Section interface. Management of the nation's climate data presents many challenges, such as diverse data, disparate digital formats, inconsistent metadata records, a variety of data service implementations, and the large volume of data and geographically distributed locations. To satisfy the needs of the users, the Climate.gov/CPC team created the Data Access and Interoperability project to design a web-based platform where interoperability between systems can be leveraged to allow greater data discovery, access, visualization, and delivery. We define *interoperability* as the ability of diverse systems to work together, or interoperate. The proposed interoperable system interface will allow users to find, display,

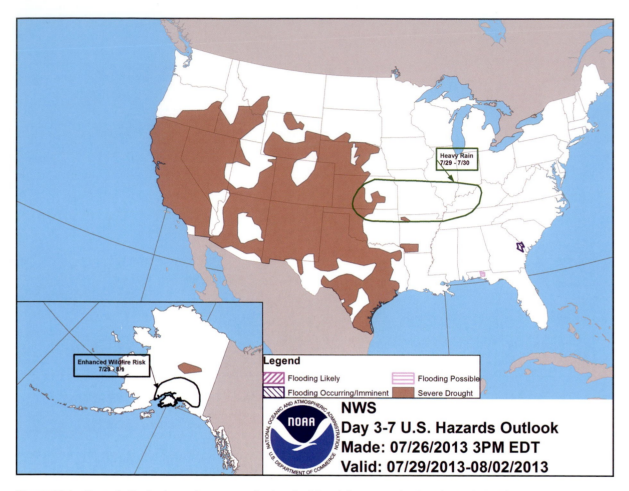

Figure 10.6 Hazards Outlook product created using ArcMap. | Courtesy of NOAA/NWS/NCEP/CPC.

manipulate, and (where applicable) download NOAA's and its partners' climate data products that are stored in and served from different data centers. Based on the definition of interoperability, the team proposed developing an Interoperable Data Platform that allows systems to integrate with each other to support the synthesis of climate data and products. This simple web-based interoperable system platform will let users discover available climate data, preview and interact with them, and acquire the data in common digital formats. This proposed system is built with standards, not data, in mind. This system will limit the diversity of data and lessen complexity in the data management with improved implementation.

The Climate.gov Interoperable Data Platform is designed around the concept of representational state transfer (REST) and implements design patterns and use cases that conform to best practices for web services. Emerging standards for automation of machine-to-machine services discovery, such as OpenSearch, and autodiscovery are being implemented throughout the Interoperable Data Platform to ensure harmonization among data service providers, integrators, and consumers. Implementation of these common specifications will not only ensure compatibility between systems within NOAA, but also with non-NOAA systems and innovators in the public. The proposed Data Interoperable System Platform will improve user experience in data discovery, access, and preview and data export due to scalable interoperability. As the team works across the organization, it will evaluate the capabilities of the participating systems to capture and assess the relative maturity of each system according to the Technology Infusion Working Group (TIWG) Interoperability Readiness Levels (IRL), which is the reference for the interoperability mapping within NOAA. This will help establish the gaps and opportunities for integrating systems across a common set of discrete aspects of interoperability.

Applying the principles of IRL will give NOAA reasonable and consistent snapshots of current readiness of systems to be interoperable, but also provide consistent targets to make the ecosystem for earth sciences data throughout NOAA even more interoperable. We have built a proof of concept for the Data Interoperable System Platform. The built system is "file agnostic," meaning that the pilot system will locate and display the data regardless of what format they are archived in. The web-based client was developed using JavaScript libraries from OpenLayers and JQuery. The OpenLayers library provides JavaScript utilities to interact with a variety of data and metadata services. JQuery provides utilities to construct the layout of the webpage itself. The main goal of this pilot initiative was to develop a proof-of-concept interoperable system for data access and display. This platform allows users to find, browse, and access NOAA's web-based data products and services served through WMS, WFS (Web Feature Services), and Esri Export Service. In the future, CPC will improve the user interface, add more functionality, and bring interoperable concepts together. The CPC will also collaborate with partners to improve the system.

Future plans

As climate and weather sciences advance, the demand for CPC data and products is increasing. These data and products are usually inaccessible to the users due to their proprietary formats or the difficulty in finding and accessing them. Therefore, data interoperability could be a big benefit for government organizations like NOAA. A truly interoperable framework improves the ability to find, preview, and access data and products in a seamless environment. By being easier to find and use, CPC data and products will obtain higher added value. In this effort, CPC pushed the available CPC geospatial data and products to an open-source GeoServer as the test case of web services and also collaborated with the Climate.gov team on interoperability. Disseminating our products as shapefiles, KMLs, and GeoTIFFs is an advancement toward improved data access and interoperability. The CPC is also working on making more data available in netCDF (Network Common Data Form), which is compliant with Climate and Forecast (CF) metadata conventions. To meet the increasing demand of geospatial data and services, NWS initiated the Enterprise GIS Project within the NOAA Integrated Dissemination Program (IDP). CPC scientists are heavily involved in this new NWS effort. One component of this program is a project to establish an enterprise geospatial dissemination tier, maintained on a continuous basis (24×7 support). This project consists of an Esri ArcGIS for Server stack as well as an open-source OpenGeo stack. Initially, the IDP GIS project will focus on disseminating NWS data only, but the future goal is to provide access to all five NOAA line offices. In this way, all of NOAA's geospatial dissemination services will be centralized, maintained in an operational environment, and have an off-site backup. Both stacks will serve Open Geospatial Consortium (OGC)-compliant services, with appropriate metadata for each service. We will work with the numerous harvesting and aggregating services that the government provides (e.g., Data.noaa.gov and Data.gov) to allow for the easy discovery and consumption of these geospatial services.

CPC continues to lead the NWS in incorporating GIS into its workflow, first by writing customized tools that allow products to be created in both the NWS proprietary software and in industry-standard geospatial format, and now by taking a lead role in the establishment of an NWS-wide enterprise geospatial data and products dissemination system. Moving toward improved data access and interoperability on our geospatial data and products will tremendously increase the viability and relevance of NWS data and products to our users.

Acknowledgments

The authors would like to thank our reviewer, Mike Charles (NOAA CPC), for the constructive suggestions and necessary edits. We would like to thank Mike Halpert, Jon Gottschalck, and Shi-Keng Yang (Sky) from NOAA Climate Prediction Center for their continuous support and encouragement. We also would like to thank Tiffany Vance, Jack Settelmaier, and Jenna Meyer from NOAA for facilitating the publication process with the Esri publication team. And last but not least, we would like to acknowledge John Nielsen-Gammon, Texas State Climatologist, for providing the inspiration for the SPI product.

References and additional resources

McKee, T. B., N. J. Doeskin, and J. Kieist. 1993. "The Relationship of Drought Frequency and Duration to Time Scales." Proceedings Eighth Conference on Applied Climatology. January 17–22. American Meteorological Society. Boston, Massachusetts.

National Aeronautics and Space Administration. 2012. "Interoperability Readiness Levels." https://earthdata.nasa.gov/sites/default/files/field/document/esdswg-irl-20120321.pdf.

National Weather Service, Climate Prediction Center. "Global Tropics Hazards and Benefits Outlook." http://www.cpc.ncep.noaa.gov/products/precip/CWlink/ghazards/.

———. "US Hazards Outlook." http://www.cpc.ncep.noaa.gov/products/predictions/threats/threats.php.

———. Homepage. http://www.cpc.ncep.noaa.gov.

———. 2014. "CPC GIS Data." http://www.cpc.ncep.noaa.gov/products/GIS/GIS_DATA/.

University of Nebraska–Lincoln. 2014. "US Drought Monitor." http://droughtmonitor.unl.edu.

CHAPTER 11

Particle tracking in ocean and atmospheric studies

Tiffany C. Vance and Kyle J. Wilcox

The atmosphere and oceans are, at first glance, very different. However, from the viewpoint of fluid dynamics, they are usefully similar. Direct analogies can be drawn between the sampling equipment and types of data collected in both domains. The same analysis techniques can be used with data gathered from both environments. Both systems can be directly linked with the use of coupled air–ocean models, and within each medium similar types of models can be used to simplify and understand dynamic systems. *General circulation models* describe the motions and properties of the ocean, the atmosphere, or both if a coupled model is being run. *Particle tracking models* can be used to describe the motions of particles in the atmosphere, and they can be used to describe the motion of particles or organisms in the ocean. Linking particle tracking models with a geographic information system (GIS) can create an application with an intuitive front end to set model parameters and better mapping and visualization of the model results, making it easier for new users to explore modeling. A GIS also allows the researcher to easily combine model results with in situ measurements to more completely describe a system. A GIS can provide critical tools for the analysis of model results, the visualization and display of spatial patterns, and the presentation of findings.

The premise of particle tracking models is linking a circulation model, which describes the motion of the medium, with a transport model for the particles. The circulation model uses basic physical principles to calculate velocities at a three-dimensional lattice of grid points. Velocities and additional properties, such as water temperature or salinity, are calculated for all points in the lattice or grid at a series of time steps or intervals. The results of the calculations at one time step are used to calculate the values at the next time step. Models of varying resolutions can be nested to define the properties over a wide spatial extent, and powerful computers and parallel programming algorithms are used to rapidly run a model for an extended time period. The particles can be assumed to be neutrally buoyant and simply transported in the fluid; they can exhibit mechanical behaviors, including the ability to fly or swim against currents; or they can exhibit biological behaviors, such as avoiding light or swimming toward the ocean floor or away from storms.

Output from multidimensional particle tracking models includes the current or wind speed and direction vectors from the underlying circulation model; the particle's location in x, y, z, and t; and calculated physical parameters, such as water temperature or salinity at the location. These types of models can also be linked to models of the development of organisms or models of physical processes acting upon mineral particles. With these more advanced models, the output could also include the developmental state and health of the organism, the weathering of a volcanic particle, or the changes in the chemical composition of a pollutant as it interacts with sunlight.

The multidimensional output can be visualized in a number of ways. One of the simplest visualizations takes an arbitrary slice through the three spatial dimensions of the circulation model data and contours the results on a plane. The contours can be animated to represent the fourth temporal dimension. Particle tracks can be overlaid on these slices at arbitrary depths or on vertical planes. However, an ideal representation of the results would display the data in at least three spatial dimensions, and would add animation for the display of the fourth dimension. Analysis of spatial patterns would be possible, and ancillary datasets could be added where needed. A GIS provides a way to combine visualization with analysis. Ancillary data such as in situ sample data from research cruises can be combined with model output showing theoretical water temperatures and wind or current speeds and directions. The location of particles and their historical track can be shown and analyzed.

Examples of particle tracking models in atmospheric, hydrologic, and marine research

A particle tracking model can describe the interaction between geological processes, such as volcanism, that create particles and the atmospheric processes that drive the dispersion of these particles (Costa, Macedonio, and Folch 2006). Atmospheric dispersion models also study the transport of particles and their associated microbial communities (Griffin 2007). Transport of nutrients such as iron from the continents to the oceans in dust particles can also be studied using a particle tracking model (Mahowald et al. 2005).

In the atmospheric sciences, Puff is a model implemented by the University of Alaska Fairbanks Geophysical Institute to track the path of volcanic eruptions (Searcy, Dean, and Stringer 1999). It uses gridded wind fields from the Weather Research and Forecasting

(WRF) model to determine the speed and direction of the path of the erupted particles in time and space. Settling and dispersion rates for the particles can be varied, and the height of the original eruption plume can be specified. The results are available via an interface that allows the user to choose a volcano and show an animation of the plume. For selected volcanoes, the output is also available as a three-dimensional visualization for the plume and two-dimensional maps of particle fallout and the plume. The output is being used for research studies but can also be used for operational applications. The Hybrid Single-Particle Lagrangian Integrated Trajectory (HYSPLIT) model (described more fully in chapter 14) is used to model the forward and backward trajectories of air parcels. It can be used to model volcanic ash paths, balloon flights, pollutant releases, and other types of dispersion and deposition (for more information, see the Air Resources Laboratory description of the HYSPLIT model: http://www.arl.noaa.gov/HYSPLIT_info.php).

Uses of models and particle tracking in hydrology include integrating the US Geological Survey's (USGS) modular finite-difference flow (MODFLOW) model with MODPATH, a particle tracking model. MODFLOW is used to simulate groundwater flow. It is three-dimensional and consists of modules to simulate a variety of hydrologic processes (Harbaugh 2005). MODPATH is a semianalytical particle tracking model that is run on top of MODFLOW to compute the path of water parcels based on the output velocities from MODFLOW (for more information, see USGS's "Summary of MODPATH": http://water.usgs.gov/ogw/modpath/). GIS applications have been tied to MODFLOW both as a way to simplify setting input parameters (Qi and Sieverling 1997) and as a way to better visualize and analyze the output (Radhakrishnan and Sengupta 2002). More recent applications include commercial tools such as the Groundwater Modeling System (GMS; for more information, see the US Army Corps of Engineers' GMS: http://chl.erdc.usace.army.mil/gms) that facilitate both the setting of input parameters and the visualization of the output. The Map and TIN modules of GMS allow the integration of GIS data and techniques with MODFLOW modeling.

In marine fisheries research, models have been used to study the transport pathways of walleye pollock larvae in Shelikof Strait, Alaska (Dougherty et al. 2012), the effects of turbulence on walleye pollock larvae (Megrey and Hinckley 2001), and the dispersion of Greenland halibut in the Bering Sea (Duffy-Anderson et al. 2012). In these studies, particle tracking models were run using the Regional Ocean Modeling System (ROMS) output, and Lagrangian floats were used to simulate particles. In some of these studies, the output was subsequently mapped and analyzed using a GIS.

LarvaMap

LarvaMap is an application to set up and run a particle tracking model for studying the transport of fish and shellfish larvae in the ocean. LarvaMap was created to make it easier for nonmodelers to set up and run models. The intent of the project was to make running models fast and intuitive enough to allow scientists to test scenarios and to run models in response to natural and anthropogenic disasters. The application uses as its input the output from a variety of ocean circulation models, including the ROMS and the US Navy's Coastal Ocean Model (NCOM). Other model outputs can be used if they are available via either an OPeNDAP (Open-source Project for a Network Data Access Protocol) or THREDDS (Thematic Real-time Environmental Distributed Data Services) server. A Java-based web front end allows the user to set parameters for the model run. The particle tracking model itself is written in Java, and the output is returned as a netCDF (Network Common Data Form) file. XML (Extensible Markup Language) files are used to pass information between the front end and the model runner and also to pass information back from the model runner. The web interface is written using the OpenScales framework and Adobe Flex.

Setting up a model run in LarvaMap requires connecting to the front end from a web browser. The user defines a case name for the model run so that the results can be identified and also so they can be shared with other researchers. The user then sets a release area for the particles by specifying a point, a rectangular area, or a polygon. These can be defined either by entering coordinates or by clicking on the map interface (figure 11.1).

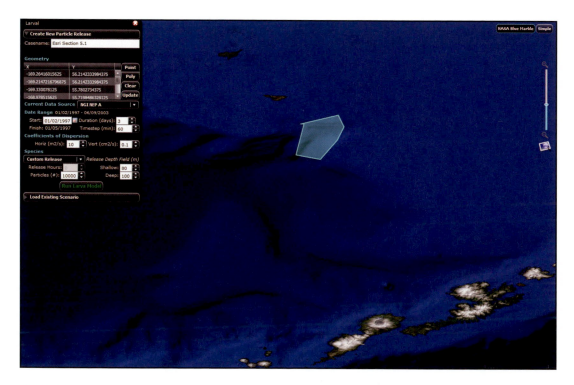

Figure 11.1 Interface for setting parameters for a LarvaMap run in the Bering Sea. The polygon to the right outlines the release area for the particles. The window on the left shows the model parameters that have been chosen. | NOAA/NASA Blue Marble from NASA's Earth Observatory.

The user specifies the number of particles to be released and their release depth(s). The user can set a time duration for the particle release to simulate fish spawning over time or some other continuous process of particle release. A number of preset scenarios for common fish species are also included for quick set up. The underlying circulation model output can be selected from a list of entries. The time range of the model output will be given, and the user can specify a start time, the duration of the model run, and a time step for the model. Finally, the user can set horizontal and vertical coefficients of dispersion suitable for the species being modeled.

Once the user has set all of the parameters and chosen to run the model, the parameters are checked to make sure that the model run's temporal extent is supported by the circulation data and that the start location is valid. A check window is returned, and the user can then either reset invalid parameters or run the model. While the model is running, a status box updates to provide feedback that the model is still running. Model runs can take from seconds to tens of minutes depending on the number of particles released, the duration of the model run, and the computing resources being used to run the model. After the model has finished running, the path of the centroid of the cloud of particles at each time step is plotted and the results are returned in a netCDF file for further analysis (figure 11.2).

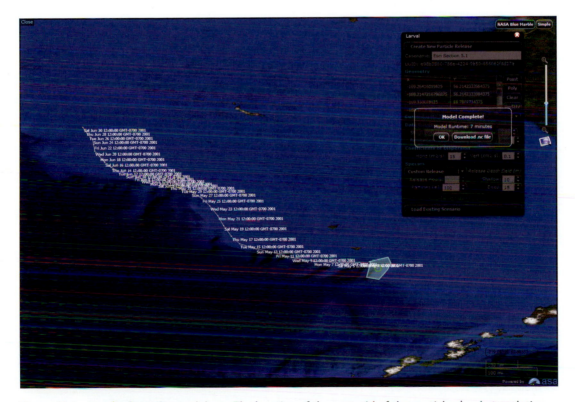

Figure 11.2   Results from the model run. The location of the centroid of the particle cloud at each time step has been added to the map. The window to the right shows the elapsed time to run the model and supports downloading the netCDF file of results. | NOAA/NASA Blue Marble from NASA's Earth Observatory.

The output files are aligned with the Climate and Forecast (CF) metadata conventions version 1.4 requirements and contain compliant units and standard names where applicable. The CF prescribe that files contain metadata that "provide a definitive description of what the data in each variable represents, and of the spatial and temporal properties of the data" (Eaton et al. 2014).

Analysis and display of particle tracking model output

Because the results are returned in a netCDF file, they can be analyzed and visualized using a variety of ArcGIS tools. The values returned include particle ID, time, latitude, longitude, depth, temperature, and salinity at the particle location. Information for each particle at each time step is included in the file. Using the Multidimension tool "Make NetCDF Feature Layer," the output netCDF file can be directly imported into ArcGIS. Two-dimensional representations of some or all of the particles can be created using the Data Management > Features > Points to Line tool, and the trajectories can displayed and analyzed (figure 11.3).

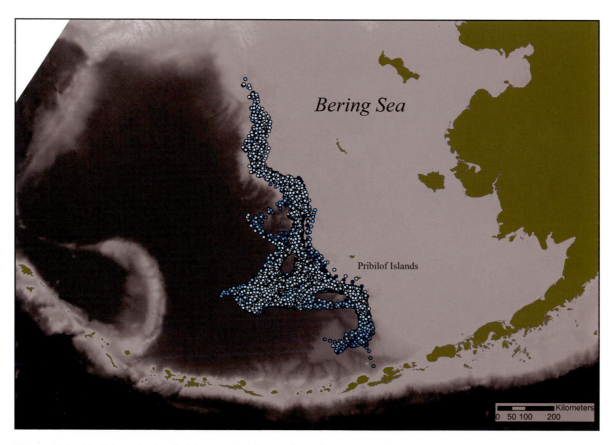

Figure 11.3 Model results loaded into ArcGIS for analysis. | Courtesy of NOAA.

The temperature and salinity data in the output file, taken from the corresponding locations in the circulation model output, can be used to create temperature histories for larvae over their path using the Data Management > Graph tools (figure 11.4).

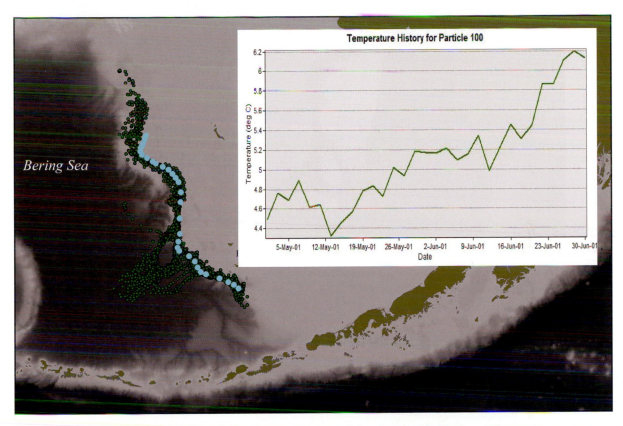

Figure 11.4 Temperature history for a single particle. The particle's path is highlighted, and the temperatures at each location, as derived from the underlying circulation model, are plotted on the graph. | Courtesy of NOAA.

The Statistical toolbox can be used to calculate the mean center and the directional distribution of the particle distribution at each time step using the Mean Center and Directional Distribution tools (figure 11.5).

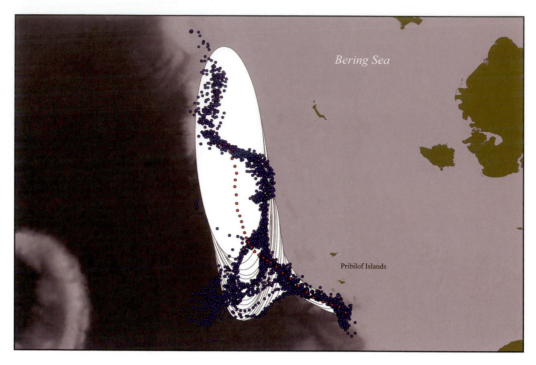

Figure 11.5 Using the Statistical toolbox to analyze paths. The mean center at each time step is shown with the red dots. The ellipse of the directional distribution of the points at each time step is also shown. | Courtesy of NOAA.

The data are fully three-dimensional, so Esri's ArcScene application can be used to create perspective views of the paths of the particles (figure 11.6).

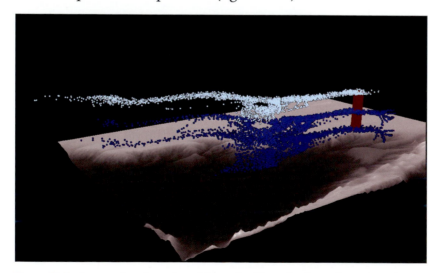

Figure 11.6 Perspective view of particle tracks. The red column shows the release points for the particles. The three colored clouds of points represent particles released at different depths (10–15 m, 50–55 m, and 90–95 m). | Courtesy of NOAA.

Because the netCDF file contains time information, it is also possible to use the file to create a "time-aware" ArcGIS file that can be used to create an animation.

Conclusion

The dispersion of inanimate or animate particles is important when responding to toxic releases, tracking sediment plumes, or determining where marine reserves might best be placed to support the recovery of endangered fish populations. Particle tracking models provide important insights into the mechanisms and paths of larval and particulate dispersal by allowing scientists to model both past and future scenarios. These types of models allow scientists to explore a simplified model of a very complex natural system. The similarities in the fluid dynamics between the oceans and the atmosphere allow similar modeling and analysis techniques to be used in both environments. Integrating a particle tracking model with a GIS makes it easier to run the model and to analyze the results. The tight integration of netCDF with ArcGIS supports this type of application and makes the full suite of ArcGIS tools available for analyses. LarvaMap has provided a robust prototype of how this kind of linked model–GIS system can work and how the particle tracking results can be analyzed using GIS tools. A variety of outputs and visualizations can be created to meet the needs of a wide range of users. With sufficient computational resources, such as those available on a cloud computing resource, these types of models and analyses can be run quickly enough to be used both for testing a variety of scenarios for the spatial management of resources and for planning and implementing responses to natural and anthropogenic disasters.

Acknowledgments

This research was supported, in part, with funds from the NOAA High Performance Computing and Communications (HPCC) Program and the National Marine Fisheries Service's Ecosystems and Fisheries Oceanography Coordinated Investigations (EcoFOCI). This is contribution EcoFOCI-N818 to NOAA's North Pacific Climate Regimes and Ecosystem Productivity research program. The findings and conclusions in the paper are those of the authors and do not necessarily represent the views of the National Marine Fisheries Service. Reference to trade names does not imply endorsement by the National Marine Fisheries Service, NOAA.

References

Costa, A., G. Macedonio, and A. Folch. 2006. "A Three-Dimensional Eulerian Model for Transport and Deposition of Volcanic Ashes." *Earth and Planetary Science Letters* 241 (3–4): 634–47.

Dougherty, A., K. Bailey, T. Vance, and W. Cheng. 2012. "Underlying Causes of Habitat-Associated Differences in Size of Age-0 Walleye Pollock (*Theragra chalcogramma*) in the Gulf of Alaska." *Marine Biology* 159 (8): 1733–44.

Duffy-Anderson, J. T., D. M. Blood, W. Cheng, L. Ciannelli, A. Matarese, D. Sohn, P. Stabeno, T. Vance, and C. Vestfals. 2013. "Combining Field Observations and Modeling Approaches to Examine Greenland Halibut (*Reinhardtius hippoglossoides*) Early Life Ecology in the Southeastern Bering Sea." *Journal of Sea Research* 75: 96–109.

Eaton, B., J. Gregory, B. Drach, K. Taylor, S. Hankin, J. Caron, R. Signell, P. Bentley, G. Rappa, H. Höck, A. Pamment, M. Juckes, A. Walsh, and J. Graybeal. 2014. "NetCDF Climate and Forecast (CF) Metadata Conventions." Version 1.7.2 Draft. March 28. http://cfconventions.org/Data/cf-convetions/cf-conventions-1.7/build/cf-conventions.pdf.

Griffin, D. W. 2007. "Atmospheric Movement of Microorganisms in Clouds of Desert Dust and Implications for Human Health." *Clinical Microbiology* 20 (3): 459–77.

Harbaugh, A. W. 2005. *MODFLOW-2005, The US Geological Survey Modular Ground-Water Model—The Ground-Water Flow Process.* Techniques and Methods 6–A16. US Geological Survey. Accessed August 28, 2012. http://pubs.water.usgs.gov/tm6a16.

Mahowald, N. M., A. R. Baker, G. Bergametti, N. Brooks, R. A. Duce, T. D. Jickells, N. Kubilay, J. M. Prospero, and I. Tegen. 2005. "Atmospheric Global Dust Cycle and Iron Inputs to the Ocean." *Global Biogeochemical Cycles* 19 (4). doi:10.1029/2004GB002402.

Megrey, B. A., and S. Hinckley. 2001. "Effect of Turbulence on Feeding of Larval Fishes: A Sensitivity Analysis Using an Individual-Based Model." *ICES Journal of Marine Science* 58 (5): 1015–29.

Qi, S., and J. Sieverling. 1997. "Using ArcInfo to Facilitate Numerical Modeling of Groundwater Flow." Paper presented at the Esri International User Conference. July 8–11. San Diego, California. http://gis.esri.com/library/userconf/proc97/proc97/to650/pap649/p649.htm.

Radhakrishnan, P., and R. Sengupta. 2002. "Groundwater Modeling in ArcView by Integrating ArcView, MODFLOW, and MODPATH." Paper presented at the Esri International User Conference. July 8–12. San Diego, California. http://gis.esri.com/library/userconf/proc97/proc97/to650/pap649/p649.htm.

Searcy C., K. Dean, and W. Stringer. 1998. "PUFF: A High-Resolution Volcanic Ash Tracking Model." *Journal of Volcanology and Geothermal Research* 80 (1–2): 1–16.

PART 4

Integrated analyses of models and observations

Parts 2 and 3 detail how climate and weather data are gathered—both via observations and models—and then displayed and analyzed in a geographic information system (GIS). Part 4 explores how to combine these data and models with other GIS data to answer questions and solve problems; for example, calculating how many people are in the path of a hurricane or what path pollutants might follow after release.

Chapter 12 describes how GIS can be used after a tornado to analyze the damage done by the storm. The data sources available and the process of compiling this data to calculate the extent of damage and the number of households affected are described.

Chapter 13 explores how information about a weather event can be combined with demographic data to explore the impact of events on infrastructure—in this case, the effects of a snowstorm on roads and schools. These kinds of explorations, or thought models, can be used to quantify the current societal impacts of storms and to support planning for future events.

Chapter 14 shows how to combine data sources in a GIS to present a unified view of an extensive weather event. It explores the complex physical processes involved in both the source and the path of a major weather system recorded by a number of sensors.

Chapter 15 illustrates how georeferenced observations of lightning strikes can be analyzed and integrated with data on wildfires to explore the types of strikes that likely trigger fires. Climatologies of lightning strikes can be created within ArcGIS, and then these results are correlated with measures of the timing and strength of El Niño events. As with the snowfall example in chapter 13, these kinds of analyses can be used for emergency planning and hazard assessment.

These chapters describe how a variety of data types, from model outputs to satellite data to observational data, can be integrated easily and quickly. The focus in this part is on analyses using desktop GIS, and how these types of integrations support decision making, define societal impacts, and enable hazard assessment.

CHAPTER 12

Joplin tornado damage analysis

Robert Toomey

Joplin tornado

On Sunday, May 22, 2011, a major multiple-vortex tornado hit the city of Joplin, Missouri, and the surrounding areas. Generating wind speeds of over 200 mph, this tornado was rated an EF5, which is the highest and most dangerous classification on the Enhanced Fujita (EF) scale (Wikipedia 2014). The tornado was at one point up to a mile in diameter and traveled almost 21.6 miles in total, about 8.8 miles of which was within the highly populated area of Jasper County and the city of Joplin. Damage to property from this storm was calculated at around 2.8 billion dollars, and 158 people died. Three people died indirectly from the storm: a police officer struck by lightning during rescue operations, a man from a heart attack, and one person from psychological trauma from the event. Along with the direct deaths, 1,150 people were reported injured, and eventually over 10,200 people filed for disaster assistance (National Climatic Data Center 2011). Table 12.1 shows the tornado scale number along with the corresponding wind speed range. Typically, the higher the wind speed and EF number, the more damage we can expect in a given area.

Table 12.1 Enhanced Fujita tornado rating by gusting wind speed

EF Number	Wind Speed (mph)
0	65–85
1	86–110
2	111–135
3	136–165
4	166–200
5	> 200

Courtesy of NOAA.

Storm damage surveys

After a serious storm event occurs, the local National Weather Service (NWS) office will send out a trained storm survey team to examine the damage area. Depending on the severity of the storm, others groups, such as academics or local emergency response, may also be included. Members of the damage survey team will typically carry a damage survey kit to assist in the damage survey (figure 12.1). A damage survey kit will typically include maps, a camera, and a Global Positioning System (GPS) for gathering point data. Software can be used to help calculate the amount of wind speed required to destroy a building. By examining the type of construction of a destroyed or damaged building, an estimate can be made of the wind speeds required to cause that damage. Damage to trees, cars, and other structures may also be used to determine wind speeds. Depending on the size and scale of the damage, aerial photos and satellite images may also be used to determine wind speeds (National Oceanic and Atmospheric Administration 2011).

Figure 12.1 Camera, GPS, computer, maps, and field guide. |
Photo by Justyn Jackson and courtesy of the National Weather Service.

Joplin tornado area analysis

Imagine that you are a regional or city manager for the area devastated by a major tornado event. Gathering data for the area of interest and performing geographic information system (GIS)–based analysis would be an important step for generating maps, statistics, and reports. Such information could be used to determine where to direct limited financial or human resources. For example, we may wish to know the answer to questions such as, "How many miles of roadways were in the tornado path?" and "Which roadways probably need to have signs replaced, debris cleared, or lights repaired?" We may want the count of housing or people affected for future city planning. We can gather data, convert it, and prepare it for GIS analysis to answer these questions.

Gathering data for analysis

For this analysis we will gather data from three major sources: the NWS, the US Census Bureau, and local county GIS offices. Data on the areas the tornado covered and the strengths of wind speeds involved can be found at the NWS. Data for US roadways and counties can be found from the US Census Bureau. The other data we need can be found at the Jasper County, Missouri, GIS data page. All of these data are currently available online for download, although you will find, in general, that hunting data down and obtaining it can be almost more work and take more skill than performing the analysis itself:

The National Weather Service (NWS 2011), http://www.crh.noaa.gov/sgf/?n=event_2011may22_summary:

- **TornadoEventMay222011.kmz**: A KMZ (Keyhole Markup language Zipped) file is a compressed file containing a KML (Keyhole Markup Language) data file, and sometimes supporting files. This package contains KML data for F1 through F5 boundary areas and a simple line path of the tornado. Each boundary represents a different Fujita scale classification for wind speed. The polygon for F1 typically contains the polygon for F2, and so on. Each increase of scale number is a higher category of wind speed and results in more damage to the area. This will be imported using the KML to Layer tool, and the boundaries will ultimately be exported as a polygon shapefile. **~8 KB.**

The TIGER Mapping Service at the US Geological Survey (USCG) Census Bureau (US Department of Commerce 2014), http://www.census.gov/cgi-bin/geo/shapefiles2012/main:

- **tl_2012_29097_edges.zip**: A ZIP file is a common format that compresses larger data files into a single smaller file to save space. This package contains the edges within Jasper County. It has the attribute ROADFLG=Y for roads, HYDROFLG=Y for streams, and RAILFLG=Y for railroads. **~2 MB.**

- **tabblock2010_29_pophu.zip**: This package contains population and housing 2010 census counts per block for the entire state of Missouri. Attribute POP10 gives us the census 2010 population. Attribute HOUSING10 gives us the census 2010 housing count. **~300 MB uncompressed.**

The Jasper County Missouri free GIS data page (Jasper County 2014), http://gis.jaspercounty. org/gisdata/free_gisdata.htm:

- **jcmo_county_boundary.zip**: Contains a shapefile defining the border of Jasper County. **~9 KB.**
- **Expedited_Debris_Removal_Area.zip**: Contains a shapefile defining a boundary of area where the majority of debris has been removed, most likely related to the most damaged areas. **~4 KB.**

Procedure and data analysis

One of the most important issues when dealing with data from multiple sources is to ensure that all the data are projected to the same coordinate system for analysis. This allows you to properly perform analyses using ArcToolbox tools such as Clip or Union. For this analysis we use the NAD 1983 StatePlane Missouri West FIP 2403 (US Feet) coordinate system within Esri's ArcMap application. The goal of your analysis will determine the coordinate system you choose.

The first step of our analysis is getting the tornado category data into a format we can use. To use the KMZ tornado data within ArcMap, we need to first use the KML to Layer tool on the TornadoEventMay222011.kmz data.

One of the created layers will be called "Multipatches." This is three-dimensional data, and for our analysis we need it to be projected onto two dimensions. To do this we need to use the Multipatch Footprint tool to create the polygon boundaries for each tornado category. These tools require the 3D Analyst and Spatial Analyst extensions to be enabled in ArcMap. The results give us a unique polygon in shapefile format for each tornado rating category. This allows us to compare and contrast this data with other shapefile sources.

To determine the total length of roads affected, we have to filter the original line data from TIGER to only include roads. We can do this using the Select tool in ArcGIS. After generating this data, we can then Clip to the tornado boundaries and generate our first image (figure 12.2). Using "calculate geometry and statistics" on the attribute table of the clipped roads tells us that about **120.59 miles of roads** are covered by the tornado.

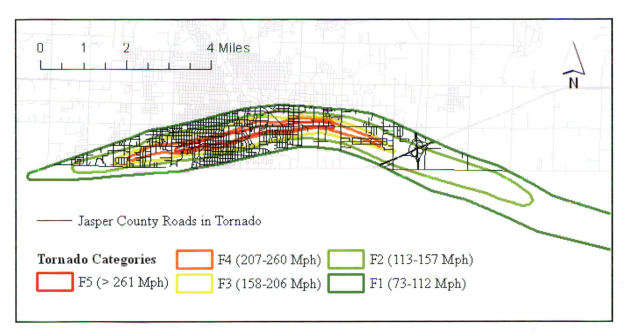

Figure 12.2 Calculating the Jasper County roads affected by the tornado using imported KMZ polygon data showing tornado categories and TIGER data for Jasper County roads. | Roads courtesy of TIGER; tornado categories courtesy of NOAA.

To determine how much of the population and housing was affected, we will first use the tornado polygon for each category to intersect the TIGER census data polygons. This leads to a slight problem. We could potentially overcount our data at the point where a tornado boundary divides a census block. Normal intersection will give us just the original data value on the inside of the intersection, which will inflate values along the border of the tornado boundary. Figure 12.3 shows the problem in more detail. Where a boundary divides a census polygon, we want the underlined value for a count, which is based on total area covered. To accomplish this, we add a field to our original census data called [OrigArea] and copy the polygon areas. Now when we run the Intersect tool we will get the new polygon area in our [Shape_Area] attribute. Using the field calculator, we can use the formula "([Shape_Area]/[OrigArea]) * [*CensusValueOfInterest*]" to generate any wanted value, such as population count. This is still flawed in that it assumes the value of interest is spread over the area evenly, which could be wrong; however, this is better than overcounting.

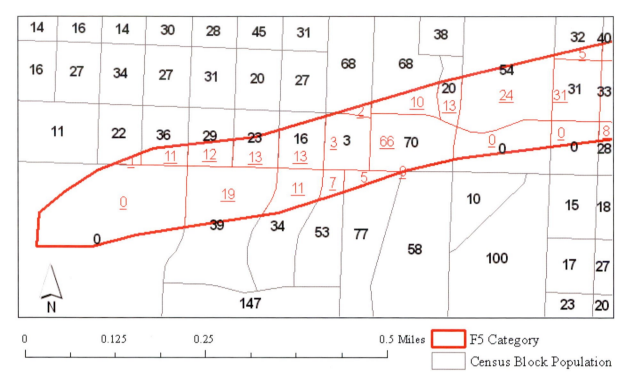

Figure 12.3 **The problem of tornado boundaries that intersect census data polygons. Correctly area-weighted values are shown underlined in red.** | Census blocks courtesy of US Census Bureau; tornado categories courtesy of NOAA.

Now we can use a combination of the Intersect and Erase tools or select and scripting to create a unique polygon area (or zone) for each of the Fujita tornado categories that does *not* contain any other category within it. Basically imagine a donut shape for the F1 category that is only the F1 contour (or the zone experiencing F1-level winds). Once we have one unique polygon per tornado category, we can apply the intersection and field calculator process we described for figure 12.3 for each tornado category, giving us a reasonable count per polygon for our census values of interest. In particular, we are interested in the POP10 and HOUSING10 counts from our census data. They represent the 2010 population census for each area and the count of housing for that area. Using the Statistics tool on our final attribute tables yields a total count for our POP10 and HOUSING10 fields, shown in table 12.2.

Table 12.2   Total counts of households and persons per tornado boundary

EF number	Total population affected	Total households affected
1	6,273	2,883
2	3,492	1,570
3	3,834	1,783
4	1,953	939
5	1,725	841
Total	**17,277**	**8,016**

Census data courtesy of US Census Bureau; tornado categories courtesy of NOAA.

Given that approximately 10,200 people filed for assistance after the tornado (from the Storm Events Database), we can estimate that about 60 percent of the people living in the path of the tornado were directly affected by the storm (10,200/17,277). This does not take into account visitors, people traveling through the area, or vacationers, but it is a reasonable estimate for analysis. Out of the total 17,277 people in the storm area, 3,678 (21 percent) of individuals experienced the extreme F4/F5 levels of wind speed. An estimated 1,780 households, or 22 percent of households in the storm, were hit by F4/F5 damage. Applying the results shown in table 12.2 and the calculated values of population and housing counts, we can generate the map layouts of figures 12.4 and 12.5.

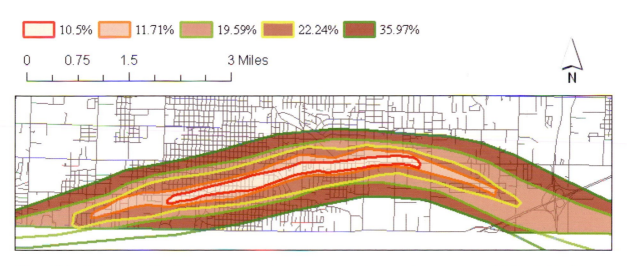

Figure 12.4   Percentage of total housing damaged by F-level zone. | Census data courtesy of US Census Bureau; tornado categories courtesy of NOAA; roads courtesy of TIGER.

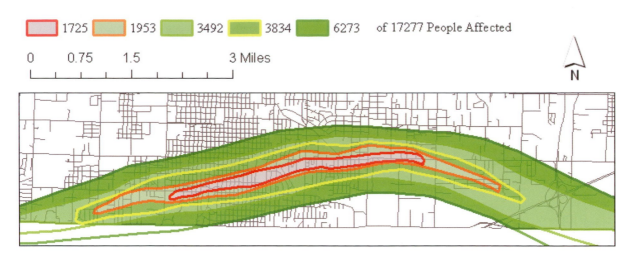

Figure 12.5 **Population of people living by F-level zone.** | Census data courtesy of US Census Bureau; tornado categories courtesy of NOAA; roads courtesy of TIGER.

One downside to the maps previously described is that although they give us a count of people and housing, they do not show us where the majority of people or houses are actually located. We will generate one final map that looks at population by area. To do this, we use the Calculate Geometry table tool in ArcMap to create and fill in an "Acre" field per polygon. Then we can divide the number of people per area by this number to generate the number of people per acre value. The results show us the highest areas by density, or where the most people live. We can see in figure 12.6 that there is a vertical band of high population density within the area hit by the highest F4/F5 wind speeds, thus showing one reason why this particular storm was so devastating to the local area.

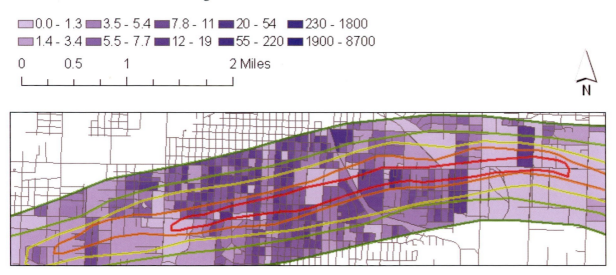

Figure 12.6 **Population by people per acre.** | Census data courtesy of US Census Bureau; tornado categories courtesy of NOAA; roads courtesy of TIGER.

References

Jasper County. 2014. "GIS Layer Inventory." http://gis.jaspercounty.org/gisdata/free_gisdata.htm.

National Climatic Data Center. 2011. "Storm Events Database." http://www.ncdc.noaa.gov/stormevents/eventdetails.jsp?id=296617.

National Oceanic and Atmospheric Administration. 2011. "Damage Surveys." http://www.srh.noaa.gov/ama/?n=damagesurveys.

National Weather Service. 2011. "Joplin Tornado Event Summary May 22, 2011." http://www.crh.noaa.gov/sgf/?n=event_2011may22_summary.

US Department of Commerce. 2014. TIGER Mapping Service. Retrieved from US Census Bureau: http://www.census.gov.

Wikipedia. 2014. "Enhanced Fujita Scale." Last modified August 5, 2014. http://en.wikipedia.org/wiki/Enhanced_Fujita_Scale.

CHAPTER 13

Integrating weather, climate, and demographic data

Mike Squires

One of the attractive features of a geographical information system (GIS) is its ability to analyze disparate datasets in the same application. This chapter discusses the use of weather and climate datasets in the form of shapefiles and ArcInfo grids along with gridded population data and other demographic and infrastructure shapefiles. This type of analysis is important because the result helps to quantify the societal impacts of weather and climate events. It is one thing to know that 3 to 18 inches of snow fell over several states, but it is much more informative to know that 9,500 miles of interstate were covered by 12 inches or more of snowfall in a particular storm or that 150 schools within some region are located in areas that received more than 12 inches of new snowfall.

The examples in this chapter will use snowfall data from the National Oceanic and Atmospheric Administration's (NOAA) National Climatic Data Center (NCDC). However, the principles described here could be applied to other types of weather and climate data, such as rainfall, drought, and temperature. An effective resource for searching for weather and climate data is NOAA's Climate.gov website (http://www.climate.gov/maps-data), which allows users to search for weather and climate data. This website also contains metadata, Open Geospatial Consortium (OGC) web services, and tools for downloading individual datasets. See chapter 6 for more information on searching for weather and climate data. The demographic and infrastructure data come from the Esri Data and Maps DVDs that ship with

ArcGIS for Desktop software. As with the climate data, users could substitute their own demographic and infrastructure data to meet their particular needs.

Infrastructure, a local example

The first example shows how to use weather and infrastructure data to estimate societal impacts of a snowstorm on point locations such as schools or hospitals for a particular region. In this case, the region is composed of the counties that are in the area of responsibility of the Greer, South Carolina, National Weather Service (NWS) Forecast Office. NWS Forecast Office areas of responsibility are known as "county warning areas." Figure 13.1 is a map showing the NWS Greer, South Carolina, county warning area. Note that the warning area includes counties in three states (South Carolina, North Carolina, and Georgia) and contains varied terrain, everything from rolling hills to mountains.

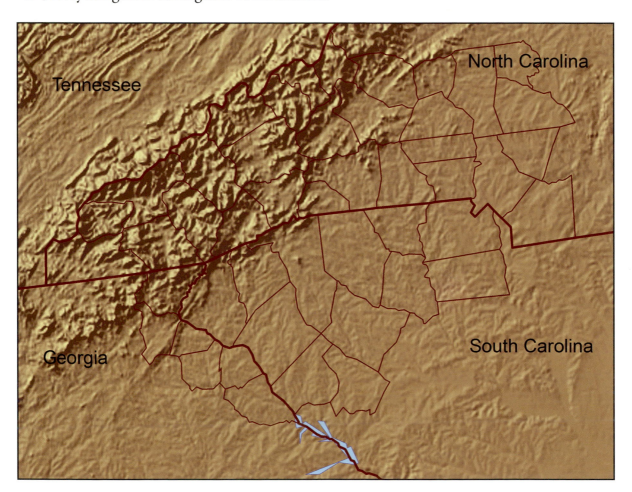

Figure 13.1   This map shows the weather warning area for the Greer, South Carolina, NWS Forecast Office. | Courtesy of NOAA and USGS.

On December 18–21, 2009, the region was hit by a massive snowstorm that closed many facilities and made travel difficult, especially in the mountains. Figure 13.2 shows the total snowfall from the storm as well as the locations of schools and interstate highways. Most of the area received over 3 inches of snowfall, and a large portion received over 6 inches of new snowfall. The mountains of western North Carolina received over a foot of snow. These amounts are significant for this southern climate. Although the map makes it clear that many schools and miles of interstate were affected, it would be helpful to quantify the number of schools or miles of interstate that were affected by various snowfall amounts.

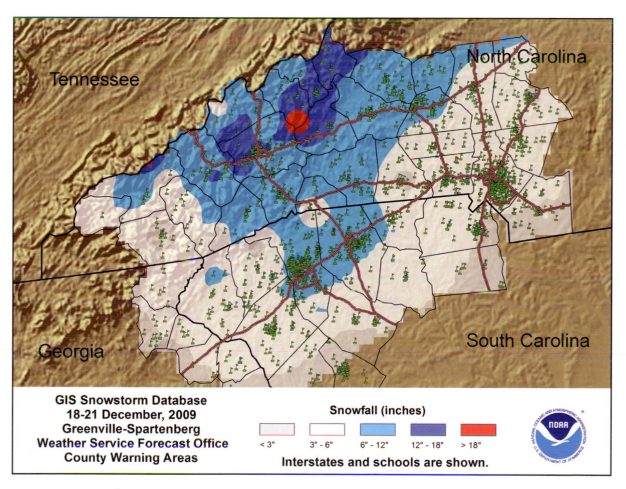

Figure 13.2 December 18–21, 2009, snowstorm and its effect on schools and interstates within the Greer, South Carolina, NWS warning area. | USGS, Esri Data & Maps, 2006; Esri Data & Maps: StreetMap. Interstates layer from members of the GIS Laboratory, Pellissippi Research Institute, University of Tennessee, Knoxville.

GIS provides tools for overlaying different spatial layers and calculating various statistics, such as counts of point features falling within specific polygon features. In this case, we will count the number of schools (points) within each category of snowfall (polygon feature). For example, how many schools were in locations that received more than 6 inches of new snowfall? Answering these types of questions helps emergency management, school administrators, and others put the storm into perspective.

To do this type of analysis, one would use a script and various geoprocessing tools. For a description of how to write a script using geoprocessing tools, see chapter 22, "Python scripting." Because this chapter is not a detailed lesson on Python scripting, "pseudo-code" will be used to describe the primary programming steps necessary to calculate various counts using point and polygon data. Pseudo-code is a high-level description of a script or program that does not require detailed knowledge of a programing language to understand. The pseudo-code used to count the number of schools in various snowfall categories is shown in the following.

Pseudo-code: Calculate point in polygon counts

1. Create a snowfall grid and convert it to polygons.
   a. *Interpolate* snowfall totals at weather stations to a continuous grid using a method such as Inverse Distance Weighted (IDW) or spline.
   b. *Reclassify* the continuous snowfall grid to a categorical grid with discrete values or bands (e.g., 0.000"—2.999", 3.000"–5.999", . . .).
   c. *Convert* the categorical snowfall grid to snowfall polygons.

2. *Spatial Join* the school shapefile with the snowfall polygons. This results in a shapefile with a separate record for each school with a new attribute that contains the categorical amount of snowfall (e.g., 3.00"–5.999").

3. *Sum* the number of schools within each snowfall category. This results in a table with a separate record for each snowfall category. The total number of schools in each category is one of the fields.

4. *Write out* the results to an ASCII (American Standard Code for Information Interchange) file.

This script produces a table that summarizes the number of schools in each snowfall category. Table 13.1 contains this information for 22 separate storms that affected the Greer, South Carolina, warning area. During the December 18–21, 2009, storm, 795 schools had over 3 inches of snowfall and 532 schools had over 6 inches of snowfall. In this part of the country, even 3 inches of new snowfall is a major event. During the March 12–15, 1993, storm there were 194 schools with over 18 inches of new snowfall. Notice in the pseudo-code that the categorical amount of snowfall is also available for individual schools after completing the spatial join.

Table 13.1 Number of schools affected by various thresholds of snowfall

Start date	End date	> 3"	> 6"	> 12"	> 18"
2/23/1993	2/27/1993	157	0	0	0
3/12/1993	3/15/1993	479	628	122	194
1/1/1994	1/5/1994	244	57	0	0
2/2/1995	2/6/1995	390	50	0	0
1/6/1996	1/9/1996	561	582	87	0
2/1/1996	2/4/1996	286	23	0	0
1/8/1997	1/12/1997	699	1	0	0
1/27/1998	1/29/1998	116	615	249	87
1/18/2000	1/22/2000	249	6	0	0
1/24/2000	1/27/2000	504	292	32	0
1/24/2000	2/1/2000	61	0	0	0
3/20/2001	3/23/2001	549	242	12	1
1/24/2004	1/29/2004	307	0	0	0
2/26/2004	2/28/2004	474	813	83	0
2/26/2009	3/3/2009	1137	60	0	0
12/18/2009	**12/21/2009**	**795**	**532**	**75**	**0**
1/27/2010	1/31/2010	582	351	0	0
2/3/2010	2/7/2010	680	163	12	0
2/5/2010	2/11/2010	146	493	37	0
2/8/2010	2/13/2010	767	0	0	0
2/12/2010	2/19/2010	302	236	158	3
2/21/2010	3/1/2010	346	322	0	0

Courtesy of NOAA.

Transportation, a regional example

The previous example used point data (schools) along with a snowfall grid to estimate societal impacts on a local scale. This example will use linear features with a snowfall grid to estimate transportation-related societal impacts on a regional scale. Specifically, the amount of snowfall affecting the interstate highway system during a major winter storm will be analyzed. The "Blizzard of 1996" was a major winter storm that affected over 57 million people, caused 3 billion dollars in damage, and killed 154 people. Figure 13.3 is a map of the storm with the interstate highway system overlaid on top of the snowfall grid.

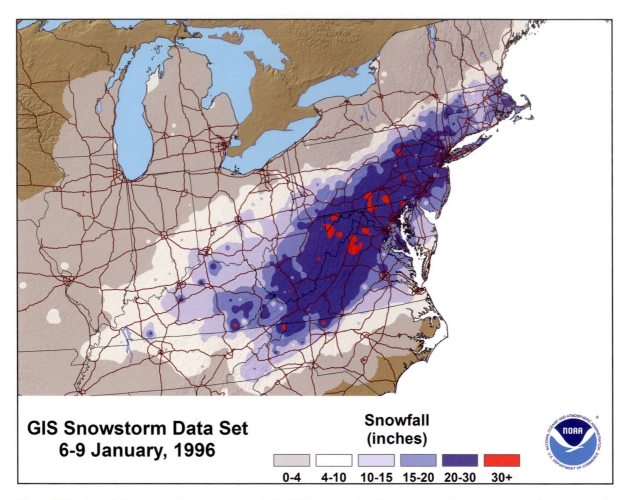

Figure 13.3   Snowfall amounts for the January 6–9, 1996, storm with the interstate highway system shown in red. | USGS, Esri Data & Maps, 2006. Interstates layer from members of the GIS Laboratory, Pellissippi Research Institute, University of Tennessee, Knoxville.

The goal in this example is to calculate the number of miles of interstate highway that had over 4, 10, 15, 20, and 30 inches of snowfall during the storm. Because the highways are linear features (as opposed to point features), this process is a little more complex than the previous example. Segments of the highways corresponding to various thresholds need to be *selected* and *clipped* out and stored in a temporary feature class. The length of each of these segments can be extracted directly from the geometry object, converted to the desired units (miles), and summed to get the total number of miles affected by a particular threshold. The following pseudo-code summarizes the procedure.

Pseudo-code: Calculate distance in polygon counts

This process must be repeated for each threshold: 4, 10, 15, 20, and 30 inches. This iteration is for snowfall between 4 and 10 inches.

1. Create a snowfall grid and convert it to polygons, as before.

2. *Select* the polygons that have 4–10 inches of snowfall.

3. *Clip* out the interstates that intersect these polygons.

4. *Assign* 4–10 inches of snowfall to each of these segments.

5. Use the geometry object to obtain the length of each of these segments.

6. *Sum* the length from all the selected segments to get the total number of miles affected by 4–10 inches of snowfall.

7. *Write out* the results to an ASCII file.

Figure 13.4 illustrates how the interstate highways are segmented and assigned snowfall categorical amounts. Segments with the same categorical amount (4–10 inches, for example) are summed to get the total number of miles for each category.

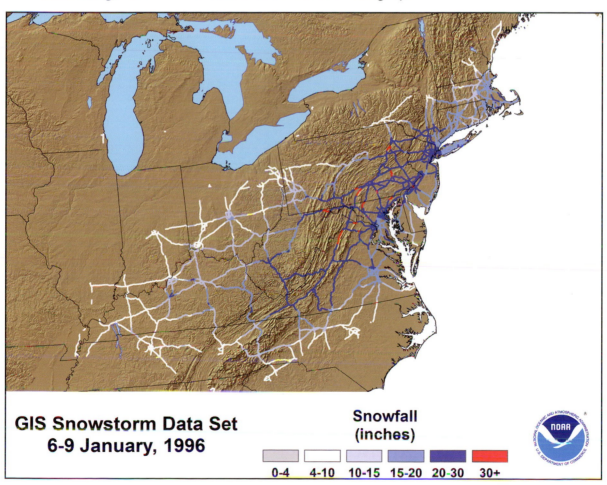

**GIS Snowstorm Data Set
6-9 January, 1996**

**Snowfall
(inches)**

0-4 4-10 10-15 15-20 20-30 30+

Figure 13.4   January 6–9, 1996, snowstorm with interstate highways color-coded by snowfall amount. | USGS, Esri Data & Maps, 2006. Interstates layer from members of the GIS Laboratory, Pellissippi Research Institute, University of Tennessee, Knoxville.

Table 13.2 contains the total number of miles of interstate highways affected by different snowfall thresholds for 25 storms. The January 1996 storm had almost 16,000 miles with greater than 4 inches of snow and 130 miles with over 30 inches of snow.

Table 13.2   Transportation impacts: Miles of interstate affected by snowfall above various snowfall thresholds

Storm date	Year	Month	> 4"	> 10"	> 15"	> 20"	> 30"
19820111_19820115	1982	1	17,228	1,163	0	0	0
19820404_19820408	1982	4	12,578	3,036	608	43	0
19830210_19830213	1983	2	10,388	7,796	4,871	1,266	6
19850129_19850203	1985	1	16,165	705	5	0	0
19870121_19870124	1987	1	14,544	6,737	734	28	0
19880105_19880109	1988	1	17,445	2,605	128	7	0
19880209_19880214	1988	2	13,224	2,696	354	4	0
19921209_19921213	1992	12	10,336	3,336	1,237	416	1
19930214_19930218	1993	2	14,782	1,216	44	0	0
19930220_19930224	1993	2	12,965	1,632	321	40	0
19930312_19930315	1993	3	17,174	12,353	7,034	2,873	198
19940116_19940119	1994	1	14,858	4,228	911	32	0
19940222_19940225	1994	2	10,987	681	0	0	0
19940222_19940225	1994	2	10,987	681	0	0	0
19950202_19950207	1995	2	11,028	3,746	284	28	0
19951218_19951222	1995	12	11,140	3,297	322	15	0
19960106_19960109	**1996**	**1**	**15,926**	**11,102**	**7,946**	**4,557**	**130**
19990101_19990104	1999	1	11,766	4,950	1,311	221	1
20001228_20010101	2000	12	9,518	824	107	5	0
20021222_20021226	2002	12	13,229	2,211	709	288	8
20030214_20030218	2003	2	14,945	8,786	6,658	2,543	9
20031204_20031208	2003	12	9,836	4,581	2,006	255	0
20040124_20040129	2004	1	18,738	2,266	122	33	0
20050121_20050124	2005	1	15,583	5,697	1,233	674	0
20051207_20051210	2005	12	12,039	1,196	22	0	0

Courtesy of NOAA.

Regional Snowfall Index

Snowstorms can have a devastating effect on various sectors of the population, including transportation, commerce, and emergency services. In an effort to quantify these effects and put them into a century-scale historical perspective, NOAA's NCDC is producing a regional snowfall impact index. Knowing the amount of snowfall is critical; however, it is important to have a sense of the societal impacts of the storm. Unfortunately, long and consistent records of economic activity, snow removal costs, school closings, and other societal activity on daily time scales are not available. However, population information can be used as a proxy for estimating societal impacts. Thus, the Regional Snowfall Index (RSI) is based on population along with the spatial extent of the storm and total snowfall from the storm. Including population information ties the index to societal impacts (Squires et al. 2014).

RSI is an evolution of the Northeast Snowfall Impact Scale (NESIS) that NCDC began producing operationally in 2005. Although NESIS was developed for storms that had a major impact in the Northeast United States, it also includes snowfall and population information from other regions as well. It can be thought of as a quasi-national index that is calibrated to Northeast snowstorms. By contrast, RSI is a regional index; a separate index is produced for each of the six NCDC climate regions in the eastern two-thirds of the nation. RSI has been calculated for 596 snowstorms that occurred between 1900 and 2014, which allows RSI to put snowstorms into a century-scale historical perspective.

The equation used to calculate the RSI is

$$RSI = \sum_{T=T_1}^{T_4} \left[\left(\frac{A_T}{\bar{A}_T} + \frac{P_T}{\bar{P}_T} \right) \right]$$

where:
T = Region-specific snowfall thresholds (inches of snowfall)
A_T = Area (square miles) affected by snowfall greater than threshold T
$\bar{A}_T$ = Mean area (square miles) affected by snowfall greater than threshold T
P_T = Population affected by snowfall greater than threshold T
$\bar{P}_T$ = Mean population affected by snowfall greater than threshold T

The regions previously referred to are the six eastern NCDC climate regions. The region-specific snowfall thresholds, T, serve to calibrate RSI to each region. For example, the regional snowfall thresholds for the South region are 2, 5, 10, and 15 inches, whereas thresholds for the Upper Midwest region are 3, 7, 14, and 21 inches. These thresholds were chosen with the help of 10- and 25-year return period statistics to help ensure objective and consistent choices across regions. Table 13.3 lists the thresholds (snowfall in inches), area (square miles), and population (2000 Census) for all the regions. Using year 2000 population information ensures that changes and variability in RSI are a result of climate variability and not changes in population. The area and population values are divided by their mean values in the equation because in a typical storm the population is one to three orders of magnitude more than the area. Using the mean area and population to standardize each term also ensures that the RSI distributions for all regions are similar despite large differences in regional snowfall climatologies, region population, and region area. This is a desirable attribute because it allows comparisons of snowstorms across regions. For example, a snowstorm in the Southeast may receive less snow than the Northeast for the same storm, but the societal impacts for the Southeast may be larger. This is because the Northeast is more resilient to snowstorms—there is more snow removal equipment and people have more experience dealing with snowstorms. Having similar index values across regions also makes it easier for the public to understand the index. Once an RSI is calculated, it is converted to a categorical score ranging from 1 (notable) through 5 (extreme). Table 13.4 shows the relationship between the RSI raw score, RSI category, and the frequency with which these categories occur. Complete details on the calculation of RSI can be found at NOAA's NCDC RSI website: http://www.ncdc.noaa.gov/snow-and-ice/rsi/references.

Table 13.3   Area and population for the NCDC Climate Regions shown in figure 13.1*

Region	Area (mi²)	Population	T1	T2	T3	T4
Ohio Valley	310,367	46,987,525	3	6	12	18
Upper Midwest	254,766	23,147,922	3	7	14	21
Northeast	178,509	60,246,523	4	10	20	30
South	563,004	36,977,926	2	5	10	15
Southeast	285,895	47,755,771	2	5	10	15
Northern Rockies and Plains	470,385	4,504,284	3	7	14	21

* T1–T4 are the specific snowfall thresholds (inches) used in the RSI algorithm.
Adapted from http://www1.ncdc.noaa.gov/pub/data/cmb/snow-and-ice/rsi/regional-snowfall-impact-scale-27th-iips-v3a.pdf.

Table 13.4   RSI Categories and the percentage of storms in each category

RSI category definitions		
Category	RSI raw score	Approximate % of storms
5	> 18	1%
4	10–18	2%
3	6–10	5%
2	3–6	13%
1	1–3	25%
0	0–1	54%

Source: http://www1.ncdc.noaa.gov/pub/data/cmb/snow-and-ice/rsi/regional-snowfall-impact-scale-27th-iips-v3a.pdf.

The process for calculating an RSI value for the Southeast for the March 12–14, 1993, storm is shown in figure 13.5. The earth tone grid is population density, with lighter colors indicating higher population. The population and snowfall grids are both 5 km resolution, and the individual grid cells align with each other. The area of snowfall and population associated with each threshold are calculated within a GIS using reclassification and zonal statistics methods and written to a table that provides all the required inputs to the RSI algorithm. The final RSI value for this storm is 20.57, which would be a Category 5 storm.

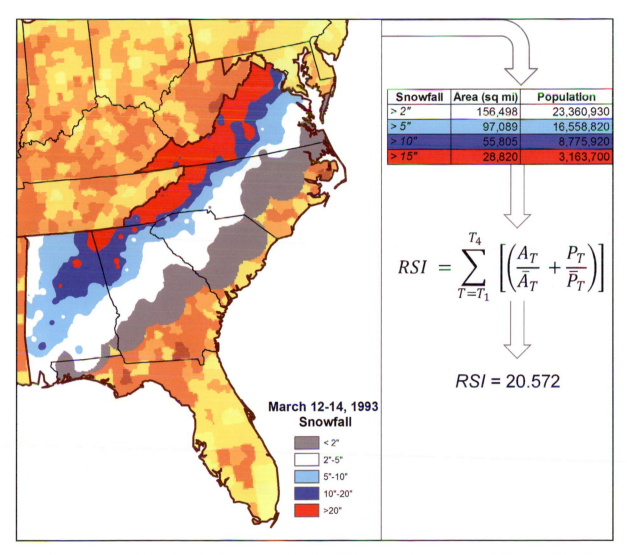

Snowfall	Area (sq mi)	Population
> 2"	156,498	23,360,930
> 5"	97,089	16,558,820
> 10"	55,805	8,775,920
> 15"	28,820	3,163,700

$$RSI = \sum_{T=T_1}^{T_4} \left[\left(\frac{A_T}{\bar{A}_T} + \frac{P_T}{\bar{P}_T} \right) \right]$$

$$RSI = 20.572$$

March 12-14, 1993 Snowfall

- < 2"
- 2"-5"
- 5"-10"
- 10"-20"
- >20"

Figure 13.5 Calculated RSI values for the storm and the equation used to calculate the RSI. | Courtesy of NOAA. Population density map: Counties2010, Data & Maps for ArcGIS.

The RSI values have no physical meaning; their purpose is to provide a relative measure of the severity of snowstorms taking into account societal impacts so that storms and their variation and change through time can be understood. It is reasonable to ask what a particular RSI value looks like in terms of a traditional snowfall map. Figure 13.6 illustrates how maps of storms in the Southeast with similar footprints but different RSI values may appear. The

Category 5 March 1993 "super storm" actually has a slightly smaller footprint (206,144 mi^2) than the Category 2 January 1982 storm (216,244 mi^2). However, the January 1982 storm has little snowfall over 10 inches and no snowfall over 15 inches. In contrast, the March 1993 storm has large areas of snowfall over 10 and 15 inches, which results in a Category 5 RSI. This comparison gives a sense how different RSI values relate to spatial distributions of snowfall and population. Due to the multidimensional nature of the RSI (snowfall area, amount, population, and juxtaposition of all three) it is possible for two storms with similar RSI values to have maps that look very different from each other.

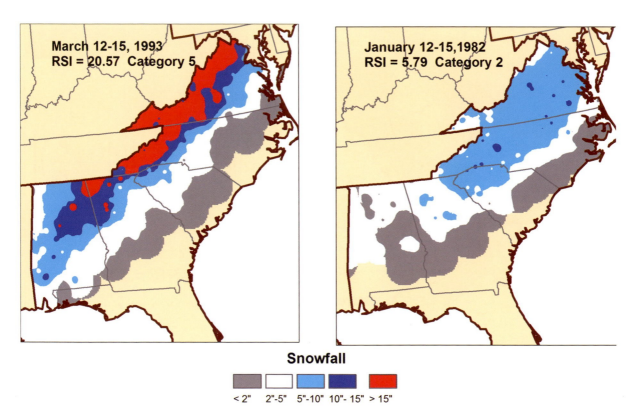

Figure 13.6 A comparison of two Southeast snow storms with similar areas but different RSI scores. | Courtesy of NOAA.

Figure 13.7 shows a December 2009 snowstorm that affected the Ohio Valley, the Northeast, and the Southeast. The total storm snowfall in each region on the map is symbolized by region-specific values. The areas of red and dark blue in the Ohio Valley and the Southeast indicate heavy snowfall relative to these regions, and hence the Category 3 and 4 rankings, respectively. The Northeast, in contrast, is only Category 1 due to the higher thresholds for this region. This is an example of how RSI is able to discriminate societal impacts between regions.

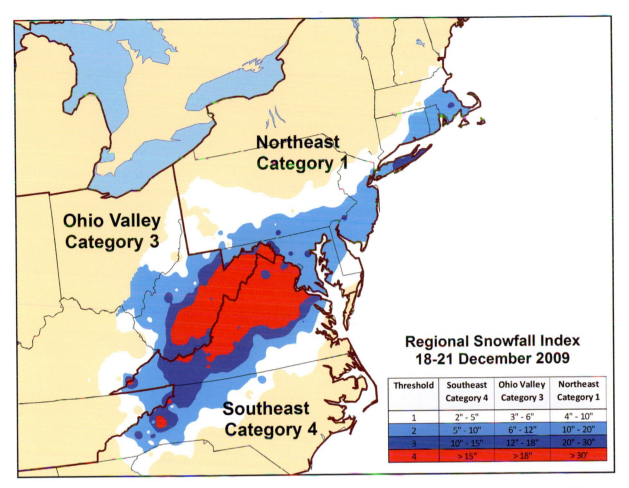

Figure 13.7 Example of RSI being computed for multiple regions showing the effect of varying thresholds for each region. | Courtesy of NOAA.

In summary, RSI—based on population and snowfall—is an effort to measure the societal impacts of snowstorms on a regional scale and to put those impacts into a century-scale historical perspective. This is important because the same storm can have different regional impacts not only as a result of a storm's evolution, but also because of regional differences in snowstorm resiliency. RSI is calculated, as needed, shortly after a storm has ended. RSI information can be found at the NOAA RSI website: http://www.ncdc.noaa.gov/snow-and-ice/rsi/. This site contains more detailed information on the RSI methodology, the snowfall and population data used to calculate RSI, and a mapping application.

Summary

This chapter described how GIS can be used to integrate weather and climate data with demographic data to provide societal impact information for snowstorms. This information is very useful for emergency managers, the news media, and policy makers. Although all the examples in this chapter used snowfall data, one could imagine analogous tasks using temperature or liquid precipitation. Regardless of the data used, when placed in GIS format, spatial tools can be used to produce valuable information.

Reference

Squires M. F., J. H. Lawrimore, R. R. Heim, D. A. Robinson, M. R. Gerbush, and T. W. Estilow. 2014. "The Regional Snowfall Index." *Bulletin of the American Meteorological Society* 95. http://dx.doi.org/10.1175/BAMS-D-13-00101.1.

CHAPTER 14

Integrating remote sensing observations and model results for weather studies

Stephanie Granger, Rob Raskin, and Michael J. Garay

The combination of measurements from multiple sources offers the potential to help researchers characterize and understand complex physical processes. The standard paradigm is that scientists write code within a visualization environment to read selected portions of the data collection, and new code is written from scratch to perform new tasks. Because these software tools typically have no concept of spatiotemporal referencing datasets, it is difficult to discover, collect, or analyze products nearby in space or time. As a result, it is challenging to exploit all the available data for any particular task or event; hence, not all atmospheric remote sensing data are used as efficiently or effectively as is possible.

Geographic information systems (GIS) are a promising solution to this data integration problem. A GIS provides services to visualize, analyze, and overlay multiparameter, georeferenced data with minimal software development effort, with a user experience that is akin to map display software, such as Google Earth, with the advantage of providing access to the actual data values and a suite of robust analytic tools. However, due to the underlying, internal two-dimensional data models of commercial GIS products, these capabilities are restricted to static two-dimensional data rather than multidimensional science products. A GIS reads in the spatial registration of a dataset from the metadata (internal or external), and although ArcGIS 10 is "time-aware," there is no analogous registration in the time dimension.

To address this problem, a prototype framework for analysis and visualization of multi-sensor, multiparameter earth science data in a unified analytical structure and data model within a GIS was developed. The resulting proof of concept provided methods including representations of vertical independent variables and a swath data structure corresponding to the common data organization of satellite-retrieved data. These features were implemented in a GIS plug-in to ArcGIS developed jointly by the National Aeronautics and Space Administration (NASA) Jet Propulsion Laboratory (JPL), the University of Redlands (UR), and the Redlands Institute.

The case study

Atmospheric rivers (ARs) are extreme precipitation events powered by a subtropical jet stream that brings moisture-laden air from the tropics to the western Pacific, essentially pulling "rivers" of moisture through the atmosphere all the way across the Pacific Ocean. In fact, AR events that pull moist air from Hawaii to the West Coast of the United States are widely known as "Pineapple Express" storms. Some of the stronger AR events produce intense precipitation and can cause major flooding in California (Ralph et al. 2004). The most dangerous storms in California have been "warm and wet" winter storms that result in concentrated rain events over large regions (Dettinger 2011). The wind and rain associated with ARs are comparable to hurricanes on the East and Gulf Coasts of the United States. Figure 14.1 shows an example of a February 2004 AR event that produced extreme precipitation in California, as seen in Special Sensor Microwave Imager (SSM/I) satellite observations of Integrated Water Vapor (IWV).

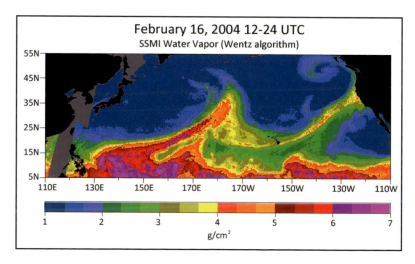

Figure 14.1   Composite SSM/I IWV from satellite overpass on February 16, 2004. The color scale represents the total amount of water vapor between the ocean surface and space. | http://www.esrl.noaa.gov/psd/atmrivers/events/, NOAA.

A January 2005 AR event was used as a case study to test the prototype plug-in and demonstrate the ability of GIS to integrate and visualize geospatial data from multiple sources. The 2005 event brought massive amounts of rain to Southern and Northern California. During one five-day period, January 6–11, over 20 inches of rain were recorded at mountain weather stations in Santa Barbara, Ventura, and Los Angeles County locations, and over 12 inches fell in Beverly Hills. The Los Angeles airport received nearly half of its annual average rainfall (12 inches) of rain in five days. On January 10, 2005, 10 lives were lost in La Conchita, California, due to a massive mudslide caused by days of intense rainfall. Figure 14.2 shows precipitation in Ventura County over a period of about three months from October 2004 leading up to and including the La Conchita landslide on January 10, 2005.

Ventura Daily Rainfall

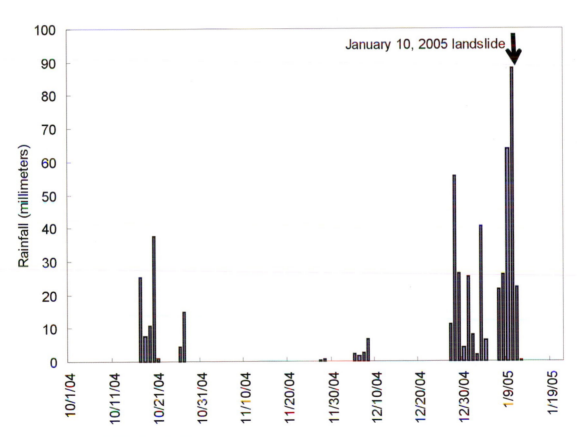

Figure 14.2 A graph tracking daily rainfall in Ventura County, California, from October 1, 2004, to mid-January 2005. The graph shows extreme precipitation in early January due to an atmospheric river. | Source: US Geological Survey (R. Jibson). Data from Wofford, 2005.

Data requirements

Integration of several disparate datasets from multiple sources is required to visualize an event of this magnitude. In order to demonstrate the utility of GIS and the prototype plug-in for integrating many datasets, several relevant observations related to the massive 2005 weather event were identified (table 14.1). These include height-resolved water vapor using measurements from NASA's Atmospheric Infrared Sounder (AIRS), daily surface wind speed and direction from NASA's QuikSCAT scatterometer, daily precipitation derived from NASA's Tropical Rainfall Measurement Mission (TRMM), sea surface temperature from the Global High Resolution Sea Surface Temperature (GHRSST) composite dataset, near-surface precipitation from ground-base Global Positioning System (GPS) sensors, and back trajectories derived using the National Oceanic and Atmospheric Administration's (NOAA) HYSPLIT (Hybrid Single-Particle Lagrangian Integrated Trajectory) model (Draxler et al. 2012) that were used to compute the potential origin and trajectory of water vapor across the Pacific leading up to the California storm. The HYSPLIT model is a complete system for computing simple air parcel trajectories and complex dispersion and deposition simulations, and was initially developed as a joint effort between NOAA and Australia's Bureau of Meteorology.

Table 14.1   Datasets, observations, and sources related to the 2005 weather event

Observation/ Measurement	Instrument	Format	Source	URL
3D water vapor	AIRS L2	HDF-EOS	Goddard Earth Sciences Data and Information Services Center	http://disc.sci.gsfc.nasa.gov
Sea surface temperature (SST)	L4 GHRSST (NCDC combined AVHRR, AMSR-E)	NetCDF	Physical Oceanography Data Active Archive Center (PO.DAAC)	http://podaac.jpl.nasa.gov
Surface winds	QuikSCAT	HDF-EOS	PO.DAAC	http://podaac.jpl.nasa.gov
Precipitation	TRMM	TIFF + TFW	Goddard Space Flight Center (GSFC)	http://trmm.gsfc.nasa.gov/data_dir/data.html
Near-surface land water vapor	Southern California Integrated GPS Network (SCIGN)	ASCII	Jet Propulsion Laboratory–Satellite Geodesy and Geodynamics Group	http://www.scign.org

(Continued)

Table 14.1   Datasets, observations, and sources related to the 2005 weather event   (*continued*)

Observation/ Measurement	Instrument	Format	Source	URL
Back trajectories	HYSPLIT model	GIS shapefile	NOAA Atmospheric Research Library	http://ready. arl.noaa.gov/ HYSPLIT.php
Basemap	Unknown source	TIFF	Esri	http://www.esri. com/software/ arcgis/arcgis-on- line-map-and- geoservices/ map-services

Courtesy of NASA/JPL.

Challenges integrating and visualizing science data products

Integrating several of the datasets identified for the case study into a GIS was relatively straight-forward; for example, output from the HYSPLIT model are automatically saved in GIS shape-file format. Other data required developing simple software scripts to convert the data from native formats (e.g., QuikSCAT wind speed and direction and SCIGN GPS) to shapefiles. However, science data products derived from the AIRS instrument represented an integration challenge requiring development of a prototype tool to enable seamless access to the NASA Data Active Archive Center (DAAC) at the Goddard Space Flight Center (GSFC). The tool also had to subset the collection "on the fly" by time, geographic region, and parameter while maintaining the unique swath construct of the measurements.

AIRS integration challenges

The AIRS sensor produces data characteristic of a large set of Earth remote-sensing data products obtained from satellites in near-polar orbits. These satellites generate a massive amount of time-dependent data that could be used effectively if integrated into standard GIS environments. However, the unique swath shape characteristic of polar-orbiting satellites (shown in figure 14.3) does not fit any standard GIS data structure (Turner 2007). A key component of the solution is the development of a four-dimensional data model that includes time and vertical dimensions and uses the satellite swath as the fundamental data structure. This approach was used to drive the development of a prototype plug-in toolbox that works with Esri ArcGIS software. The toolbox enabled spatial and temporal integration of a multidimensional, multiparameter data product into a unified GIS framework. It also provided a method for interactively interrogating AIRS satellite observations in volumetric space. The toolbox was developed by leveraging the Intel Array Visualizer and its File Loader, a freely available game component that includes application programming interfaces (APIs) to read common scientific formats and visualize three-dimensional data. The Intel software was folded into ArcObjects via Python calls. The proof-of-concept plug-in tool accessed AIRS data at the Goddard DAAC via file transfer protocol (FTP) calls and used the Intel package to transparently read the native Hierarchical Data Format—Earth Observing System (HDF-EOS) format (figure 14.4).

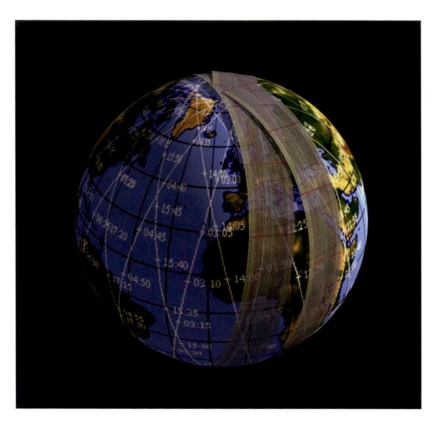

Figure 14.3 Swath pattern from a polar-orbiting satellite (e.g., Terra or Aqua). | Courtesy of T. Turner, University of Redlands, Redlands, CA.

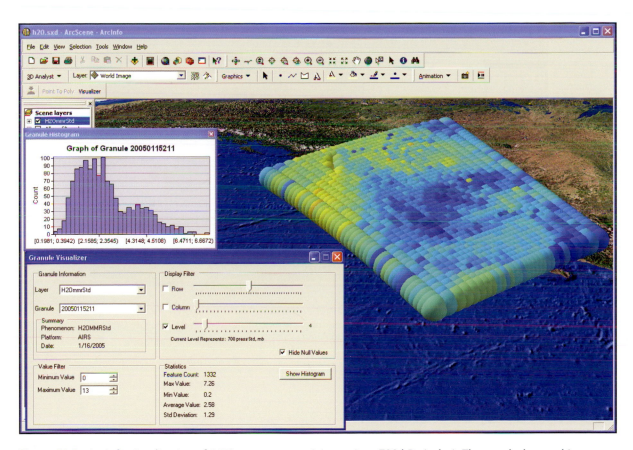

Figure 14.4 ArcInfo visualization of AIRS water vapor mixing ratio at 700 hPa (color). The graph shows a histogram of values, and sliders control the display of variables and provide information. | NASA/JPL. Courtesy of the California Institute of Technology.

Visualization of an extreme weather event in GIS

An example of the resulting visualization using the prototype tool is shown in figure 14.5. In this figure, a granule of AIRS water vapor data in the northeastern Pacific is shown as a point cloud superimposed on a background of GHRSST sea surface temperatures and QuikSCAT wind vectors. TRMM precipitation values are color-coded in blue superimposed over the ocean. To the right of the image, water vapor amounts from GPS are shown color-coded by absolute magnitude for various stations. Back trajectories from the NOAA HYSPLIT model are shown as dotted lines, indicating the relationship between the atmospheric water vapor over the Pacific and water vapor over land. A histogram of the AIRS data values is also shown in the top center of the image. Visualizations such as these could help scientists study and quantify spatiotemporal variability of atmospheric river events and their paths.

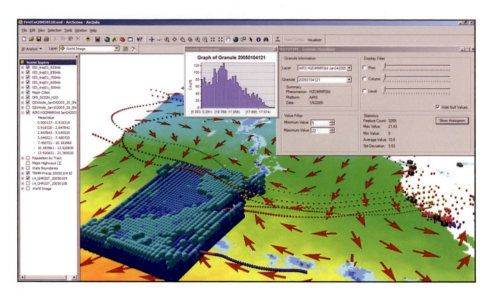

Figure 14.5   ArcGIS visualization of AIRS water vapor as a point cloud, QuikSCAT wind vectors, TRMM precipitation, HYSPLIT back trajectories, GHRSST SST, and SCIGN GPS Integrated Water Vapor for January 4, 2005. | NASA/JPL. Courtesy of the California Institute of Technology.

Results and conclusions

Understanding and predicting water cycles and water resources are important for sustainability worldwide (Intergovernmental Panel on Climate Change 2007). GIS technology enables incorporation of multisensor, multiparameter observations to provide a holistic, multidimensional view of these phenomena as a system that could lead to improved understanding of AR events. In order to incorporate all the data, a framework that includes representations of independent variables for time and vertical variables and a swath data structure that corresponds to the common data organization of satellite-retrieved data is needed. Recent advancements in GIS tools (addition of time and vertical dimensions) will help to facilitate continued development of the required framework. Retaining information on the instrument swath and (ultimately) the individual sensor footprint preserves the maximum amount of data fidelity and resolution. This facilitates an appropriate choice of tools for data interpolation, intercomparisons, and blending at later processing and analysis stages.

Acknowledgments

This research was carried out at the Jet Propulsion Laboratory, California Institute of Technology, under a contract with the National Aeronautics and Space Administration.

The authors gratefully acknowledge the NOAA Air Resources Laboratory (ARL) for the provision of the HYSPLIT transport and dispersion model and READY website (http://ready.arl.noaa.gov) used in this publication.

References

Dettinger, M. 2011. "Climate Change, Atmospheric Rivers, and Floods in California—A Multimodal Analysis of Storm Frequency and Magnitude Changes." *Journal of the American Water Resources Association* 47 (3): 514–23. doi:10.1111/j.1752-1688.2011.00546.x.

Draxler, R. R., and G. D. Rolph. 2012. HYSPLIT (HYbrid Single-Particle Lagrangian Integrated Trajectory) Model Access via NOAA ARL READY website, http://ready.arl.noaa.gov/HYSPLIT.php. NOAA Air Resources Laboratory, Silver Spring, MD.

Intergovernmental Panel on Climate Change. 2007. "Summary for Policymakers." In *Climate Change 2007: The Physical Science Basis. Contribution of Working Group I to the Fourth Assessment Report of the Intergovernmental Panel on Climate Change*, edited by S. Solomon, D. Qin, M. Manning, Z. Chen, M. Marquis, K. B. Averyt, M. Tigor, and H. L. Miller. Cambridge, UK, and New York: Cambridge University Press.

Jibson, R. 2005. "Landslide Hazards at La Conchita, California." USGS Open File Report—2005-1067. http://pubs.usgs.gov/of/2005/1067/508of05-1067.html.

Ralph, F. M., P. J. Neiman, and G. A. Wick. 2004. "Satellite and CALJET Aircraft Observations of Atmospheric Rivers over the Eastern North Pacific Ocean during the Winter of 1997/98." *Monthly Weather Review* 132: 1721–45.

Turner, A. 2007. "Consilience of Geographic Information Systems and Earth Sciences." In *Proceedings of the American Geophysical Union Fall Meeting*. December 10–14, 2007. San Francisco, CA.

Wofford, M. 2005. "Ventura, California, Weather Conditions." Accessed January 28, 2005. http://www.venturaweather.com/daily.htm.

CHAPTER 15

Lightning applications

Arlene Laing, Mark LaJoie, and Steven Reader

Cloud-to-ground lightning is a substantial threat to lives, commercial activity, and personal property (Curran, Holle, and Lopez 2000). Improving our knowledge of lightning distribution and the factors that influence lightning is vital to better prediction and reduction of lightning hazards. Lightning studies are suited to geographic information system (GIS) techniques because flashes are georeferenced and the response to the consequences of lightning, such as wildfires, requires visualization and mapping to be effective. The variability of lightning is more easily monitored and understood if its multiple meteorological influences can be integrated with tools such as the Man computer Interactive Data Access System (McIDAS-X), software created at the University of Wisconsin in 1973 for interactive analysis of satellite and other meteorological data (Lazzara et al. 1999).

Although the El Niño Southern Oscillation (ENSO; Philander 1990) has been linked to many weather phenomena and hazards (Ropelewski and Halpert 1986), comparatively few studies have examined the relationship between ENSO and lightning. This chapter describes how GIS is used to aggregate lightning distribution on a 2.5 km scale grid at monthly, seasonal, and annual scales and to explore how those distributions vary under ENSO extremes. The area of interest includes the Gulf Coast from Texas to South Carolina, which was selected because of its high flash-density rates and because it is a region where the ENSO impact is very clearly demonstrated for both temperature and precipitation patterns.

Lightning and fires in Florida

During the spring and early summer of 1998, over 2,300 fires scorched nearly a half million acres of Florida at a cost of over 620 million dollars. The Florida Division of Forestry (FDOF) attributed lightning as the primary ignition source (31 percent) during this 1998 outbreak. Precipitation was about 200 percent above normal for the 1997–1998 El Niño winter. However, subsequent dry conditions (rainfall less than 50 percent of normal) left more fuel available for combustion. Although drought conditions and wildfire threat existed through late May to early July 1998, the numbers of lightning-initiated fires and acres burned varied daily. Widely used drought indices are inadequate for application on a daily basis. For instance, the five-day period, June 18–22, 1998, presented much difficulty for fire forecasting. The number of new fires went from 46 to 85, and then just as quickly decreased to 34. Spatial analysis was performed on lightning data (location, peak current, polarity, and multiplicity) and fire data using Esri's ArcGIS software.

Figure 15.1 shows an example of the spatial and temporal relationship between flash occurrence, fire initiation, and the polarity of igniting flashes. Most of the 1998 lightning fires were associated with negative flashes.

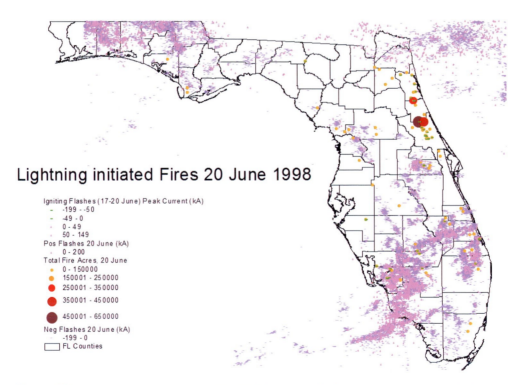

Lightning initiated Fires 20 June 1998

Igniting Flashes (17-20 June) Peak Current (kA)
-    -199 - -50
-    -49 - 0
·   0 - 49
·   50 - 149
Pos Flashes 20 June (kA)
·   0 - 200
Total Fire Acres, 20 June
·   0 - 150000
●   150001 - 250000
●   250001 - 350000
●   350001 - 450000
●   450001 - 650000
Neg Flashes 20 June (kA)
     -199 - 0
☐   FL Counties

Figure 15.1 Lightning and fires, June 20, 1998. Negative flashes are green, positive flashes are magenta and purple, and circles mark the fires. The size of the circle increases and the shade darkens with increasing acres burned. | Fire data courtesy of the Florida Division of Forestry; lightning data from Global Atmospherics Inc., previous owner of the NLDN.

Meteorological analysis using the McIDAS-X software helped to link the variability of lightning with atmospheric conditions that favor high flash rates, such as sea breeze thunderstorms (figures 15.2a and 15.2b). Meteorological conditions were determined from surface and upper air station observations, visible and infrared satellite imagery, and radar observations. GIS analysis of lightning in combination with localized winds, relative humidity, lower tropospheric instability, and rainfall provides guidance for mitigation of wildfire hazard.

(a)   (b)

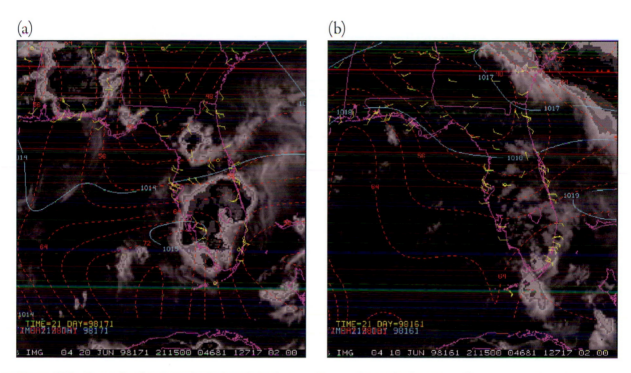

Figure 15.2 Example of meteorological analysis that combines enhanced infrared satellite image with surface observations using McIDAS-X for (a) June 20 (active convection and outbreak of lightning fires) and (b) June 10 (suppressed convection, one lightning fire reported). Thunderstorms are outlined in white, dark interior areas are the most intense, red dashed lines are relative humidity (%), cyan lines are pressure (hPa), and wind barbs are in yellow. | Data are from the National Oceanic and Atmospheric Administration (NOAA).

Lightning climatologies

The National Lightning Detection Network (NLDN), owned and operated by Vaisala Inc., detects cloud-to-ground (CG) lightning flashes over the contiguous United States and, with decreasing efficiency, over adjacent waters (Cummins et al. 1998). The longest NLDN-based lightning climatologies in the United States have found that the Gulf Coast has the highest flash density, measured in flashes per km^2, with the peak over central Florida (Orville and Huffines 2001; Orville et al. 2002). Lightning flash data were provided as point data in tables, with each of the nearly 55 million records containing attributes such as latitude, longitude, date, time, polarity, and strength.

Flash density

Each monthly lightning file was imported into ArcMap as a point feature layer, saved in shapefile format, and projected to a custom Albers equal area projection (figures 15.3a and 15.3b), which preserves area and facilitates analysis of flash per unit area. Flashes were then assigned to a fine-resolution grid by (1) importing the dBase table component of each shape file into the S-PLUS statistical package (Insightful Corporation 2003), (2) running a custom script to aggregate and bin individual flashes into 2.5 km × 2.5 km grid cells (816 × 418), (3) assigning each resultant grid box a corresponding flash count, and (4) exporting the data as monthly ASCII files. The grid corners and geographic extent of the domain was specified as header information in each file, rendering each readable by ArcMap as monthly raster grids that match the study domain precisely.

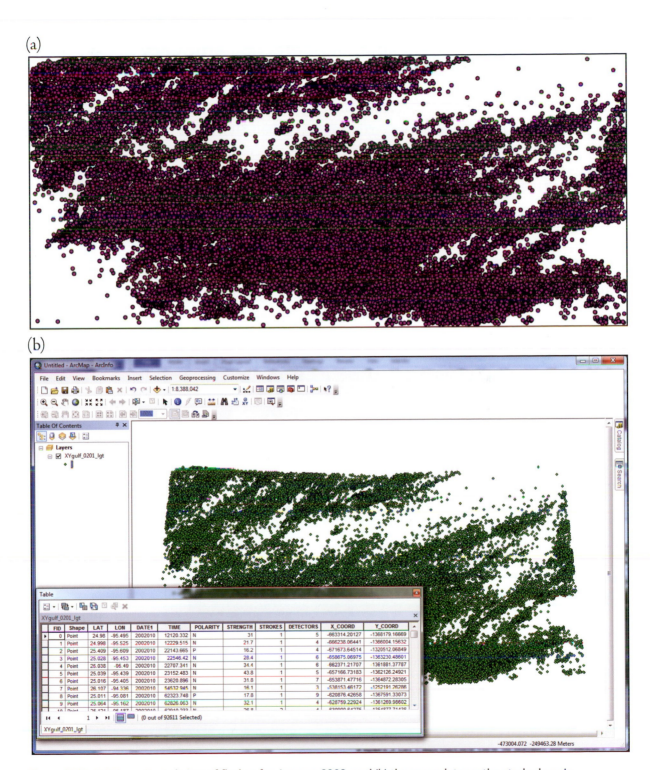

Figure 15.3 (a) Unprojected view of flashes for January 2002, and (b) the same data on the study domain projection. Inset in (b) shows the attribute table for lightning flashes. | Lightning data courtesy of US Air Force Combat Climatology Center (AFCCC), who purchased the data from Vaisala Inc., current owner and operator of the NLDN; background state and county border data originated with Tele Atlas and were distributed by Esri.

Correction for changes in lightning detection efficiency

The NLDN sensors were upgraded in the period from 2002 to 2003, which made the network more sensitive and led to an increase of flash detection efficiency (DE) to between 90 and 95 percent (Jerauld et al. 2005). Correction factors for relative DE for each year were obtained from Vaisala Inc. (K. Cummins, personal communication 2007). The correction factors used in this study are relative to 1999.

The DE correction values are arranged in a 2° × 2° grid and provided as tables (in database file [DBF] format). The DBF files are imported as events into ArcMap and converted to polygon shapefiles. The shapefiles are exported. Then a new unit polygon shape is created for the whole domain area. Both the unit polygon and the shapefile of the DE data field are then added to ArcMap.

The Gulf Coast region is subsetted from the national values (figure 15.4). The DE correction table is imported to ArcMap and converted to a feature using a Visual Basic script.

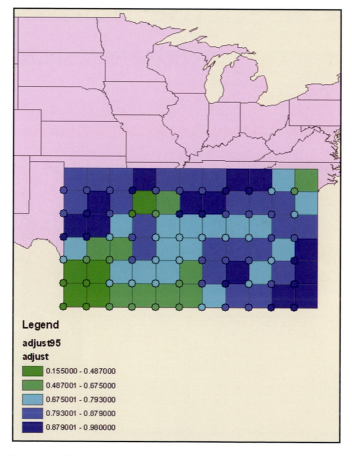

Figure 15.4   Grids of 1995 density efficiency correction factors for the study domain. | Lightning data courtesy of US Air Force Combat Climatology Center (AFCCC), who purchased the data from Vaisala Inc., current owner and operator of the NLDN; background state and county border data originated with Tele Atlas and were distributed by Esri.

The DE correction layer is added to ArcMap and reprojected to match the flash density grids (figure 15.5). The cell spacing is set to 2.5 km to match flash density grid boxes. A new flash density map is produced by dividing the current flash density grid by the DE correction grid. Histograms of the difference field showed that the flash density change was less than 1 flash km² for most of the affected cells. ArcGIS zonal statistics are used to estimate new annual domain totals whose time series are compared with annualized sea surface temperature (SST) anomalies in the tropical central Pacific.

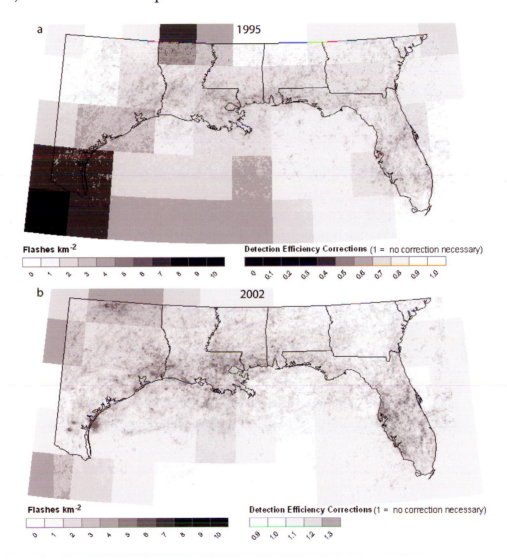

Figure 15.5 Examples of mean flash density (km²) and detection efficiency values (relative to 1999) for (a) 1995 and (b) 2002. Detection efficiency values that are "too low" are darker. Higher values of flash density are darker. | Lightning data courtesy of US Air Force Combat Climatology Center (AFCCC), who purchased the data from Vaisala Inc., current owner and operator of the NLDN; background state and county border data originated with Tele Atlas and were distributed by Esri.

Correlation of lightning and equatorial Pacific SST anomalies

The extremes of ENSO, termed El Niño and La Niña, encompass a wide range of climatic conditions (Philander 1990). The ENSO index used for this study is derived from direct SST measurements (Smith and Reynolds 2004). The Oceanic Niño Index was formally defined as the "three-month average of sea surface temperature departures from normal" in the Niño 3.4 region of the Pacific (Department of Commerce 2003). For the period from 1995 to 2002, a 96-month time series of these SST anomaly values was downloaded from the Climate Prediction Center.

Simple Pearson's correlations were computed between concurrent monthly pairings of Niño 3.4 SST and CG lightning flash deviation values from the study area. For each grid, the lightning flash deviation from the monthly mean is calculated, and each eight-month time series of values is compared with the corresponding eight-member series of Niño 3.4 SST anomaly values. Thus, SST anomalies are compared to above or below "normal" monthly lightning values in any given bin. The correlation values computed by the script for each user-specified domain were then written out to monthly text files, and the text files imported into ArcMap and visualized over a basemap of the study area. To achieve this, the ArcMap ET GeoWizards tools were used to create a blank grid matching the user-specified subdomains. The blank grid squares were then populated with matching correlation values from the text files (e.g., figure 15.6a and 15.6b).

(a)

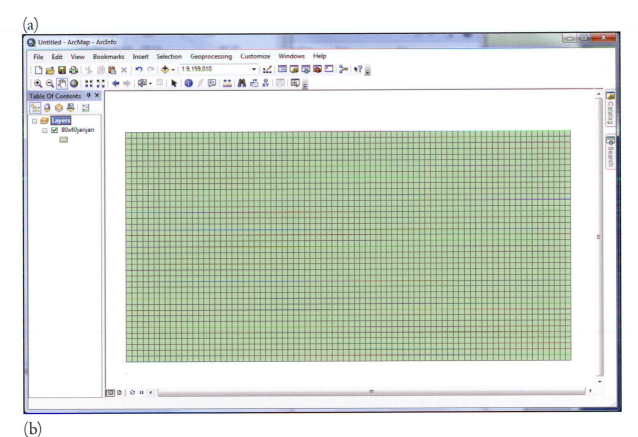

(b)

Nino 3.4 - Lightning Deviation Correlations

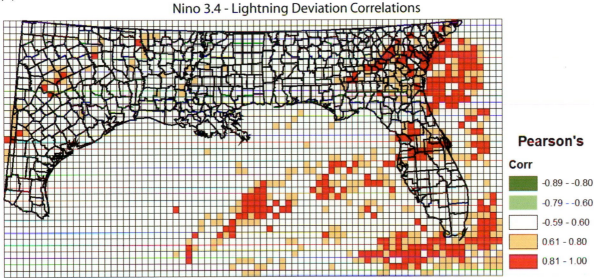

Pearson's

Corr

	-0.89 - -0.80
	-0.79 - -0.60
	-0.59 - 0.60
	0.61 - 0.80
	0.81 - 1.00

Figure 15.6 Example of (a) the domain grid for which monthly correlations are made between lightning anomalies and the Oceanic Niño Index, and (b) a map of monthly correlation for December. | Nino 3.4 SST anomaly data courtesy of NOAA. Lightning data courtesy of US Air Force Combat Climatology Center (AFCCC), who purchased the data from Vaisala Inc., current owner and operator of the NLDN; background state and county border data originated with Tele Atlas and were distributed by Esri.

Conclusion

GIS and other analytic tools allow exploration of the relationships between lightning and wildfires. They enable users to create lightning climatologies, relate ENSO phases to lightning distribution, and present the results as maps and graphs that are suitable for emergency management and hazard mitigation. GIS techniques are used to map flash density using Albers equal area projection, which preserves area (a key property when analyzing flashes per unit area), adjusts flash density maps for changes in the detection efficiency of the lightning detection network, estimates new annual domain totals using zonal statistics, and maps correlations of monthly flash deviations with SST anomalies in the equatorial Pacific Niño 3.4 region. Although eight years is inadequate to establish a long-term pattern, results imply that the ENSO influences lightning across the US Gulf Coast (Laing et al. 2008). The ENSO–lightning relationship has implications for hazard assessment of public safety and can be a useful tool for long-term seasonal planning (e.g., wildfire management).

References

Curran, B. E., R. L. Holle, and R. E. López. 2000. "Lightning Casualties and Damages in the United States from 1959 to 1994." *Journal of Climate* 13: 3448–64.

Cummins, K. L., M. J. Murphy, E. A. Bardo, W. L. Hiscox, R. B. Pyle, and A. E. Pifer. 1998. "A Combined TOA/MDF Technology Upgrade of the US National Lightning Detection Network." *Journal of Geophysical Research* 103 (D8): 9035–44.

Department of Commerce. 2003. "NOAA Gets US Consensus for El Niño/La Niña Index, Definitions." NOAA Press Release NOAA03-119. September 30, 2003.

Insightful Corporation. 2003. S-Plus version 6.2. http://www.insightful.com/products/splus/.

Jerauld, J., V. A. Rakov, M. A. Uman, K. J. Rambo, D. M. Jordan, K. L. Cummins, and J. A. Cramer. 2005. "An Evaluation of the Performance Characteristics of the US National Lightning Detection Network in Florida Using Rocket-Triggered Lightning." *Journal of Geophysical Research* 110: D19106. doi:10.1029/2005JD005924.

Lazzara, M., J. M. Benson, R. J. Fox, D. J. Laitsch, J. P. Rueden, D. A. Santek, D. M. Wade, T. M. Whittaker, and J. T. Young. 1999. "The Man Computer Interactive Data Access System: 25 Years of Interactive Processing." *Bulletin of the American Meteorological Society* 80 (2): 71–284.

Laing, A. G., M. LaJoie, S. Reader, and K. Pfeiffer. 2008. "The Influence of El Niño-Southern Oscillation on Lightning in the Gulf Coast of the United States, Part II: Monthly Correlations." *Monthly Weather Review* 136 (7): 2544–56.

Orville, R. E., and G. R. Huffines. 2001. "Cloud-to-Ground Lightning in the United States: NLDN Results in the First Decade, 1989–98." *Monthly Weather Review* 129: 1179–93.

Orville, R. E., G. R. Huffines, W. R. Burrows, R. L. Holle, and K. L. Cummins. 2002. "The North American Lightning Detection Network (NALDN)—First Results: 1998–2002." *Monthly Weather Review* 130: 2098–109.

Philander, S. G. H. 1990. *El Niño, La Niña and the Southern Oscillation.* San Diego, CA: Academic Press.

Ropelewski, C. F., and M. S. Halpert. 1986. "North American Precipitation and Temperature Patterns Associated with the El Niño Southern Oscillation (ENSO)." *Monthly Weather Review.* 114: 2352–62.

Smith, T. M., and R. W. Reynolds. 2004. "Improved Extended Reconstruction of SST (1854–1997)." *Journal of Climate* 17: 2466–2477.

PART 5

Web services

Whereas part 4 concentrated on local use and analyses of data, part 5 is about making these data and modeling results available to collaborating scientists and the broader community of people interested in everything from hourly weather to future climate. Web services and other Internet tools can make weather and climate information easily accessible and usable for mashups and other informal mapping techniques. Social media can make the conversation about the weather and climate a two-way street, with formal and informal experts contributing observations and analyses.

Chapter 16 reviews a typology of web map services for weather and climate data and provides examples of each category. These can provide a range of interactivity and can allow data to be integrated and adapted for many uses.

Chapter 17 explores integrating map and web services into a single presentation. These can be ArcGIS for Server or open-source services, as long as they are described using standard metadata descriptions.

Chapter 18 describes the integration and use of web services for military meteorological and oceanographic (METOC) applications. These kinds of combined views of weather and ocean conditions are critical when planning military operations and also have civilian applications. These tools can be used both to disseminate information and to create new worlds of observational data.

CHAPTER 16

Weather-based web map services

Kevin Butler and Tiffany Vance

In his book *The Visual Display of Quantitative Data,* Edward Tufte (1992) portrays maps as one of the most efficient, or "data dense," methods of communicating quantitative information. Maps have always been central to the atmospheric sciences. From portraying simple weather observations to complex representations of spatiotemporal harmonic analyses, maps provide the atmospheric scientist with rich information about the location and distribution of atmospheric events and features. Widespread mapping of surface weather observations in the United States began in the mid-1900s with the advent of the national telegraph system (figure 16.1). From its early beginnings, cartography—the science, technology, and art of making maps—has embraced changes in technology. One of the largest technological transformations in cartography has been the migration from paper-based maps to web- or Internet-based maps.

Figure 16.1   An early US Signal Service weather map: September 1, 1872. | Courtesy of National Oceanic and Atmospheric Administration/Department of Commerce.

Web-based maps hold particular interest for the atmospheric scientist for two reasons. First, improved data collection capabilities and global scale numerical climate models generate massive quantities of data. Because these data reference the atmosphere, they are explicitly spatial, meaning that the data are associated with a particular location on the earth. Maps have always been the primary mechanism for communicating spatial information. Secondly, weather observations are transient. Their usefulness is short-lived and, in many instances, they are only valuable until the next observation is recorded. Traditional paper map production followed a labor-intensive and time-consuming process of data collection, compilation, manual production, printing, and distribution. This process is not effective for transient weather observations. Once an initial map has been produced, web-based map services compress the process of compilation, production, and distribution into a few seconds, as the new data are viewable immediately.

   One of the earliest web-based maps was the Xerox PARC Map Viewer produced at Xerox's Palo Alto Research Center in 1993. This map was static, meaning that although the user could pan and zoom, the content of the map did not change. Esri began developing custom mapping applications in 1995 that could not only display information on a map but could also perform basic geoprocessing capabilities, such as geocoding and buffer analysis. In 1998, Esri released

ArcView IMS (Internet Mapping Service), which led to the development and deployment of thousands of interactive web-based mapping applications on the web. ArcGIS for Server was released in 2004 and exposed a full suite of geoprocessing capabilities to web-based map developers. All of these products required some level of programming or customization skills to develop and deploy web-based maps and applications. Today, web mapping is nearly ubiquitous, and high-quality maps can be generated with no programming skills.

Kraak typology updated

In 2001, Jan-Menno Kraak, a prominent cartographer, developed a typology of web-based maps. Essentially he divided web-based maps into two categories: static and dynamic. He further divided dynamic maps into categories of increasing interactivity or analytical complexity. Acknowledging the Kraak typology, we include the following five categories of maps: static, dynamically generated or updated, mashups, capable of analytics, and big data or crowdsourced with geoevent-driven views (figure 16.2). The following section provides a description and real-world example of each type of map in our typology.

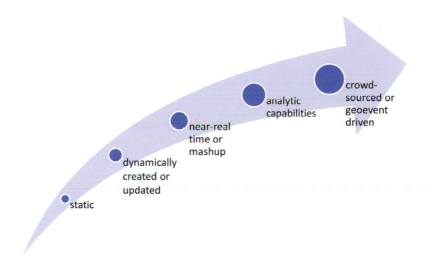

Figure 16.2 Typology of web-based maps. | Inspired by Kraak (2001).

Static and animated web maps

Static web maps are essentially a graphical "snapshot" of a map embedded in a web page. The user cannot change the scale of the map or pan and zoom around the map. Static maps are useful when the cartographer needs to display data that do not change rapidly. With static maps, the cartographer can choose the optimal typography and symbology in order to communicate the map's message without worrying about how it will appear at different display scales. This ability to set symbology allows the cartographer to use the standard conventions for the display of meteorological data, such as wind barbs and symbols for warm and cold fronts. The National Oceanic and Atmospheric Administration's (NOAA) National Weather Service Storm Prediction Center uses static web-based maps to explore the impact of tornados (figure 16.3). A static map is appropriate in this instance because the underlying data are historical, and thus not changing, and the data cover a fixed spatial scale.

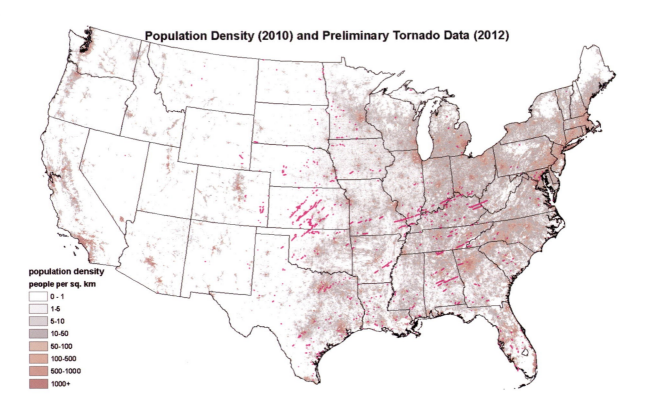

Figure 16.3 A static web-based map: Population density and tornado occurrence, 2012. | NOAA's National Weather Service Storm Prediction Center.

Dynamically created/updated maps

Dynamically created maps allow the user to zoom and pan around the map and to zoom to areas of interest. The underlying data for dynamic maps are automatically updated. This updating might occur every minute, hourly, daily, or even annually depending upon the data involved. Dynamic maps can be interactive—allowing the user to select layers, time ranges, etc.—or they can simply display a pregenerated map based upon the most recent version of the data. These dynamically updated maps can also serve as a gateway to the underlying data and to associated web pages. A prime example of this would be the National Weather Service's (NWS) main map page: http://www.nws.noaa.gov (figure 16.4). This page is continually updated and recreated as watches and warnings are issued. A dynamically created and interactive map of hurricane tracks that allows the user to specify geographic areas, time ranges, and intensities can be found at http://www.csc.noaa.gov/hurricanes/#.

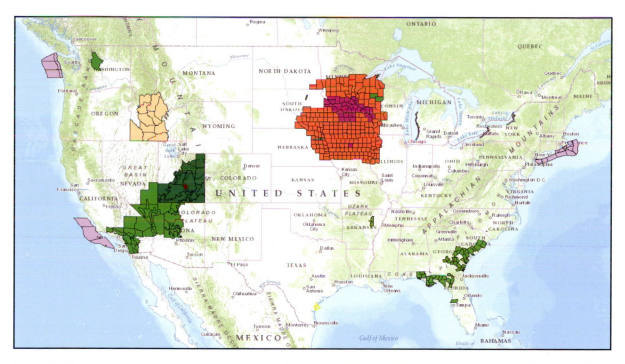

Figure 16.4 **A dynamic map of weather watches and warnings.** | National Weather Service, National Oceanic and Atmospheric Administration. http://www.nws.noaa.gov.

Dynamically created maps can also be made available as a map service with fixed representation and symbology, or the data in the map can be made available via web services or as data files downloadable from a web page. In this case, the data could be made available as shapefiles, KML (Keyhole Markup Language)/KMZ (Keyhole Markup language Zipped) files, or as a web service. Web services allow a cartographer to integrate data into a map or web page without having to download and store the data. By connecting to a live service, the data can also be continually updated as the data provider gathers new information. Standards such as those for Web Feature Services (WFS) and Web Coverage Services (WCS; discussed in chapter 17) provide consistent formats and interaction mechanisms. Examples include NWS data in KML/KMZ files at http://www.srh.noaa.gov/gis/kml/ and as a georeferenced image or Open Geospatial Consortium (OGC)-format web service at http://www.nws.noaa.gov/gis/otherpage.html. In these maps, the underlying data are automatically updated, and a user retrieving the files or services would receive the most recent version of the data. Other examples include the NWS warning and watch polygons at http://www.nws.noaa.gov/gis/shapepage.htm. This site provides shapefiles that are updated every minute, 24 hours a day, seven days a week. A map service for watches and warnings easily used in an ArcMap template or map is available at http://gis.srh.noaa.gov/ArcGIS/rest/services/watchWarn/. Older warnings and watches are automatically removed from the files. Other examples include sea ice extent maps found at http://pafc.arh.noaa.gov/data/ice/shapefiles/ and river and flooding data at http://www.nws.noaa.gov/gis/shapepage.htm.

Real-time maps and web services/distributed data sources

Real-time or near-real-time maps are frequently "mashups" of data from various sources and use a variety of data services, including Web Map Services (WMS) or WFS. They can either aggregate a single type of data from various sources or locations (e.g., the RIDGE radar composite as a map service found at http://www.nws.noaa.gov/gis/otherpage.html) or they can aggregate data from a variety of data sources (e.g., nowCOAST, shown in figure 16.5, which is intended to be a "portal to real-time coastal observations and NOAA forecasts": http://nowcoast.noaa.gov). NowCOAST is a real-time service that places an emphasis on real-time imagery and forecasts and combines them to provide a synoptic view of conditions across the United States. Another aspect of nowCOAST is its ability to point to georeferenced links, which are tabular datasets that are accessed by clicking points on the map. These are from a variety of distributed data sources and are not limited to NOAA sites.

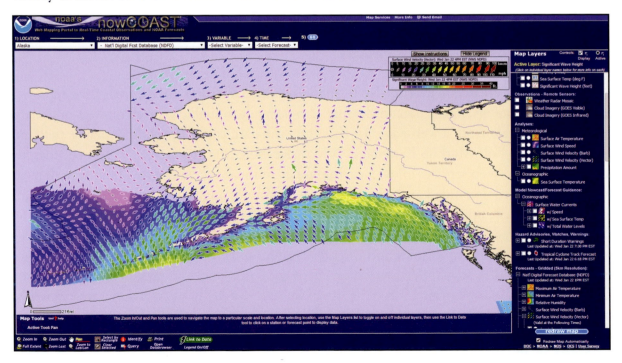

Figure 16.5 NowCOAST map of wind speeds and forecast of significant wave heights. | National Ocean Service, National Oceanic and Atmospheric Administration, http://www.nowcoast.noaa.gov.

Analytic maps

Analytic maps allow the user to perform analyses and geoprocessing via a web interface. Geoprocessing services allow web-based maps to perform many of the analytical functions found in ArcGIS for Desktop. The geoprocessing service can be customized to perform a single analysis or it can involve a number of geoprocessing tasks chained together. The analytical services allow the user to perform many of the same types of analyses that can be performed in ArcGIS: overlaying points, aggregating points, and creating buffers. A service that performs a specific type of weather or climate analysis can be created and customized, as needed. The power of a server or cloud computing resource can be used to process complicated analyses quickly. The service can be made available via ArcGIS for Server or take advantage of the analytics available on ArcGIS Online. If the map is served via ArcGIS Online, the calculations themselves are performed using Esri's secure cloud, which provides considerable computing power.

An excellent example of an analytic map is StreamStats from the US Geological Survey (USGS). StreamStats allows the user to run a variety of hydrologic-processing tools via a web interface. The user can zoom and pan around a map and then choose common hydrologic analyses, such as tracing the path of a raindrop through a watershed, defining a watershed using a DEM (digital elevation model), or showing the path and profile of a stream or river. Figure 16.6 shows the result returned by the Watershed from a Point tool. The user simply clicks to create a point, and the watershed for that point is automatically calculated and visualized as a polygon on the map.

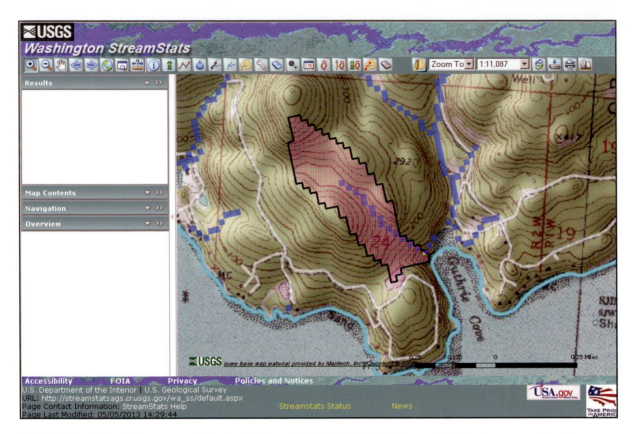

Figure 16.6 StreamStats-generated watershed analysis. | US Geological Survey, http://water.usgs.gov/osw/streamstats/Washington.html. Some basemap material provided by Maptech, Inc., ©2008.

Crowdsourced maps

The most recent development in web mapping is the use of crowdsourced data to create maps. These types of maps can be used to describe and analyze small-scale phenomena that might not be easily extracted from models or widely spaced synoptic observations. Chapter 7 covers the integration of social media and GIS thoroughly, but two examples show the power of integrating data gathered by the public with GIS base data and applications. The PING Project (http://www.nssl.noaa.gov/projects/ping/) uses information from volunteers to validate NEXRAD radar data by providing observations from close to the ground, where the radars cannot detect precipitation (figure 16.7). Volunteers can submit their reports via a web page or a mobile application. The locations of reports from volunteers are mapped in near real time and can themselves provide a continually updated map of precipitation patterns.

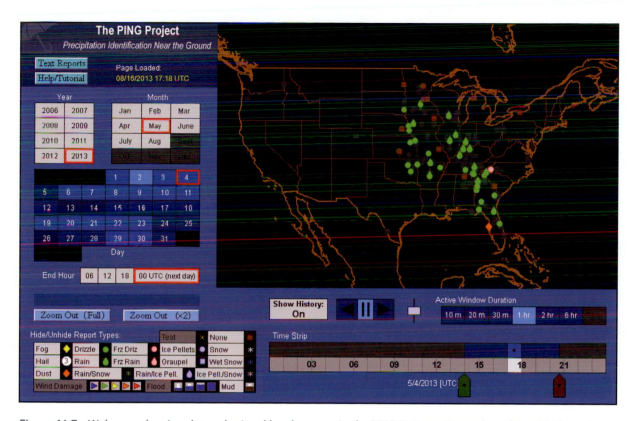

Figure 16.7 Web map showing data submitted by observers in the PING Project. Green dots show drizzle, red dots show ice pellets, and the brown squares show locations where it is reported that no precipitation is occurring. | National Severe Storms Laboratory, National Oceanic and Atmospheric Administration, http://www.nssl.noaa.gov/ projects/ping/display/.

ArcGIS Online supports templates for displaying social media that are especially powerful if there is agreement on a hashtag to use for a particular event (http://www.arcgis. com/apps/SocialMedia/index.html?appid=e4332149201e4fc28b006576fc93057d). Esri's Public Information Map (http://www.esri.com/services/disaster-response/severe-weather/ latest-news-map) combines base data on precipitation and severe weather statements with pictures posted on Flickr, YouTube content, and Twitter posts (figure 16.8).

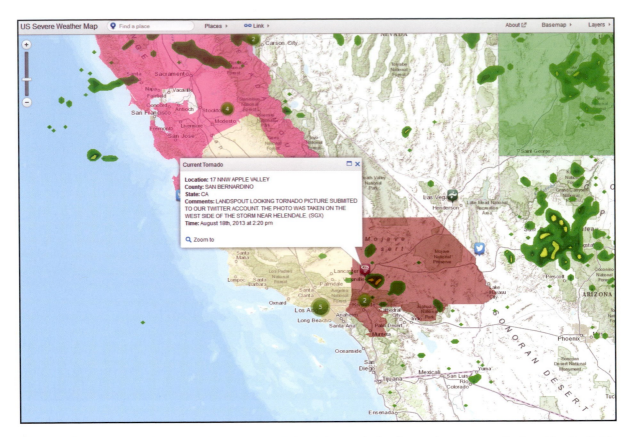

Figure 16.8 Location and content of a tweet about the sighting of a land spout/waterspout displayed by the Public Information Map. | Basemap data sources: Esri, DeLorme, FAO, USGS, NOAA, EPA; AccuWeather, Inc.; Environment Canada; ©2013 Esri.

Conclusions

In the 18 years since the advent of web mapping, there has been tremendous progress: from static maps that were exciting simply because you could easily make a map a part of a web page to dynamic maps that would always be up-to-date to web maps that are nearly functionally equivalent to desktop ArcGIS in their ability to perform analyses to the recent developments that allow mapping and analysis of "big data." ArcGIS Online will continue to expand its suite of geoprocessing tools and cartographic capabilities. The map is the primary interface to geoprocessing in the desktop GIS environment. As web-based geoprocessing capabilities improve, the web map will serve the same purpose for cloud-based analyses. For example, Esri has released a web service where a user can pass an x,y location to a web service, get back a polygon of the custom-delineated watershed, and overlay it with precipitation data to calculate total precipitation for the basin. Using other hosted data in the cloud, such as that on soils, elevation, and land cover, the user can calculate runoff. All of these tasks can be orchestrated through a collection of web services (hosted data and hosted analysis). At this point there will be no difference between a desktop weather analysis and one done over the web.

Acknowledgments

This publication was supported, in part, with funds from the National Marine Fisheries Service's Ecosystems and Fisheries Oceanography Coordinated Investigations (EcoFOCI). The findings and conclusions in the paper are those of the author and do not necessarily represent the views of the National Marine Fisheries Service. Reference to trade names does not imply endorsement by the National Marine Fisheries Service, NOAA.

References

Kraak, M. J. 2001. "Web Maps and Atlases." In *Webcartography: Developments and Prospects*, edited by M. J. Kraak and A. Brown, 135–40. London: Taylor and Francis.

Tufte, E. R. 1992. *The Visual Display of Quantitative Information*. Cheshire, CT: Graphics Press.

CHAPTER 17

Interoperability interfaces

Chris MacDermaid and Jebb Stewart

One of the problems with disseminating atmospheric data is that there are multiple traditional protocols for accessing these data, including FTP (file transfer protocol), HTTP (Hypertext Transfer Protocol), and SCP (Secure Copy Protocol). In addition, a number of interfaces have been built on top of these protocols, such as DBNet (Distributed Brokered Networking), ADDE (Abstract Data Distribution Environment), THREDDS (Thematic Real-time Environmental Distributed Data Services), and OPeNDAP (Open-source Project for a Network Data Access Protocol). Each of these interfaces has their strengths and resolves issues with disseminating atmospheric data, but trying to build a client to interface with all these services is daunting. In this chapter we look at using Open Geospatial Consortium (OGC) web service standards for disseminating atmospheric data and offer several lessons learned from the NOAA Earth Information Service (NEIS) project (http://www.esrl.noaa.gov/neis/). The goal of this project was to construct a framework of layered services designed to help National Oceanic and Atmospheric Administration's (NOAA) mission areas by facilitating the discovery, access, integration, and understanding of all NOAA data.

OGC web services interface standards

There are many types of atmospheric-related data for climate, weather, and the coasts, and many different ways to disseminate these data. It would be difficult for a client to negotiate all the different interfaces needed for accessing these data. Ideally, the client should communicate with the data dissemination service without regard to how the service is implemented. One general approach to the problem is to use the OGC web service interface standards to access the data. Atmospheric data can be disseminated using the OGC Web Map Service (WMS), Web Coverage Service (WCS), Web Feature Service (WFS), and Sensor Observation Service (SOS). Although the data formats with each of these interfaces by necessity may be different, common elements among the services are abstracted out in the OGC Web Services (OWS) Common Standard (figure 17.1).

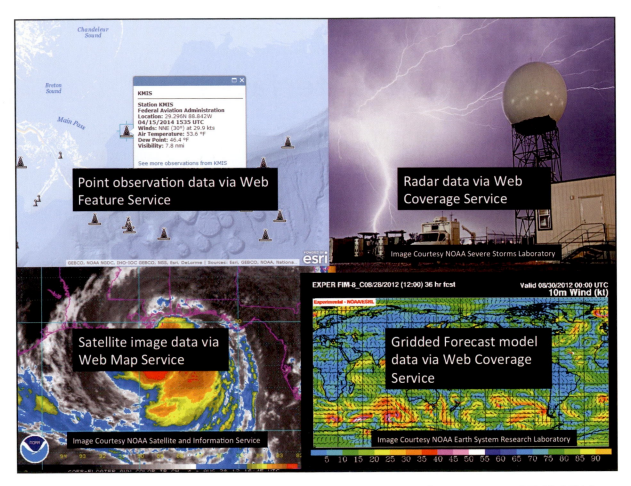

Figure 17.1 OGC services for atmospheric data. | Courtesy of NOAA. Basemap data sources: Esri, GEBCO, NOAA, NGOC, IHO-IOC, NGS, and DeLorme.

For atmospheric data that can be disseminated as an image, the WMS provides a standard interface for requesting images that are widely used in the atmospheric data community. Note that although the WMS delivers an image, the underlying data represented are not limited to imagery. Disseminating data through this interface will meet many clients' needs for atmospheric data, but it only provides an image and not the source data. To provide access to the source data, the WCS interface is needed for coverage data such as gridded forecast and climate model data. Similarly, the WFS is needed for access to feature data such as weather station and buoy observations.

Each of these services allows clients to select a subset of the data based on temporal, spatial, and other query constraints. For interoperability between the services, the OGC developed the OWS Common Standard, which specifies the aspects that are common to OWS interface implementations. The complete documentation for the standard can found on the OGC website at http://www.opengeospatial.org/standards/common.

To be compliant with the OGC specification, each OGC web service interface is required to provide the metadata for the service through a *GetCapabilities* operation. This operation allows the client to retrieve metadata about the capabilities provided by the service. Although this is not required for an OGC-compliant web service interface, an OGC web service interface can optionally provide metadata using different data structures and formats, such as the Web Service Description Language (WSDL). Guidelines for creating and using a WSDL are described in the annex of the OGC web service interface implementation standard (Open Geospatial Consortium 2010).

The mandatory parameters in a *GetCapabilities* metadata document include the service type identifier, the versions supported, the response formats, and the languages supported. This service metadata makes a server partially self-describing. In addition, the metadata document can contain metadata about the service and data content. An example of the service section and the other metadata from a NOAA WMS for radar data follows.

An example of a *GetCapabilities* service section from a NOAA WMS:

```
<Service>
<Name>WMS</Name>
<Title>Watches, warnings, advisories</Title>
<Abstract>This service contains a layer depicting a mosaic
of the NWS radar in CONUS and the
watches/warning/advisory polygons.
</Abstract>
<KeywordList><Keyword></Keyword></KeywordList>
<OnlineResource xlink:type="simple"

xlink:href="http://gis.srh.noaa.gov/ArcGIS/services/
Radar _ warnings/MapServer/WMSServer?"/>
<ContactInformation>
<ContactPersonPrimary>
<ContactPerson>Ira Graffman</ContactPerson>
<ContactOrganization>NOAA/National Weather Service
</ContactOrganization>
</ContactPersonPrimary>
<ContactPosition>OST/SEC GIS Lead</ContactPosition>
<ContactAddress>
<AddressType>Postal</AddressType>
<Address>1325 East West Highway - w/ost33</Address>
<City>Silver Spring</City>
<StateOrProvince>MD</StateOrProvince>
<PostCode>20904</PostCode>
<Country>USA</Country>
</ContactAddress>
<ContactVoiceTelephone>555 555 5555</ContactVoiceTelephone>
<ContactFacsimileTelephone></ContactFacsimileTelephone>
<ContactElectronicMailAddress>john.q.public@noaa.gov
</ContactElectronicMailAddress>
</ContactInformation>
<Fees>None</Fees>
<AccessConstraints>None</AccessConstraints>
<MaxWidth>2048</MaxWidth>
<MaxHeight>2048</MaxHeight>
</Service>
```

NOAA Earth Information System

Across NOAA and other government agencies, a wide variety of data and information systems meet various agency missions. To meet NOAA's mission (i.e., to understand and predict changes in climate, weather, oceans, and coasts; to share that knowledge and information with others; and to conserve and manage coastal and marine ecosystems and resources) its data and systems need to be easily accessible and interoperable. Achieving this would lead to a more efficient organization. Earth System Research Laboratory (ESRL) is developing a concept called the NOAA Earth Information System (NEIS) that explores these interoperable interface capabilities. The NEIS framework is implemented through interoperable services in several distinct categories (figure 17.2). These services allow users to acquire and process data and generate visual representations in an expected, consistent way, regardless of where the data physically reside or what format the data are stored in.

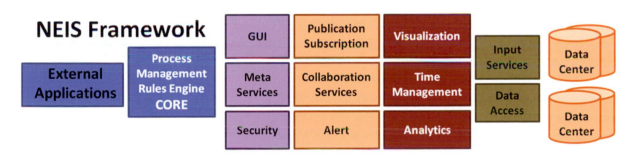

Figure 17.2   NEIS services framework. | Courtesy of NOAA.

For more information about this project, please visit the NEIS website: http://www.esrl.noaa.gov/neis.

A major function of a system such as this is seamless data integration. A user must be able to discover, visualize, and process data from different sources without knowing where the data physically reside, the physical storage format of the data, the underlying operating system of the hardware, or the implementation programing language of the services themselves. To facilitate this functionality, common interfaces must be defined and agreed upon by all interested parties.

Through the use of standardized web services, an application can programmatically and consistently determine what data are available through a particular service provider, information about the data, the file formats in which data can be delivered, and the geospatial and temporal coverage of the data. By having these well-defined interoperable interfaces available, the complexity and potential problems of an application itself are reduced. Additionally, application developers can then concentrate on innovation to solve problems for their users, rather than the intricacies of different services and standards.

Discovering data is not a trivial exercise. Metadata can reside in multiple locations, and a generic search for a simple term can return thousands of results. NEIS is using several technologies to improve this experience. For storing and harvesting metadata records from other services, NEIS is using the Esri Geoportal Server. The Geoportal Server implements the OGC Catalog Service for the Web (CSW) interface and can harvest information from a variety of other interoperable interfaces. The NEIS system harvests information from the Geoportal Server catalog via the CSW interface. If the metadata record contains service endpoints, a location where the data can be retrieved programmatically, these endpoints are also harvested to retrieve additional information about the data. All this content is then indexed for searching into a separate Apache Solr instance. Apache Solr is a powerful enterprise search server that provides NEIS several unique capabilities to assist in discovering data. In addition to standards-based open interfaces for requesting information, Apache Solr allows data to be indexed with facets, one of the numerous aspects of data, such as whether the data are related to oceanic, atmospheric, chemical, or biological domains. These facets allow users to refine their search to specific categorical datasets.

For visualizing data, currently the NEIS system relies heavily on the WMS standard specification for product generation and access to rendered data. This specification defines a specific request structure to generate georeferenced raster images that are then visualized along with data from other sources in the NEIS system. The request can be crafted such that an image is generated for a specific time and a specific geospatial domain. The ability to specify a subset of data rather than dealing with the entire dataset significantly reduces the volume of data transferred between client and service, improving the overall user experience. Because NEIS understands the OGC WMS web interface, additional data can be made immediately available to the application without significant changes to the application through hosting data behind a WMS interface.

A visualization application, TerraViz, was developed by the Global Systems Division (GSD) of ESRL to showcase the possibilities of these interoperable interfaces to discover (figure 17.3) and display (figure 17.4) data from disparate data sources.

Figure 17.3 NEIS search screen showing temporal, geospatial, and facet search filtering capability. | Courtesy of NOAA, NASA, and Xplanet.

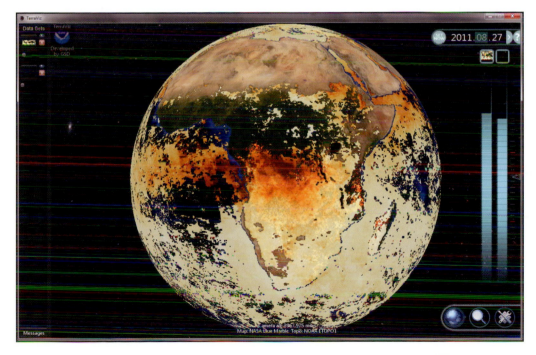

Figure 17.4 An example of integrating datasets via interoperable services using NEIS/TerraViz. | Courtesy of NOAA, NASA, and Xplanet. Map from NASA Blue Marble. Topography data from NOAA ETOPO1.

To make data available to NEIS in an interoperable way, a data provider needs to provide its data through one of the standardized services described previously and create a standardized metadata file using the International Organization for Standardization (ISO) 19115 format. This metadata file describes the data, along with information about the standardized service endpoint. This metadata can either be harvested from another service or uploaded to the NEIS Geoportal Server. Once the metadata information is available behind a CSW service, the data are immediately available to the NEIS framework and can be accessed or integrated with all other datasets currently available in the system. For example, for point data in shapefile format, the WFS is the best service for making these data accessible. Existing solutions, such as ArcGIS for Server, provide WFS capability for data contained in shapefiles. A data provider can install and configure ArcGIS for Server to host its data and then create the necessary ISO 19115 metadata file with information about this service in order for the data to be discovered programmatically. Once the metadata file is accessible through a CSW interface, NEIS and TerraViz have immediate access and can visualize or integrate these data quickly within the framework.

Conclusion

NEIS is one of many communities within NOAA looking to define and use interoperable interfaces to improve existing services. Each community may choose different technology and implementations to meet their objectives, but the basic concepts behind each are the same. Interoperable interfaces facilitate the discovery, understanding, access, and visualization of data. For interoperable interfaces to be successful, several key issues must be addressed:

- Metadata and related dictionaries are vital. A user community must agree to terms and definitions that facilitate common understanding of data. Semantic agreement on content based on common vocabularies is required.

- Interoperable interfaces should be limited. A variety of interoperable interfaces perform similar functionality. Further, several versions of these interfaces may exist with slightly different requirements as the governing standards body continues to learn and improve the standards. The user community should require an agreement on the set of specific interoperable interfaces and related versions to be used.

- Data and information exchange formats are important. Well-defined interoperable interfaces go a long way toward integrating disparate datasets. In addition to the service interfaces, an agreement on data formats exchanged by these services is required within the user community. These formats are often self-describing and use the previously mentioned common vocabulary.

- Best practices for implementation of standards: the standards define an expected interoperable interface for certain actions. However, the standards may not strictly define every little detail of what the interface provides. For example, an interface may require a time field for filtering or request. But time can be represented in a variety of formats, and so different implementations may represent time differently. This can lead to services meeting the standard but not being coherent or consistent in their response to a request. User communities should establish and enforce best practices of implementation of interfaces to ensure that systems are truly interoperable.

Through the use of interoperable interfaces, common and consistent services exist to help facilitate the discovery, understanding, access, and integration of data across a wide variety of applications. Because these standards are well known and defined up-front, making new data available to an application using these interoperable interfaces does not require changes to the actual application or interface. These interfaces help reduce the complexity of applications and allow application developers to focus on creating new tools and systems to take advantage of these interoperable interfaces. Ultimately, interoperable interfaces are a keystone to improving access to data and efficient sharing of information.

References and additional resources

Apache Solr. http://lucene.apache.org/solr/.

Esri Geoportal Server. http://geoportal.sourceforge.net.

International Organization for Standardization. "ISO 19115 Metadata Standard." http://www.iso.org/iso/catalogue_detail.htm?csnumber=26020.

NOAA Earth Information System. http://www.esrl.noaa.gov/neis.

Open Geospatial Consortium. http://www.opengeospatial.org.

———. "OGC Web Services Common Standard." http://www.opengeospatial.org/standards/common.

———. "OGC Web Map Service." http://www.opengeospatial.org/standards/wms/.

———. "OGC Web Coverage Service." http://www.opengeospatial.org/standards/wcs/.

CHAPTER 18

METOC web services

Martin Rutherford and Paul Sliogeris

METOC is the term traditionally used by the military, and particularly the Navy, to refer to meteorology and oceanography and its use in planning and conducting maritime operations. More recently, following the 2004 Boxing Day tsunami in Indonesia and the devastating earthquake in Haiti in 2010, the term "operations" has also included Humanitarian Assistance and Disaster Relief (HADR) operations.

The maritime environment is harsh and unforgiving and provides little shelter for a ship caught in the open ocean experiencing extreme winds and waves generated by a tropical storm or rapidly deepening mid-latitude depression. In high latitudes, sea ice, icebergs, and superstructure icing from freezing precipitation or spray present a potentially catastrophic hazard.

In a hostile military situation, knowledge of the environment is a key information advantage that can be gained through either knowing something the adversaries do not or being able to process and act on the same information available to all parties more quickly. Analysis of the environment can determine the best locations in which to deploy submarine and mines—or to avoid them—or to determine the optimum radar settings to detect incoming aircraft and, conversely, the best height for an aircraft to fly to avoid early detection.

In a world constrained by financial resources and dwindling fuel reserves, naval vessels, like merchant ships, have to consider optimum track ship routing, taking currents and storms into account when planning long ocean passages. The availability of information relevant to maritime safety, maritime operations, and efficiency in passage planning and resource management will be discussed together with technologies and techniques for publishing the information as web services, thus allowing the mariner or military planner to access and query the information through both desktop applications and web browsers.

In *The Art of War* (c. 400–320 BC), Sun Tzu advises, "Know the ground, know the weather; your victory will then be total." Weather has often proved decisive in military history. Kublai Khan's attempt to conquer Japan was foiled by major storms, giving rise to the term *kamikaze*. The failure of Napoleon and Hitler to defeat Russia is attributed, in part, to the harsh winter conditions experienced by their armies. The Dunkirk Evacuation and the D-Day Invasion during the Second World War benefitted from favorable weather conditions. The date of the Normandy landings was determined by forecast weather conditions.

During Operation Desert Storm in 1991, US air combat forces could not conduct effective photo-reconnaissance or bombing raids because they could not see the targets through the clouds. Land forces and ground combat operations also suffered as rain turned sand to mud and wadis to rivers and bogs. Iraq stopped reporting weather observations soon after invading Kuwait, so Coalition forces relied on interpretation of weather satellite images. Using satellite imagery this way is not new, particularly in the maritime domain, where observations are scarce and generally only available on the major shipping routes.

Rapid Environmental Assessment

Rapid Environmental Assessment (REA) is the process of collection, production, and dissemination of geospatial and environmental information about a particular area (the battlespace) in a coordinated, systematic, and timely manner. The information includes hydrographic, topographic, oceanographic, and atmospheric parameters and may be quasi-static (e.g., topography, coastlines, landforms), historical (e.g., past weather observations), climatological (e.g., statistics derived from the historical observations), observed (either in situ or by remote sensing), or forecast. Figure 18.1 shows the typical information required for a comprehensive assessment of the maritime battlespace. To the military, a successful REA gives military personnel the awareness and information to make effective decisions and optimally employ platforms, weapons systems, and sensors in the battlespace.

The North Atlantic Treaty Organization (NATO) divides REA into three categories:

- **Category 1**. Archived data searches, satellite remote sensing, computer modeling, and other data analyses. In effect, everything that can be found out about a location without going there.

- **Categories 2 and 3.** In situ environmental data collection, both overt and clandestine, prior to an operation. The aim of REA categories 2 and 3 is to confirm category 1 knowledge and to address the unknowns.

- **Category 4.** Operational or in-stride environmental data collected by the main force as part of its operation.

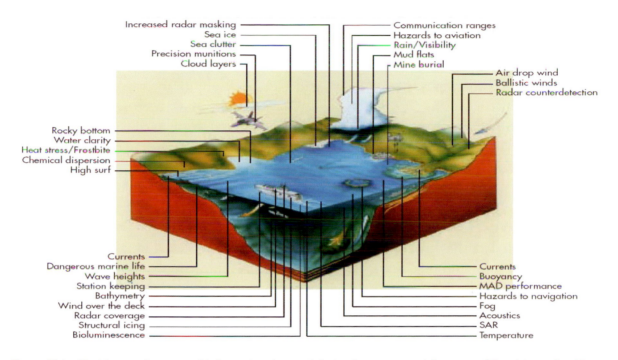

Figure 18.1   Maritime environmental information data and derived parameters. | Courtesy of Royal Australian Navy Hydrography, Meteorology, and Oceanography Branch.

Foundation data

Whereas REA refers to the process of collection, production, and dissemination of environmental information, foundation data are the core parameters and attributes that form the information baseline and from which specialized or custom products can be derived and decisions made. For example, a surf forecast relies on the following geospatial layers: shoreline orientation and topography, bathymetry, swell characteristics (period, height, wavelength, and orientation relative to the shore), tide, nearshore ocean currents, wind, and atmospheric pressure. REA collects, predicts, and manages the foundation data layers used to predict the swell in a product-agnostic way. Taking a foundation-layer approach avoids duplication because many products rely on the same foundation parameters. To collect and manage each at a product level would mean unnecessary duplication. Winds and atmospheric pressure may, for example, be products in their own right.

The foundation data custodian is responsible for maintaining and providing all of the baseline information (allowing users to derive custom products or to make decisions based on the parameters themselves) but may not necessarily be responsible for all the uses of the data.

The foundation custodians are typically the subject matter experts for each of the data types. Continuing with the surf example, Army surveyors may be responsible for providing the shoreline orientation and nearshore topography; Navy hydrographers for the shallow-water bathymetry and tides; and METOCs (Meteorological and Oceanographic) for swell, ocean current, wind and pressure observations, and predictions.

In the Australian Defence Force, responsibility for foundation maritime REA data lies with the Navy Hydrography, Meteorology, and Oceanography Branch (HM Branch). The HM Branch has been using Open Geospatial Consortium (OGC) web services for over a decade as a means of disseminating foundation layers collected through the REA process. The following sections describe examples of foundation data published as web services by the HM Branch.

"Static" web services

"Static" refers to data that are constant throughout the REA process. Static data are used for situational awareness and put locations and their features into context. Two primary situational awareness products used for maritime operations and provided as web map services by the HM Branch, bathymetry and nautical charts, are discussed in the following sections.

Bathymetry

Bathymetry is presented as a surface derived from individual depth soundings. The General Bathymetric Chart of the Oceans (GEBCO) is one of the HM Branch's situational awareness bathymetry products.

GEBCO data comes from the British Oceanographic Data Centre (https://www.bodc. ac.uk/data/online_delivery/gebco/) and are processed by loading the supplied grid file into a geodatabase using the ArcGIS Copy Raster tool. A hillshade is created from this raster by entering the following values into the Hillshade tool and setting its transparency to 50 percent:

- Azimuth: 315
- Altitude: 45
- Model Shadows: false
- Z Factor: 0.0001 (a 10-fold vertical exaggeration)

An ArcGIS Map Service Definition file with an appropriate color ramp is created and published as an OGC Web Map Service (WMS) using ArcGIS for Server with a representational state transfer (REST) endpoint.

Users can get the GEBCO data from an Open Layers web-based client from the METOC Products and Services website (figure 18.2) or use the REST endpoint to load the service into a browser such as ArcGIS for Desktop (figure 18.3).

Figure 18.2   GEBCO displayed via a web browser. | Courtesy of Royal Australian Navy Hydrography, Meteorology, and Oceanography Branch. Data from the GEBCO world map, http://www.gebco.net and https://www.bodc.ac.uk/data/online_delivery/gebco/.

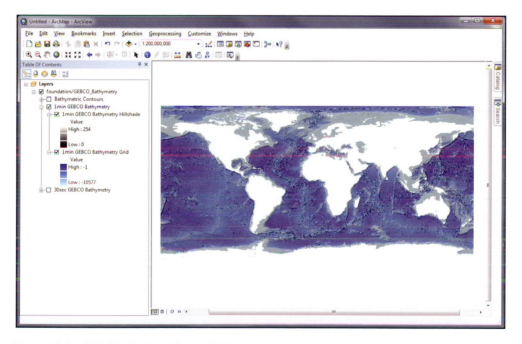

Figure 18.3   GEBCO displayed in ArcGIS for Desktop. | Courtesy of Royal Australian Navy Hydrography, Meteorology, and Oceanography Branch. Data from the GEBCO world map, http://www.gebco.net and https://www.bodc.ac.uk/data/online_delivery/gebco/.

Nautical charts

A nautical chart is far more data rich than a bathymetric surface. Nautical charts provide a graphical representation of maritime features, particularly those significant to navigation, so they are more detailed in shallow and coastal waters. The Australian Hydrographic Office produces both raster and vector nautical charts of the Australian Area of Charting Responsibility, which includes Papua New Guinea. As part of the raster chart production process, a GeoTIFF version that can be used in web services and GIS is produced.

The AusGeoTIFF Chart Service provides over 800 charts and chartlets as a single-scale dependent situational awareness layer (figures 18.4 and 18.5). The service is web and GIS enabled and provides the most current nautical charts. The following procedure is used to create the map service:

- Prepare the GeoTIFFs by copying the files to an appropriate file store, ensuring that they are all in a common projection and geographic coordinate system.

- Build a (referenced) mosaic dataset using the Create Mosaic Dataset tool and add the files to the mosaic with the Add Rasters to Mosaic Dataset tool.

- Create a set of chart footprints and add attributes to this feature class populated from the raster properties and chart metadata.

- Publish this map document and create the cache.

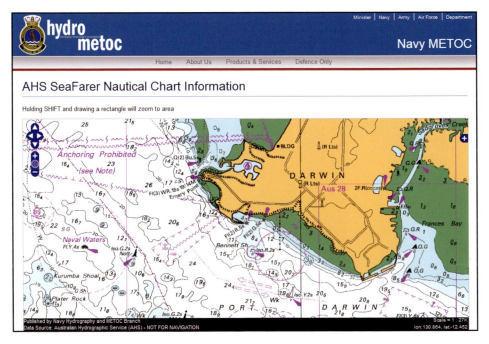

Figure 18.4 Example of a detailed nautical chart for the Darwin Wharves area. | Courtesy of Royal Australian Navy Hydrography, Meteorology, and Oceanography Branch. Chart from the Australian Hydrographic Office.

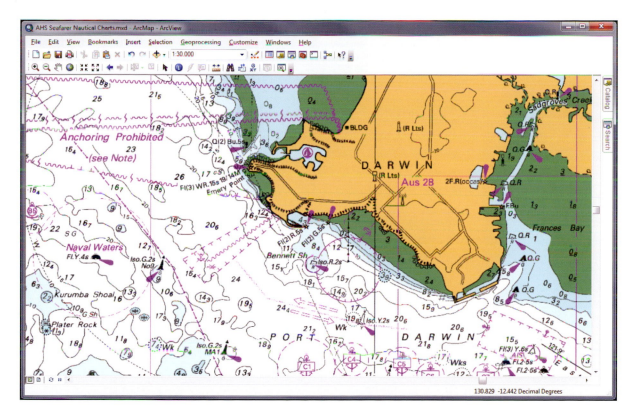

Figure 18.5 Displaying approaches to the Darwin chart in ArcGIS for Desktop. | Courtesy of Royal Australian Navy Hydrography, Meteorology, and Oceanography Branch. Chart from the Australian Hydrographic Service.

Volumetric web services: The real 3D

To a METOC, 3D means volume, or at least n × 2D, not the rendering of the height attribute of an (x, y) surface, to give it a real-world perspective. A hill or a building, although it might be rendered in a way to make it appear three-dimensional, does not generally have interior points with attributes at all (x, y, z) or (x, y, z, t) points. The atmosphere and ocean, however, do, and the interior air/sea temperatures, winds/currents, and moisture/salinity values are important to climate scientists, dynamic modelers, and the military alike.

Typical ocean and atmospheric climatologies and numerical models produce layers or slices of the environment at standard levels. The World Ocean Atlas (http://www.nodc.noaa.gov/OC5/WOA09/pr_woa09.html), for example, is categorized to 40 standard depth levels, with 10 m increments near the surface increasing to 500 m increments below 2,000 m. The vertical levels within netCDF (Network Common Data Form) files, which contain the multidimensional information can be easily viewed and analyzed in ArcGIS for Desktop because individual levels can be selected through the vertical dimension properties (figure 18.6).

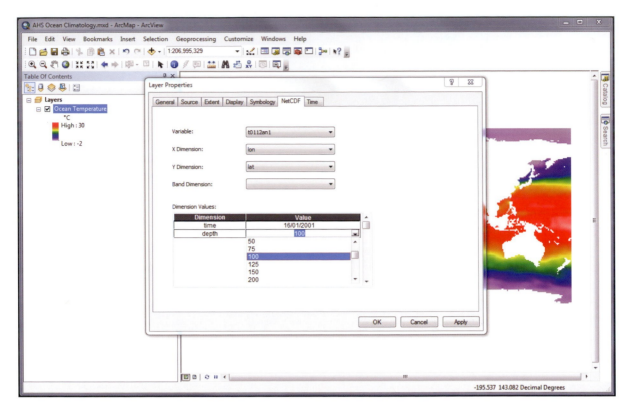

Figure 18.6 Selecting vertical dimensions from a netCDF file. | Courtesy of Royal Australian Navy Hydrography, Meteorology, and Oceanography Branch.

The netCDF format, and other similar multidimensional formats such as GRIB (Gridded Binary Form) and HDF (Hierarchical Data Format), is still not truly volumetric because the data are constrained to defined levels. To interpolate a value at *any* depth, you need a custom geoprocessing tool that uses the functionality in the Raster Calculator tool to calculate values in between the defined levels. Conceivably, this tool could be published as a web geoprocessing service, enabling a volumetric map service with volumetric interpolation to be performed on the fly.

Annex C of OGC's OpenGIS Web Map Server Implementation Specification (http://portal.opengeospatial.org/files/?artifact_id=14416) describes how multidimensional data are handled within the service requests, and metadata through optional *Dimension* elements enclosed within *Layer* elements. The World Ocean Atlas example previously described, once published as a WMS 1.3.0–compliant service, would have its vertical dimension declared as follows:

```
<Dimension name="elevation" units="m" default="0">-0,-10,-20,-30,-50,-75,-100,-125,-150,-200,
-250,-300,-400,-500,-600,-700,-800,-900,-1000,-1100,-1200,-1300,-1400,-1500,-1750,-2000,
-2500,-3000,-3500,-4000,-4500,-5000,-5500,-6000,-6500,-7000,-7500,-8000,-8500,-
9000</Dimension>
```

Services with evenly defined intervals are easier to describe by declaring the lower bounds, upper bounds, and its resolution as follows:

```
<Dimension name="elevation" units="m" default="0">-10000/0/100</Dimension>
```

Time-dependent web services

In *War and Peace,* Tolstoy states, "The strongest of all warriors are these two—Time and Patience." Time (together with volume) is what differentiates METOC from most other aspects of military geospatial information. Every piece of data or information must be put into a temporal context. What was it like? What is it like? What will it be like? When is the best time to . . . ? Each of these temporal questions presents its own challenges in data management and information dissemination.

Time-dependent web services can be published in one of two ways: as a time series of independent web services (the traditional way), where each layer within the service represents a single time instance or period, or as a single time-aware web service. ArcGIS clients from version 10.0 are able to consume a time-aware service and enable temporal navigation through a time slider. Browser-based clients can request individual time steps from a time-aware service by calling on the *Dimension* element in a similar manner as with the volumetric services above:

```
<Dimension name="time" units="ISO8601" default="2003-10-17">1996-01-01/2003-10-17/
P1D</Dimension>
```

The ISO 8601 format is used to specify a time period. In the previous example, the temporal period is defined as 1 day starting from 1 Jan 1996 and ending 17 Oct 2003; therefore, this single service contains many published time steps.

The following Group for High Resolution Sea Surface Temperature (GHRSST) images highlight the difference between the two methods of publishing temporal services as viewed within an ArcGIS client. Figure 18.7 shows the traditional method of publishing each time step as a single layer, and figure 18.8 highlights a time-aware service with a time slider. Finally, a browser-based client can be configured to work with either type of service, as shown in the Open Layers client in figure 18.9.

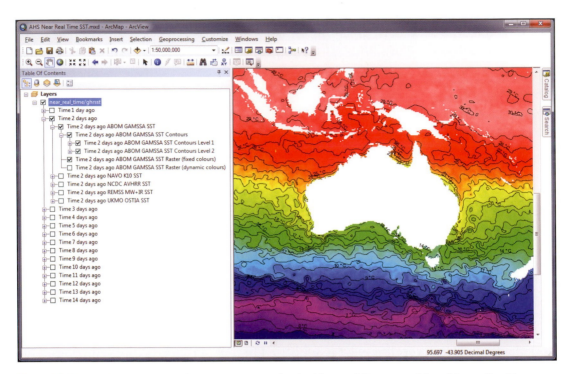

Figure 18.7 GHRSST service with time steps as individual layers. | Courtesy of Royal Australian Navy Hydrography, Meteorology, and Oceanography Branch. GHRSST data from https://www.ghrsst.org.

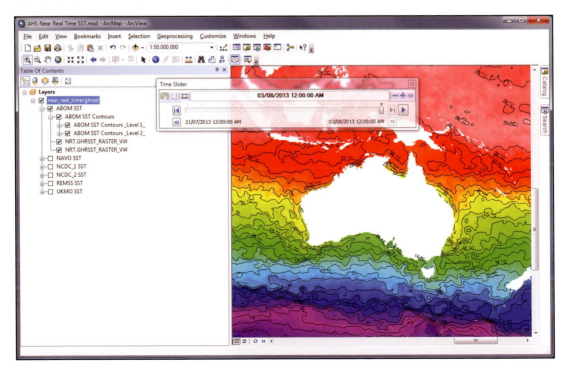

Figure 18.8 GHRSST service showing time-aware display with a time slider. | Courtesy of Royal Australian Navy Hydrography, Meteorology, and Oceanography Branch. GHRSST data from https://www.ghrsst.org.

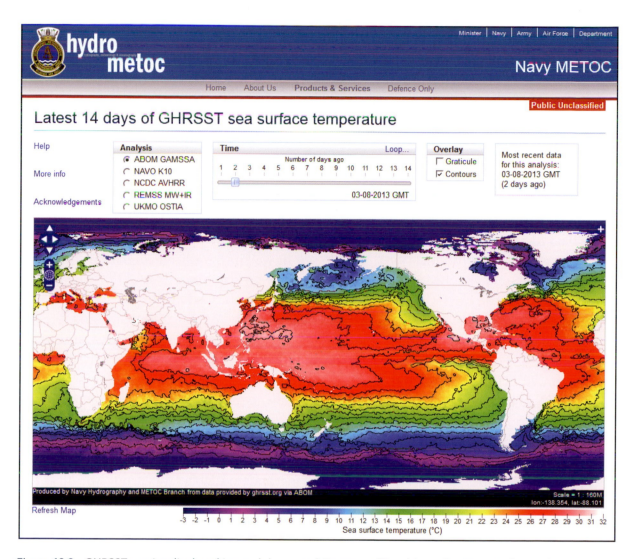

Figure 18.9 GHRSST service displayed in a web browser. | Courtesy of Royal Australian Navy Hydrography, Meteorology, and Oceanography Branch. GHRSST data from https://www.ghrsst.org.

It is not possible to define a time period for climatological services using the ISO 8601 format. A couple of workarounds are necessary. Consider a dataset that spans several decades from 01 Jul 1987 to 31 Dec 2011 (such as the Cross-Calibrated Multi-Platform Ocean Surface Wind Vector L2.5 First-Look SSM/I-F14 Microwave Analyses: http://podaac.jpl.nasa.gov/dataset/CCMP_MEASURES_ATLAS_L3_OW_L2_5_SSMI_F14_WIND_VECTORS_FLK) that is sufficient to calculate typical monthly averages for a given area of operations or battlespace. The ISO 8601 format requires a four-digit year as a minimum, whereas each time dimension in this service represents the average of the month for the entire period. One approach is to select the latest year to describe the period, such as January = 2011-01, February = 2011-02, and so on. A more correct (but unmanageable) approach would be

January = 1988-01-01/1988-01-31, 1989-01-01/1989-01-31, and so on. Another approach, as suggested in the netCDF Climate and Forecast (CF) metadata convention (http://ferret.wrc. noaa.gov/noaa_coop/coop_cdf_profile.html) is to use 0000, representing no particular year; so January would be 0000-01, February = 0000-02, and so on. To enable the time slider in ArcGIS the climatological time field can be either an ISO 8601 format or an integer loosely based on that format, such as YYYYMM or YYYYJJJ (ISO 8601 requires the hyphen "-").

Time-dependent volumetric web services

Putting the spatial and temporal dimensions together results in multidimensional services, where data can be accessed or viewed through three-dimensional space and time. The services' source data are also multidimensional, and do not fit well into traditional relational database management system (RDBMS)-like files or enterprise geodatabases. NetCDF is the perfect container for this and can be natively read, and therefore published as a service by ArcGIS for Desktop since version 9.2. Currently, there are still a number of constraints to using ArcGIS for Server to publish netCDF files. For example, the data must be on a regular, unrotated Cartesian grid. For other more complex multidimensional netCDF files, THREDDS by Unidata provides OGC WMS and WCS services. Numerical models are typically stored in a THREDDS Data Catalogue and are presented to clients such as ArcGIS through its WMS and WCS endpoints.

Forecasts and near-real-time data are probably the most challenging to manage because temporal volatility is high and minimizing latency between source and use is fundamental. There is no silver bullet for this type of data. The methods available range from storing as feature datasets and rasters within geodatabases to preprocessing and using flat files and images to using netCDF with dissemination tools such as ArcGIS, THREDDS, and ncWMS. Feature classes work well for defined loading sizes and often work better through direct DBMS table load/deletes; however, when data volumes become large the time taken to load and destroy data in the tables negatively affects the currency of the information.

Conclusions

The geospatial "real world" is a complex volumetric time-varying mix of variables and parameters linked by the laws of physics. In a military context, personnel and platforms and their sensors, communications, and weapons systems are influenced by the environment. Knowledge of the physical battlespace and its effects gives us a great advantage. GIS and geospatial web services are effective at representing the complex environment and using powerful query and decision tools to provide advice on the best course of action at an operational and tactical level.

ArcGIS provides a range of tools to enable the publishing of METOC datasets as web services. The increased use of web processing services for geoprocessing will further extend the functionality and usefulness of METOC data. One can imagine smart applications in mobile phones and in-vehicle navigation systems, including dynamic and searchable ocean and weather parameters, in the near future. For the military planner, this may provide spatiotemporal options for activities such as launching and recovery of aircraft, conducting boat transfers, or performing underway refueling. For the nonmilitary user, this may provide the current sea temperature and wave swell information and precipitation and cloud data.

References and additional resources

Australian Government, Department of Defence. "Defence Capability Plan, Joint Projects." http://www.defence.gov.au/dmo/id/dcp/html/jp/JP1770.html.

CF MetaData. "CF Conventions and Metadata." http://cfconventions.org.

Federation of American Scientists. "Desert Storm—Military Space Weather Systems." Last modified April 7, 1997. http://www.fas.org/spp/military/docops/operate/ds/weather.htm.

Johnson, P. 2005. "Rapid Environmental Assessment Emerging Requirements for Military Hydrography." http://www.thsoa.org/hy05/02_1.pdf.

Nese, J. 2008. "The Weather of D-Day." *Weather Whys.* Podcast video, June 4. http://podcasts.wpsu.org/D06202008153019.mp4.

Unidata. "Network Common Data Form." http://www.unidata.ucar.edu/software/netcdf/.

———. "THREDDS Data Server." http://www.unidata.ucar.edu/software/tds/.

Wikipedia. "Mongol Invasions of Japan." Last modified July 16, 2014. http://en.wikipedia.org/wiki/Mongol_invasions_of_Japan.

———. "Russian Winter." Last modified June 26, 2014. http://en.wikipedia.org/wiki/Russian_Winter.

PART 6

Tools and resources

Previous parts of this book provided the conceptual foundations for mapping and modeling weather and climate data. Part 6 takes a more pragmatic approach and introduces specific tools and resources for acquiring, reading, analyzing, and visualizing multidimensional weather and climate data in a geographic information system (GIS).

Chapter 19 provides a succinct description of the details of the netCDF (Network Common Data Form) data model and introduces some essential netCDF vocabulary.

Chapter 20 discusses the geoprocessing tools that translate the multidimensional format of netCDF into the more common two-dimensional GIS format. These geoprocessing tools support a variety of data types and enable the direct use of netCDF data in desktop and server geoprocessing workflows.

Chapter 21 introduces temporal data and techniques for visualizing it in both space and time. It walks through the steps necessary to enable ArcGIS to correctly display and share temporal data.

Chapter 22 discusses how Python code supports geographic analysis, conversion, and management of data and the extension of the analytical capabilities of ArcGIS. It explains how Python code for ArcGIS can be easily shared via modules.

Chapter 23 describes an open-source software package, the Weather and Climate Toolkit, used for visualization and export of multidimensional data. This chapter describes how the tool can be used and how it works with common software packages used in the scientific community.

CHAPTER 19

NetCDF and related information sources

Ben Domenico

NetCDF (Network Common Data Form) is a set of interfaces for array-oriented data access and a freely distributed collection of data access libraries for C, FORTRAN, C++, Java, and other languages. The netCDF libraries support a machine-independent format for representing scientific data. Together, the interfaces, libraries, and format support the creation, access, and sharing of scientific data. Esri supports netCDF by providing a variety of tools to read and write netCDF files and to display and analyze netCDF data in maps. These tools are described in detail in chapter 20.

NetCDF data are:

- Self-Describing. A netCDF file includes information about the data it contains.

- Portable. A netCDF file can be accessed by computers with different ways of storing integers, characters, and floating-point numbers.

- Scalable. A small subset of a large dataset may be accessed efficiently.

- Appendable. Data may be appended to a properly structured netCDF file without copying the dataset or redefining its structure.

- Sharable. One writer and multiple readers may simultaneously access the same netCDF file.
- Archivable. Access to all earlier forms of netCDF data will be supported by current and future versions of the software.

NetCDF in meteorology

NetCDF can be used to store many kinds of data, but it was originally developed for the earth science community. NetCDF views the world of scientific data in the same way that an atmospheric scientist might: as sets of related arrays. These arrays can contain various physical quantities (such as pressure and temperature) located at points at a particular latitude, longitude, vertical level, and time.

Dimensions have a length and a name. The axis information (latitude, longitude, level, and time) would be stored as netCDF dimensions. Variables are N-dimensional arrays of data, with a name and an associated set of netCDF dimensions. The physical quantities (pressure, temperature) would be stored as netCDF variables. It is also customary to add one variable for each dimension to hold the values along that axis. These variables are called *coordinate variables*. The latitude coordinate variable would be a one-dimensional variable (with latitude as its dimension), and it would hold the latitude values at each point along the axis.

A scientist might also like to store supporting information, such as the units or information about how the data were produced. The metadata would be stored as netCDF attributes. Attributes are always single values or one-dimensional arrays. Text in a string, which is a one-dimensional array of ASCII characters, could provide the metadata for the physical quantities.

The netCDF classic data model

The classic netCDF data model consists of variables, dimensions, and attributes. This way of thinking about data was introduced with the very first netCDF release and is still the core of all netCDF files (figure 19.1).

NetCDF Data has

Variables   (eg *temperature, pressure*)

Attributes   (eg *units*)

Dimensions (eg *lat, lon, level, time*)

Each variable has

Name, shape, type, attributes

N-dimensional array of values

Each attribute has

Name, type, value(s)

Each dimension has

Name, length

Variables *may share* dimensions

Represents shared coordinates, grids

Variable and attribute values are of type

Numeric: 8-bit **byte**, 16-bit **short**, 32-bit **int**, 32-bit **float**, 64-bit **double**

Character: arrays of **char** for text

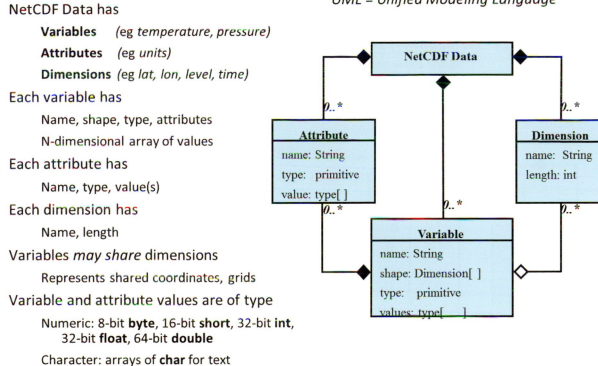

Figure 19.1   The netCDF classic data model. | Courtesy of Unidata/UCAR.

The enhanced data model in netCDF-4/HDF5 files

Files created with the later versions of the netCDF format, such as netCDF-4, have access to an enhanced data model, which includes named groups. Groups, like directories in a Unix file system, are hierarchically organized to an arbitrary depth. They can be used to organize large numbers of variables (figure 19.2).

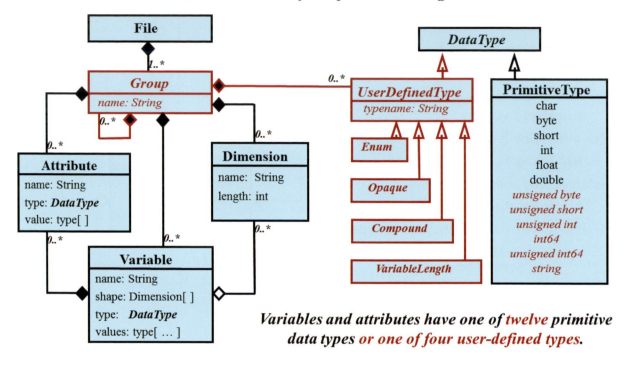

A file has a top-level unnamed group. Each group may contain one or more named subgroups, user-defined types, variables, dimensions, and attributes. Variables also have attributes. Variables may share dimensions, indicating a common grid. One or more dimensions may be of unlimited length.

Variables and attributes have one of twelve primitive data types or one of four user-defined types.

Figure 19.2 The enhanced netCDF data model. | Courtesy of Unidata/UCAR.

Each group acts as an entire netCDF dataset in the classic model; that is, each group may have attributes, dimensions, and variables, as well as other groups. The default group is the root group, which allows the classic netCDF data model to fit neatly into the new model. Dimensions are scoped such that they can be seen in all descendant groups; that is, dimensions can be shared between variables in different groups if they are defined in a parent group. In netCDF-4 files, the user may also define a type. For example, a compound type may hold information from an array of C structures; a variable-length type allows the user to read and write arrays of variable length values.

Variables, groups, and types share a namespace. Within the same group, variables, groups, and types must have unique names (i.e., a type and variable may not have the same name within the same group, and similarly for subgroups of that group). Groups and user-defined types are only available in files created in the netCDF-4/Hierarchical Data Format (HDF) 5 format. They are not available for classic or 64-bit offset format files.

The Climate and Forecast (CF) conventions and metadata

The CF conventions provide a set of use conventions for netCDF data files. They provide conventions for describing the data variables and also for the spatial and temporal dimensions of the data. Esri's ArcGIS software handles CF-compliant netCDF data and relies on the conventions to make reading and writing netCDF files consistent. The CF conventions are not intended to be discovery metadata, and they do not provide cataloging or other search information. The CF conventions are based on and extend the Cooperative Ocean/Atmosphere Research Data Service (COARDS) conventions (http://ferret.wrc.noaa.gov/noaa_coop/coop_cdf_profile.html), which were created to describe oceanic and atmospheric netCDF data. The CF conventions provide a way to precisely define coordinate axes for latitude, longitude, a vertical coordinate, and time. They also provide extensions to describe nonrectangular horizontal grids, nonspatiotemporal axes, climatological time coordinates, and references to grid cell boundaries from models.

Origin information can provide limited discovery metadata by including information such as the title, source, and history of the data. Standard names are used to describe variables. The units for the variable, pointers to metadata, and descriptions of fill and null values can be included. Dimensions can be used to describe the spatiotemporal location of one- to four-dimensional data. Each dimension has a unique coordinate variable. The CF conventions allow for scalar coordinate variables and auxiliary coordinate variables that are not monotonic. The coordinates attribute is used to associate data variables with coordinate variables.

For more details, see the CF conventions document at http://cfconventions.org.

Resources for other netCDF implementations and related data types

- **NetCDF in the Open Geospatial Consortium (OGC) arena:** The OGC has adopted netCDF with CF (Climate and Forecast) conventions as an international binary encoding standard. The OGC material regarding CF-netCDF can be found at http://www.opengeospatial.org/standards/netcdf.

- **Related data models for scientific data:**
  - ☐ OPeNDAP (Open-source Project for a Network Data Access Protocol): http://opendap.org
  - ☐ HDF: http://www.hdfgroup.org

- **The THREDDS (THematic Real-time Environmental Distributed Data Services) web services for netCDF:** http://www.unidata.ucar.edu

- **Library of Congress Digital Preservation Standards Description:** http://www. digitalpreservation.gov/ndsa/working_groups/standards.html

Search for these terms:
- ☐ NetCDF-3, Network Common Data Form, version 3
- ☐ NetCDF-4, Network Common Data Form, version 4
- ☐ NetCDF-4C, Network Common Data Form, version 4, classic model

- **NetCDF materials from the most recent Unidata netCDF training workshop:** http://www.unidata.ucar.edu/software/netcdf/workshops/most-recent/

- The netCDF software was developed by Glenn Davis, Russ Rew, Ed Hartnett, John Caron, Steve Emmerson, and Harvey Davies at the Unidata Program Center in Boulder, Colorado, with contributions from many other netCDF users. For a complete history of netCDF, see http://www.unidata.ucar.edu/software/netcdf/docs/background.html.

References and additional resources

Nativi, S., J. Caron, B. Domenico, and L. Bigagli. 2008. "Unidata's Common Data Model Mapping to the ISO 19123 Data Model." *Earth Science Informatics* 1 (2): 58–78. http://www.springer link.com/content/t5g828928v82n6ju/fulltext.html.

Nativi, S., B. Domenico, J. Caron, and L. Bigagli. 2006. "Extending THREDDS Middleware to Serve OGC Community." *Advances in Geosciences* 8: 57–62.

Nativi, S., J. Caron, E. Davis, and B. Domenico. 2005. "Design and Implementation of NetCDF Markup Language (NcML) and Its GML-Based Extension (NcML-GML)." *Computers & Geosciences Journal* 31 (9): 1104–18.

CHAPTER 20

NetCDF tools

Kevin Butler

NetCDF (Network Common Data Form) is a self-describing, machine-independent data format widely used throughout the atmospheric sciences community. As outlined in chapter 19, it is a multidimensional format, meaning that it can store information for variables at different time intervals and different atmospheric pressure levels, for example. It is often helpful to think of a netCDF file as a cube of data. In contrast, data used in a GIS context are most often represented two-dimensionally. Esri created a series of geoprocessing tools that translates the multidimensional format of netCDF into the more common two-dimensional GIS format. The tools do not convert the data but provide an "on the fly" translation. Translating is faster than converting and does not require the creation of a second copy of the data. These geoprocessing tools enable the direct use of netCDF data in desktop and server geoprocessing workflows. The tools support a variety of data types. Atmospheric scientific data, like all spatially referenced data, can be represented in one of three forms: raster, vector, or tabular attributes. The raster model is used to represent continuous surfaces such as precipitation or solar radiation. Vector data models are used for discrete features in geographic space such as the location of weather stations. Attribute files contain information about each geographic feature, but this information is not represented on a map. Esri's tools allow you to consume data in all of these formats. These tools will be illustrated using real-world examples of netCDF data.

Continuous surfaces: Working with gridded National Weather Service data

One of the tools used by atmospheric scientists is the predictive atmospheric model. Cooperative research ventures have produced a large number of models at scales ranging from local to global. Much of the source data, as well as the model results, are freely available via the web. The challenge has become not the *availability* of data but the *integration* of atmospheric modeling data into other analyses. One of the most widely used models is a reanalysis model available from the National Weather Services' (NWS) National Centers for Environmental Prediction (NCEP). This model uses a state-of-the-art analysis and forecasting system to assimilate data from 1948 to the present. The final model runs have been aggregated into daily, monthly, and annual time series. The data are available in netCDF format.

Because temperature is a continuous surface, we can explore the NCEP data as a raster layer. The Multidimension toolbox in ArcGIS for Desktop contains tools that work specifically with netCDF files. Using the Make NetCDF Raster Layer tool, the NCEP Reanalysis data can be read into ArcMap as a raster layer. Figure 20.1 shows a symbolized map created with the output of the Make NetCDF Raster Layer tool.

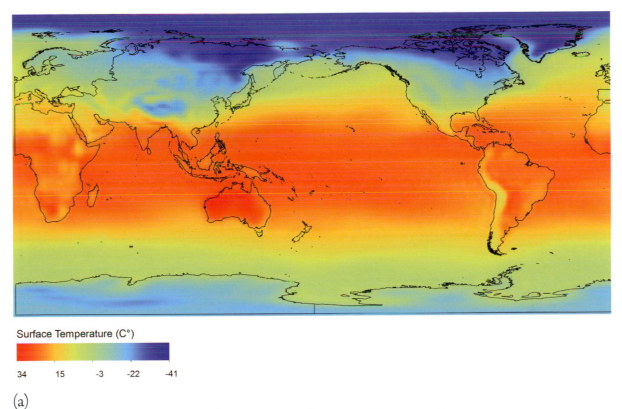

Surface Temperature (C°)

34   15   -3   -22   -41

(a)

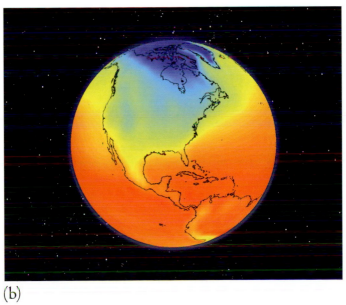

(b)

Figure 20.1   (a) Global surface air temperature, 1948. (b) The same data represented on a three-dimensional globe. |
NCEP Reanalysis data provided by the NOAA/OAR/ESRL PSD, Boulder, Colorado, USA, from their website at http://
www.esrl.noaa.gov/psd/.

Figure 20.2 shows the relationship between the contents of the netCDF file and the parameters for the Make NetCDF Raster Layer tool. The user specifies which variable to extract (e.g., monthly mean air temperature), the names of the dimensions containing the spatial coordinates for the data points (lat and lon), and the name of the output raster layer (air_Layer).

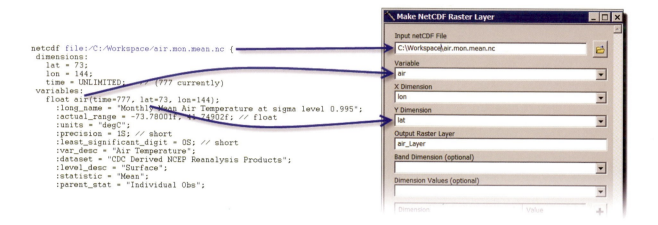

```
netcdf file:/C:/Workspace/air.mon.mean.nc {
  dimensions:
    lat = 73;
    lon = 144;
    time = UNLIMITED;  // (777 currently)
  variables:
    float air(time=777, lat=73, lon=144);
      :long_name = "Monthly Mean Air Temperature at sigma level 0.995";
      :actual_range = -73.78001f, 41.74902f; // float
      :units = "degC";
      :precision = 1S; // short
      :least_significant_digit = 0S; // short
      :var_desc = "Air Temperature";
      :dataset = "CDC Derived NCEP Reanalysis Products";
      :level_desc = "Surface";
      :statistic = "Mean";
      :parent_stat = "Individual Obs";
```

Make NetCDF Raster Layer

Input netCDF File
C:\Workspace\air.mon.mean.nc

Variable
air

X Dimension
lon

Y Dimension
lat

Output Raster Layer
air_Layer

Band Dimension (optional)

Dimension Values (optional)

Dimension   Value

Figure 20.2 Relationship between netCDF CDL and Make NetCDF Raster Layer tool. See chapter 19 for a complete description of netCDF CDL.

Once the netCDF raster layer has been created, it can be used as input for other geoprocessing tools. For example, the Zonal Statistics to Table tool can be used to summarize the air temperature data by continent, producing the table shown in figure 20.3.

Table

ZonalStats

CONTINENT	COUNT	AREA	MIN	MAX	RANGE	MEAN	STD	SUM
Africa	399	2493.75	7.527424	30.05129	22.52386	20.56893	4.304673	8207.002
Asia	863	5393.75	-40.30226	27.55451	67.85677	-7.917104	18.41155	-6832.46
Australia	111	693.75	12.66968	33.65354	20.98386	27.02341	4.533697	2999.599
North America	596	3725	-41.00968	24.82709	65.83677	-15.15763	15.62564	-9033.947
Oceania	4	25	11.47259	16.44324	4.97065	13.99726	1.948998	55.98906
South America	242	1512.5	5.975809	27.91355	21.93774	20.95535	4.628405	5071.195
Antarctica	960	6000	-24.32677	1.960323	26.28709	-14.27886	5.249391	-13707.7
Europe	230	1437.5	-27.35839	14.26033	41.61871	-4.625591	8.390899	-1063.886

|◄ ◄   0 ► ►| (0 out of 8 Selected)

ZonalStats

Figure 20.3 Surface air temperature summarized by continent.

Vector fields: Depicting surface wind speed and direction

Whereas some atmospheric phenomena are best represented as continuous surfaces (e.g., solar radiation or precipitation), other variables, such as surface wind, are better represented as vector fields. The term *vector* implies that two characteristics of a phenomenon, magnitude and direction, are taken into account. Many atmospheric variables, such as surface wind, cannot be fully described without measuring both their speed and direction. A vector field is simply a means to represent both the magnitude and direction of a vector (i.e., wind speed and direction). Vector fields should not be confused with vector representations of GIS data. In the context of GIS, the term *vector* most often refers to the representation of discrete geographical objects (e.g., roads or weather stations) as points, lines, or polygons.

To visualize vector fields in GIS, they are often converted to points having two attributes: magnitude and direction. These points can be represented cartographically in several ways. For example, the magnitude attribute of surface winds can be used to determine which wind barb symbol to use for a point, and the direction attribute can be used to control the rotation of the wind barb, which indicates the direction from which the wind is blowing. Alternatively, if surface wind is represented using arrows, the magnitude attribute can be used to control the color or size of the arrows, and the direction attribute can be used to control the rotation of the arrow on the map.

In order to represent vector fields cartographically, they must be represented as features (points) in the GIS. This can be accomplished using the Make NetCDF Feature Layer tool from the Multidimension toolbox. This tool reads spatially referenced data from a netCDF and creates an in-memory point feature layer. This point feature layer can be used as input for other geoprocessing tools (e.g., hotspot analysis or interpolation tools) or simply represented cartographically.

To illustrate the cartographic representation of surface wind, data from the NWS National Digital Forecast Database (NDFD) will be used. The NDFD contains gridded forecasts of sensible weather variables such as temperature, sky cover, wind speed, wind direction, and wind gust. These data are free to the public and available for the conterminous United States, Puerto Rico, Guam, and the US Virgin Islands. Figure 20.4 shows the parameters of the Make NetCDF Feature Layer tool used to create the point feature layer.

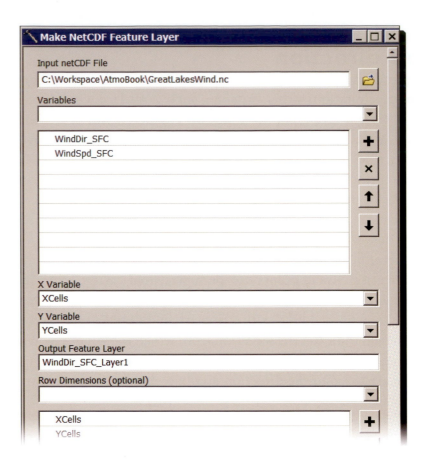

Figure 20.4 Make NetCDF Feature Layer tool used to import wind speed and wind direction.

Once the Make NetCDF Feature Layer tool has been run, the gridded dataset will be represented as simple points in ArcMap. In order to depict wind speed and direction in the same map, the points will be symbolized as arrows, colored to represent various categories of wind speed and rotated to indicate wind direction. To accomplish this, the layer is rendered with a graduated colors renderer using the wind speed variable. Increasing color hue indicates greater wind speed. Next, using the advanced symbology features, the arrows are rotated to indicate wind direction. The rotation is calculated using the geographic style where the angle of rotation is measured from true north. In the case of surface winds, an expression was used to add 180 degrees to the value of the wind direction variable so that the rotation would represent the "from direction" of the wind. Figure 20.5 illustrates the workflow used to create the symbology used on the map in figure 20.6.

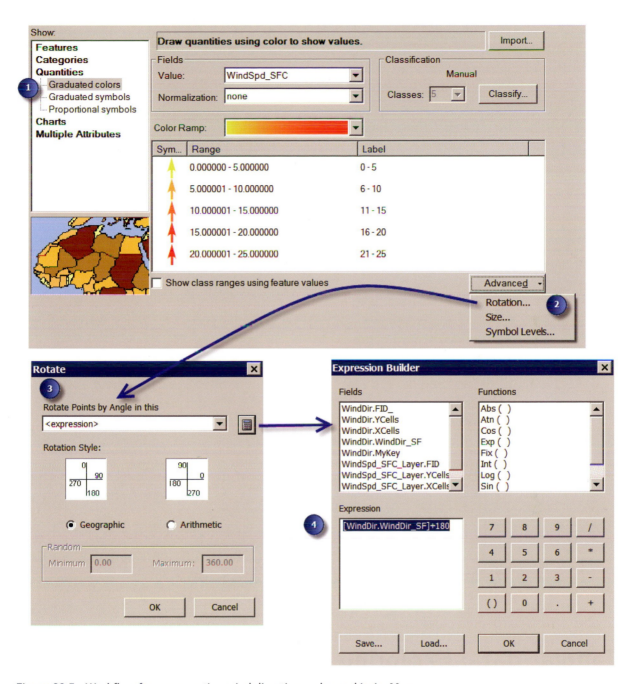

Figure 20.5 Workflow for representing wind direction and speed in ArcMap.

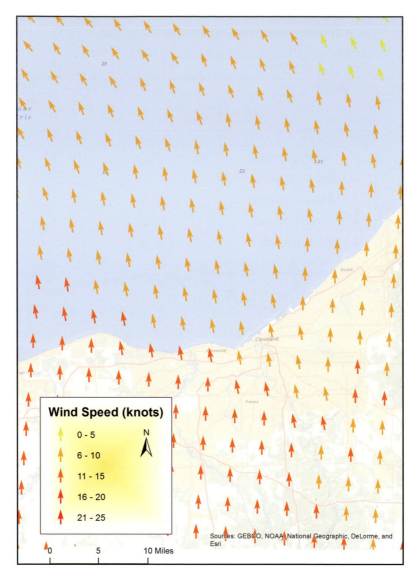

Figure 20.6   **Wind speed and direction near Cleveland, Ohio.** | Basemap data sources: GEBCO, NOAA, National Geographic, DeLorme, and Esri.

Tabular data: Exploring atmospheric ozone concentration

The issue of atmospheric ozone concentration has captured the attention of both the public and the scientific community since the discovery of reduced stratospheric ozone levels above Antarctica in the early 1980s. Concerns over the effects of ozone depletion led to an international agreement to reduce the production and use of human-produced ozone-depleting substances. This international agreement, known as the Montreal Protocol 1987, was ultimately adopted by 197 political entities. Monitoring atmospheric ozone levels is important to both the scientific community and of interest to the general public.

Because there are natural (i.e., nonanthropogenic) variations in atmospheric ozone concentration, it is important to examine ozone levels across time. One way to visualize change across time is to create a graph. To accomplish this, the netCDF data can be represented in ArcMap as a stand-alone table. Stand-alone tables are helpful when netCDF files do not contain spatially referenced data or the analysis method used requires the input data to be in tabular format. Ozone data for the following example were extracted from the European Centre for Medium-Range Weather Forecasts (ECMWF). ECMWF is an independent intergovernmental organization providing medium-range forecasts (approximately one week forward) for a variety of meteorological variables. In addition to conventional meteorological variables, the ECMWF provides data on total column ozone.

Although the ECMWF dataset contains ozone data for the entire globe, we will create a graph for one specific location in eastern New Jersey. The Make NetCDF Table View tool is used to extract ozone data for a specific latitude and longitude (figure 20.7). This is accomplished by specifying Dimension Values in the tool dialog. Specifying time as a row dimension causes the tool to create a table with a row for each unique time contained in the netCDF file. The resulting table has a column for the ozone concentration, and each row represents a unique date. Using the Graphing Wizard in ArcMap, it is easy to create a vertical line graph where the horizontal axis represents time and the vertical axis ozone concentration (figure 20.8).

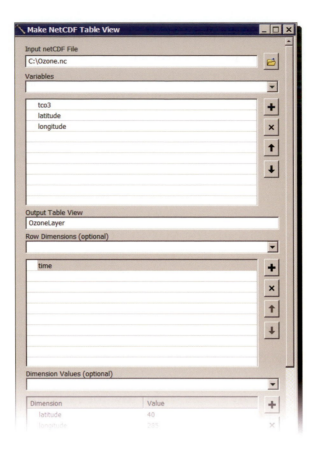

(a)

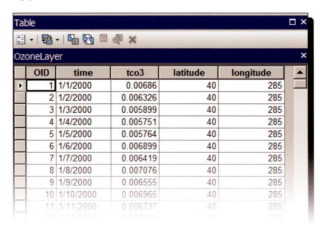

(b)

Figure 20.7 (a) Make NetCDF Raster Layer tool used to extract ozone data at a specific latitude and longitude value.

(b) Stand-alone table produced by the tool. | Ozone data courtesy of the European Centre for Medium-Range Weather Forecasts (ECMWF).

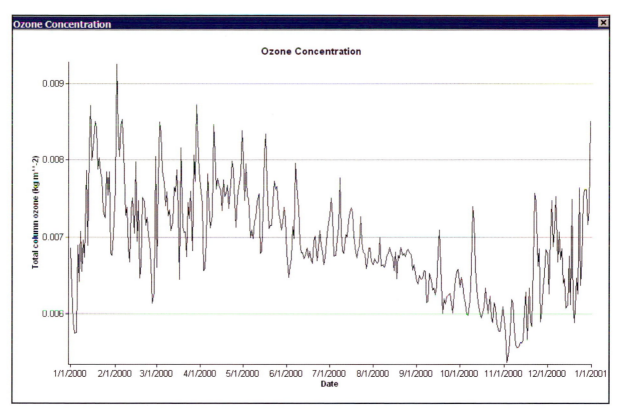

Figure 20.8 Ozone concentration depicted using a graph. | Ozone data courtesy of the European Centre for Medium-Range Weather Forecasts (ECMWF).

Creating netCDF data using ArcMap

The tools previously described read netCDF data so that the data can be visualized or integrated into a geoprocessing workflow. Geoprocessing workflows are composed of a series of geoprocessing tools chained together so the output of one tool in the chain is input for the next. A typical geoprocessing tool performs an operation on an ArcGIS dataset and produces a new dataset as the result of the tool. This new dataset is typically a raster, feature, or table. ArcGIS has a series of tools for transforming these native formats into a netCDF file.

Using the Raster to NetCDF tool, you can export a raster or a raster catalog to a netCDF file. Raster cell values are exported as netCDF variables. Longitude and latitude, or x- and y-coordinate values, are exported as coordinate variables. A single-band raster is exported as a variable of rank 2, which means it has two dimensions representing x- and y-coordinates. A multiband raster is exported with an additional dimension to represent different bands. Fields from a raster catalog are exported as additional dimensions. The Raster to NetCDF tool always creates a new netCDF file or overwrites an existing one. It does not append to an existing netCDF file.

You can export point features to a netCDF file. A field from the feature attribute table can be exported either as a netCDF variable or as a dimension. Usually, the fields storing unique identifiers of features, such as IDs of rainfall stations or values identifying different events such as date of a time series, are exported as dimensions. However, fields storing measurement values, such as wind speed, wind direction, rainfall, and so on, are exported as variables. When no field is specified as dimension, the default dimension RecordID is created for exporting feature attributes in a variable. RecordID represents the OID of a feature. Longitude and latitude or x- and y-coordinate values are exported as separate coordinate variables and linked to a variable through the coordinates attribute. The z- and m-values of the input features are exported as variables specified by the Z Variable and M Variable parameters. The Feature to NetCDF tool always creates a new netCDF file or overwrites an existing one. It does not append to an existing netCDF file.

Tip: Displaying netCDF files in ArcCatalog

By default, ArcCatalog only displays native GIS file types such as rasters or geodatabases. This way, the catalog is not cluttered with unnecessary file types, such as word processing documents. The netCDF file type (.nc) is not recognized by ArcCatalog by default. However, it is easy to add this file type to ArcCatalog. Displaying the netCDF file extension allows you to drag files from the Catalog into the ArcMap Table of Contents or into tool dialog boxes. To add the .nc file extension, perform the following tasks:

1. In ArcMap, click the Options button on the Catalog window.

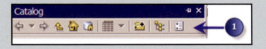

Figure 20.9 Catalog toolbar.

2. Click the New Type . . . button.
3. Type **nc** in the "File extension" input box.
4. Type **NetCDF** in the "Description of type" input box.
5. Optionally, click the Change Icon . . . button, and then choose an icon to represent the netCDF files.

Tip: Drag and drop

Need to quickly preview a netCDF file? From Windows Explorer, you can drag and drop a netCDF file into ArcMap's Table of Contents. If the file contains variables with two or more dimensions, a raster layer is created and displayed using the first variable.

CHAPTER 21

Space-time visualization

Steve Kopp

Most spatial data in atmospheric science are associated with time, usually the time it was observed to occur or the forecast time it is expected to occur. This section will briefly introduce temporal data and techniques for visualizing it in both space and time.

To work with temporal data in a geographic information system (GIS) you first must specify the source of the time information. Because it is possible to have more than one field or dimension in the data containing time information, you need to specify which field of dimension to use.

In Esri's ArcGIS software, you set the time properties of your data on the Time tab of the Layer Properties dialog box. Start by selecting the "Enable time on this layer" box.

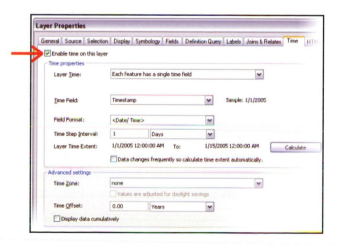

Figure 21.1   Enabling time in a layer in ArcGIS.

Animating point observations from weather stations

Observations of values changing through time as a fixed point, such as temperature at a weather station, is the easiest type of visualization using the simplest form of data.

Once the "Enable time on this layer" box is selected in the dialog box, some properties will populate by default. You will want to review the following settings to ensure that they are correct:

1. First, specify whether the time information in your point feature class is a single field of start time or if it is two fields for start time and end time. In this case, our temperature observations occurred at points in time, not over a time range, so we have a single field.

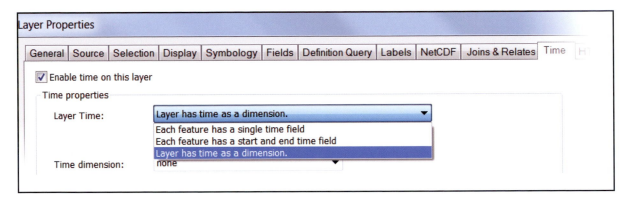

Figure 21.2   Defining the properties of the time layer.

2. Now specify information about the time. If the time field type is not "DATE," you will need to select its time format from the list. To improve performance and usability, store your time values in a date field.

3. The software will try to determine the time step interval. If it is incorrect, you can change it here.

4. The time extent is used to control the time window of the map. If you do not know the full time extent, you can ask the software to calculate it for you.

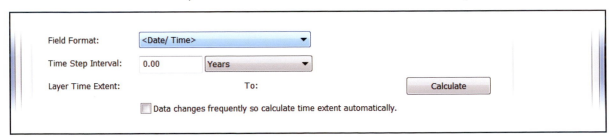

Figure 21.3   Ask the software to calculate the time extent of a layer if you do not know it.

Controlling the time slider and time display

Once you have enabled time in a layer, the time slider 🕐 becomes active in the Tools toolbar.

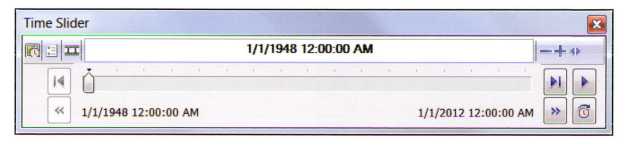

Figure 21.4   The time slider.

The most common parameter people want to control in the display of their temporal data is the format of the time drawn in the map. This is controlled from the properties ▤ of the time slider.

There are many other parameters you can use to control how you interact with time in the map, set a time zone to synch up all layers, set a time extent that is smaller than the time range of all layers, or control the playback speed during animation.

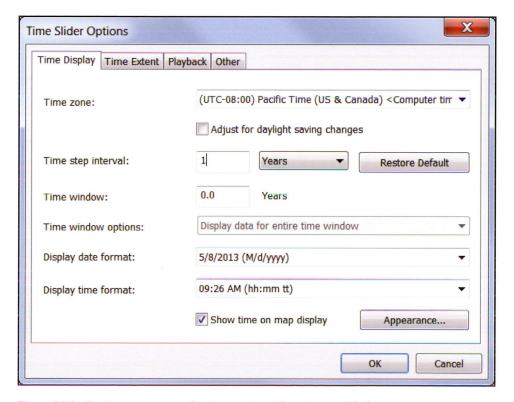

Figure 21.5   Setting parameters for interaction with a time-enabled map.

Figures 21.6 and 21.7 were created using the time slider to view different time slices in a dataset. The precipitation data from the Vegetation/Ecosystem Modeling and Analysis Project (VEMAP Phase 2) were loaded as a time-aware layer. Figure 21.6 shows the layer for 1948. In figure 21.7, the time slider advanced the time frame to data from 1996.

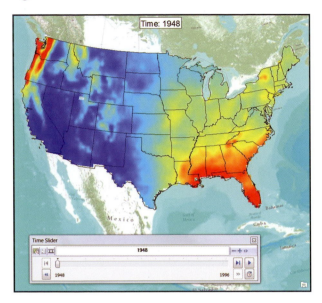

Figure 21.6   Total annual precipitation: 1948. | Data courtesy of the VEMAP Phase 2 (Vegetation/Ecosystem Modeling and Analysis Project (Kittel et al. 1995), and the Ecosystem Dynamics and Atmosphere Section, National Center for Atmospheric Research. Basemap data sources: Esri DeLorme, HERE, TomTom, Intermap, increment P Corporation, GEBCO, USGS, FAO, NPA, NRCAN, GeoBase, IGN, Kadaster NL, Ordnance Survey, Esri Japan, METI, Esri China (Hong Kong), Swisstopo, MapmyIndia, and the GIS user community.

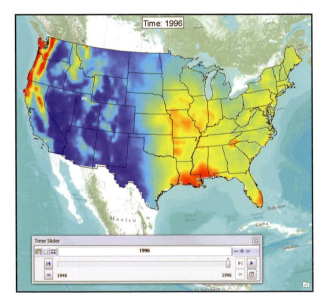

Figure 21.7   Total annual precipitation: 1996. | Data courtesy of the VEMAP Phase 2 (Vegetation/Ecosystem Modeling and Analysis Project (Kittel et al. 1995), and the Ecosystem Dynamics and Atmosphere Section, National Center for Atmospheric Research. Basemap data sources: Esri DeLorme, HERE, TomTom, Intermap, increment P Corporation, GEBCO, USGS, FAO, NPA, NRCAN, GeoBase, IGN, Kadaster NL, Ordnance Survey, Esri Japan, METI, Esri China (Hong Kong), Swisstopo, MapmyIndia, and the GIS user community.

Sharing your temporal visualization

Once we have created a temporal map, the next step is to share it with others. Sharing your animation with other ArcGIS users is as simple as sharing the layer package or map package, and the time information will also be carried over. When you need to share your space-time visualization with people who do not have access to GIS software, you can create a movie to share. However, the most dynamic way to share space-time visualizations is as time-enabled map services. By creating a map service, you can update the data continually, and you do not need to share new files.

Creating an animated movie

To create a movie of your visualization, open it in ArcGIS for Desktop and click the Export to Video icon ⏭ on the time slider.

1. Open the Time Slider window by clicking the Time Slider button 🕐 on the Tools toolbar.

2. Click the Options button ⊞ to open the Time Slider Options dialog box, and then click the Playback tab.

3. Choose Play in specified duration.

4. Specify the playback duration in seconds. This sets how long the video will run. Click the Export to Video button ⏭ to open the Export animation dialog box.

5. Click the Save in arrow and choose a location.

6. In the File name text box, type the name of the video file you want to create.

7. Click the Save as type arrow, and then choose the type of video file you want to create. You can export it as an Audio Video Interleave (.avi) file or as an Apple QuickTime movie (.mov) file.

8. Optionally, click the Help button to learn about the different properties you can set to define the quality of the exported video.

9. Click Export and choose the compressor and compression quality you want to use. Depending on the export format (AVI or QuickTime), the compression dialog boxes may appear different. On these dialog boxes, you can specify the compression properties. The two most important compression properties to consider when exporting videos are the following:

   - Picking the right codec for applying compression to the output videos.
   - Specifying the frame rate of the output video. The frame rate defines how many frames are captured in 1 second of the output video.

Tip: To create a high-quality video with clear text and data, use a codec that does not apply lossy compression, such as Full Frames (Uncompressed) for exporting AVI files.

You can also export your animation as a collection of sequential images in Windows Bitmap (.bmp) or JPEG (.jpg) format. These images can then be used as input frames to create videos (AVI or QuickTime format) using the Raster To Video geoprocessing tool or other third-party video creation software.

Creating temporal map services

Another way to share your time-enabled meteorological data is through a temporal map service. Map services make a map that you have made available to others on a server. They are designed to work in many web and intranet scenarios. The same map service may be used in ArcMap by one user, a web application by another user, ArcGIS Online by another user, and a mobile application by still another user. Temporal map services attempt to duplicate the functionality of desktop animation on the web. When you publish your map to an ArcGIS for Server instance, the time information in your time-enabled layers and map is preserved and accessible through the map service. For example, figure 21.6 shows a time-enabled service viewed on ArcGIS Online. The ArcGIS Online viewer recognizes that the service is time enabled and generates the web equivalent of a time slider at the bottom of the map (figure 21.7).

To view a time-enabled web map, follow these steps:

1. Look for a time slider at the bottom of the web map. If the time slider is not visible, the map does not contain any time-aware layers or the time-aware layers are not currently visible.

2. Click the Play button to begin the map animation.

3. If you want, use the sliders to manually adjust the time period that appears on the map.

4. Click the Pause button to pause the animation.

5. Click the Previous button to go back to the last data interval.

6. Click the Next button to advance to the next data interval.

7. To adjust the playback speed, click the Time Settings button ⚒ to the right of the slider and move the slider toward Slower or Faster.

Time Settings
Playback Speed
Slower
Faster
Show advanced options
OK
Cancel

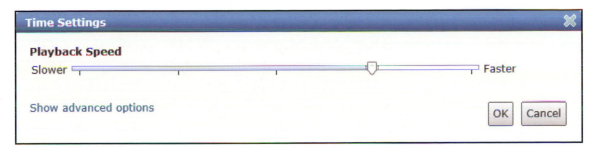

Figure 21.8 Setting the playback speed for an animation.

Options such as start and end time and the time display interval can be adjusted using the Advanced Options dialog box.

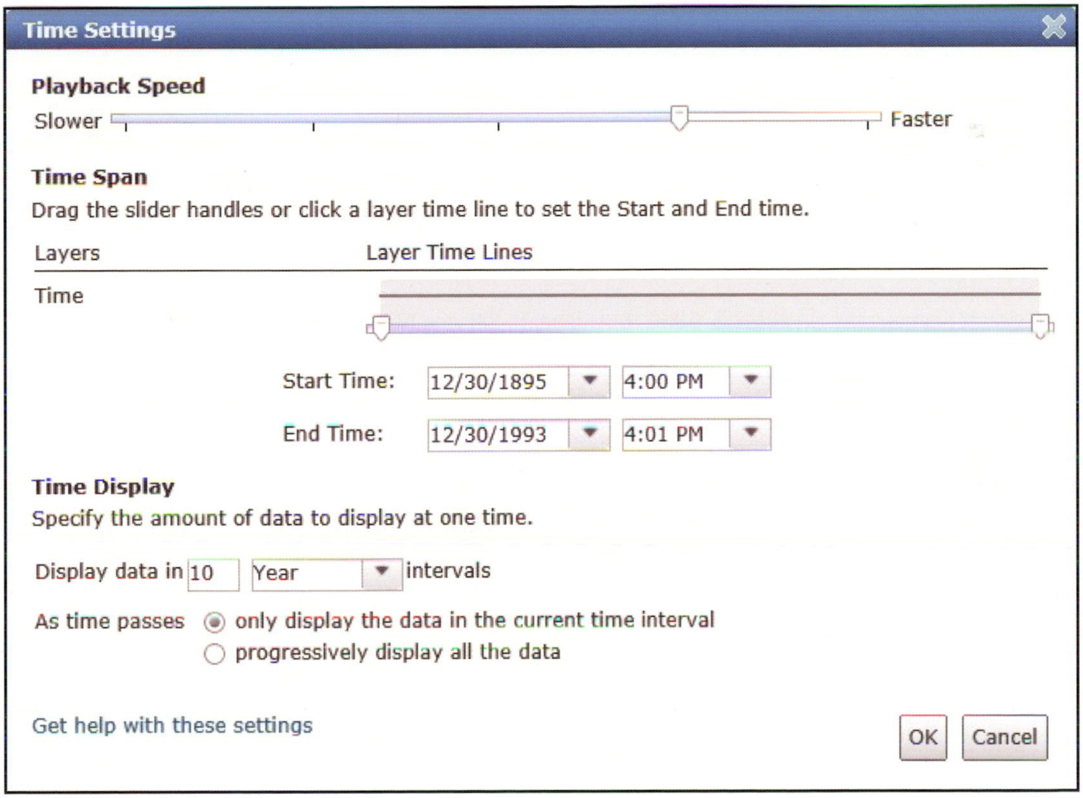

Time Settings
Playback Speed
Slower
Faster
Time Span
Drag the slider handles or click a layer time line to set the Start and End time.
Layers
Layer Time Lines
Time
Start Time:
12/30/1895
4:00 PM
End Time:
12/30/1993
4:01 PM
Time Display
Specify the amount of data to display at one time.
Display data in
10
Year
intervals
As time passes
only display the data in the current time interval
progressively display all the data
Get help with these settings
OK
Cancel

Figure 21.9 Setting the start and end time for a playback.

The time-enabled map previously described is being served by ArcGIS for Server. Many clients can query the server and display the map. In addition to ArcGIS Online, map viewers exist for the Java and Adobe Flex environments. The map service can be consumed by ArcGIS for Desktop or ArcGIS Explorer.

In order to make the map available to as many clients as possible, ArcGIS supports the Open Geospatial Consortium (OGC) Web Map Service (WMS) specification. OGC web services provide a way for you to make your maps and data available in an open, internationally recognized format over the web. OGC has defined specifications for making maps and data available on the web to anyone with a supported client application. All developers are free to use the OGC specifications to create these supported clients. In some cases, the client can be as simple as a web browser.

Publishing an ArcGIS for Desktop map as a service and making it a WMS time-enabled map requires a few steps:

1. Open your map document in ArcMap and choose File > Share As > Service from the main menu.

2. Choose the ArcGIS for Server instance that will host your published map and provide a name for the service. The Service Editor appears.

3. In the Service Editor, specify the properties of the map service. This is where you specify that you want your service to be able to serve OGC-compliant maps.

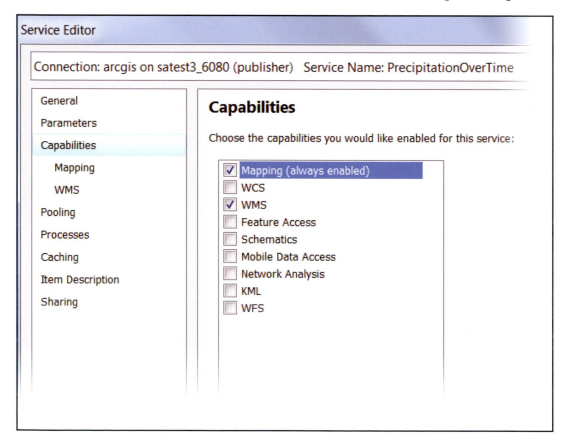

Figure 21.10   Enabling capabilities for a map service.

If you chose to have your map served with WMS capabilities and your original map document contains time-enabled layers, ArcGIS for Server will automatically create a WMS-T compatible service.

4. After analyzing the map using a wizard and correcting any errors, click Publish.

Your map service is now running on the server and can be accessed by users and clients on your network (figure 21.11). If your server administrator allows web access to the service, your service is also now available on the web.

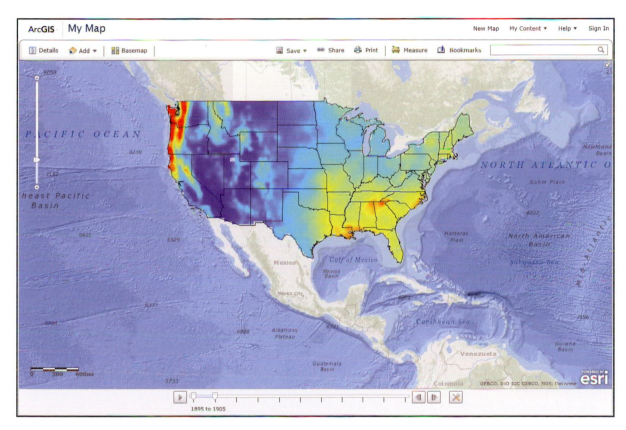

Figure 21.11 Precipitation data for the continental United States viewed on ArcGIS Online. | Data courtesy of the VEMAP Phase 2 (Vegetation/Ecosystem Modeling and Analysis Project (Kittel et al. 1995), and the Ecosystem Dynamics and Atmosphere Section, National Center for Atmospheric Research. Basemap data sources: Esri, GEBCO, IOC GEBCO, NOAA, National Geographic, DeLorme, HERE, Geonames.org, and other contributors.

Reference
Kittel, T. G. F., N. A. Rosenbloom, T. H. Painter, D. S. Schimel, and VEMAP Modeling Participants. 1995. "The VEMAP Integrated Database for Modeling United States Ecosystem/Vegetation Sensitivity to Climate Change." *Journal of Biogeography* 22: 857–62.

CHAPTER 22

Python scripting

Kevin Butler

Python is a free, cross-platform, understandable, open-source programming language that has been widely adopted in the GIS community. It is the scripting language of choice for the geoprocessing environment because it is embedded within the ArcGIS for Desktop and ArcGIS for Server products. Using Python, you can perform geographic analysis, convert and manage data, and extend the analytical capabilities of ArcGIS.

The integration of ArcGIS and Python is made possible through the ArcPy site package. ArcPy provides Python developers access to the entire geoprocessing toolbox, including tools found in the ArcGIS suite of extensions. For example, the following code loads the ArcPy site package and adds a field to roads feature class.

```
>>> import arcpy
>>> arcpy.AddField _ management("c:/Ohio.gdb/roads",
"LENGTH _ MILES", "TEXT")
```

Any number of geoprocessing tools can be strung together to create a GIS workflow. However, this functionality is not unique to Python. ModelBuilder, a visual programming language for building workflows in ArcGIS, can string together sequences of geoprocessing tools, feeding the output of one tool into another tool as input. The true power of Python, in the context of geoprocessing, comes from its ability to provide advanced iteration and branching while easily accessing geoprocessing functionality.

Managing data with Python: The NetCDFFileProperties class

In addition to providing access to geoprocessing tools, ArcPy ships with several Python classes. These Python classes are "blueprints" for describing and manipulating objects in ArcGIS, such as a spatial reference or an extent. Classes often contain sections of prebuilt code called *methods*. Using the methods of a class reduces the amount of code that you have to write yourself. NetCDFFileProperties is one example of an ArcPy class. It contains methods for describing the contents of a netCDF (Network Common Data Form) file, a file format often used in climate analysis and weather forecasting. The netCDF format was designed to store multidimensional scientific data, and therefore may have a very complicated structure. Suppose you have a large number of netCDF files and you need to extract information about each variable to create a report of all of your data holdings. Discovering what variables the netCDF file contains and gathering information about those variables can be accomplished using a short section of Python code (figure 22.1).

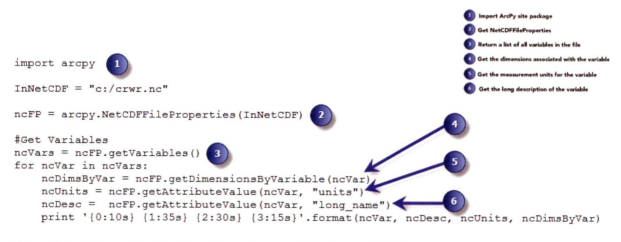

Figure 22.1   Code used to identify and learn about variables in a netCDF file.

For each variable in the netCDF file, the code shown in figure 22.1 will print the name of the variable, its description, units of measurements, and the dimensions that define its shape (e.g., latitude and longitude). This script could easily be modified to process all netCDF files in a directory in order to build a complete catalog of all of your data holdings.

Automating workflows with Python: Converting and aggregating data

The netCDF data model has become an important tool for disseminating scientific data. In situ measurements or the output of computational climate models are created for long time periods, often at global scales. To facilitate the distribution of these files across the Internet, they are often disaggregated so that a single file contains only data for one month or one year, for example. For the purposes of analysis or visualization, it is desirable to have the entire temporal span of the data represented in a single file. The Climate Prediction Center (CPC) Unified Gauge-Based Analysis of Daily Precipitation over CONUS product available from the National Oceanic and Atmospheric Administration's (NOAA) Earth System Research Laboratory Physical Science Division employs this disaggregated distribution mechanism. The complete CPC datasets contain precipitation values over the conterminous United States from 1948 through 2006. Each year of data is distributed as a single netCDF file. To create a complete animation or to calculate averages over the entire temporal span the data for individual years must be aggregated into a single file.

Fortunately, the ArcPy site package has a mechanism for looping through and processing all files in a directory. In figure 22.2, ArcPy's ListFiles method is used to scan a directory for any files beginning with the text "precip" that have the .nc extension. For each of these files, an in-memory feature class is created and then appended to an existing feature class in a file geodatabase.

Figure 22.2   ArcPy's ListFiles method.

Given the large temporal span and high spatial resolution (0.25 degrees latitude by 0.25 degrees longitude) of this dataset, approximately four million points are required to represent each year of data. Processing the data a year at a time and then appending it to a disk-based storage format makes working with such a large dataset possible.

Extending analytical capabilities: Working with NumPy

One of the chief benefits of the Python development environment is that it is extensible. Other developers create collections of Python code that solve a specific problem or provide additional functionality and distribute the code as modules. You can begin using these modules in your

Python code by simply importing the modules. One of the most widely used extensions to the Python language is the NumPy module. This extension adds support for the storage and analysis of large multidimensional arrays and matrices.

Meteorological data are inherently time enabled, so they lend themselves to time series analysis. One common method employed is Fourier analysis. This technique takes a complex waveform (e.g., the variation of temperature or insolation across time) and breaks it down into simplified harmonics represented as trigonometric functions. These simplified functions generalize, or smooth, the "noisy" variations in the original waveform. Several harmonics may be required to fully explain the variation in the original complex waveform. Each harmonic is described by an amplitude and a phase (figure 22.3). Amplitude is the height of the wave's crest above or below the data's mean value. Phase is the location of the first crest with respect to the origin.

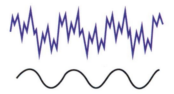

Figure 22.3 Complex waveform (upper) decomposed into a simpler waveform (lower).

Fourier analysis has the general form $G(t) = G_{0+\sum_{m=1}^{N} R_m \cos\left(\frac{2\pi m}{p}\right)t+\varphi_m}$, where t is the time of year, p is the period, N is the number of months, R_m is the mth amplitude, and $ø_m$ is the mth phase. The proportion of total variance explained by each harmonic is $V_h = (a_h^2 + b_h^2)/2\sigma_x^2$, where a and b are the real and imaginary components of the transform, respectively, and $2\sigma_x^2$ is the variance of the original data.

The harmonic analysis code presented in figure 22.4 (page 260) was run against a netCDF dataset containing monthly mean temperature data for 2001 through 2010. The analysis was performed for a single location near Columbus, Ohio. When applied to temperature data, the goal of harmonic analysis is to summarize temperature variation throughout the year as a single mathematical equation known as an annual function. Twelve records representing the mean temperature for each month were extracted and transformed using the Fourier method. This process was repeated for each year. Table 22.1 shows the parameters of the first two harmonics and the percentage of variance explained by each. Calculating the parameters of the harmonics is the first step in building the annual function. The first harmonic represents annual variation in temperature values, and the second harmonic represents semiannual variations. In this example, the majority of the variance in the temperature data is explained by the first harmonic. This means that it does a good job of describing the overall pattern of temperature increase and decrease.

Table 22.1 Parameters of the first two harmonics and the percentage of variance explained by each

| Year | First harmonic | | | Second harmonic | | Percent of variance | | |
	Average	Amplitude	Phase	Amplitude	Phase	First	Second	SD
2001	10.75	11.83	2.98	1.22	2.29	96.46	1.03	8.51
2002	10.71	12.25	3.06	1.52	−1.33	97.14	1.50	8.79
2003	9.59	12.94	3.01	2.11	3.04	94.97	2.53	9.39
2004	10.44	12.54	3.03	2.26	3.13	96.09	3.11	9.05
2005	10.66	13.42	3.00	0.97	−2.06	97.45	0.51	9.61
2006	11.12	10.93	3.04	0.90	0.24	96.17	0.65	7.88
2007	10.89	13.27	2.97	1.47	3.02	93.24	1.15	9.72
2008	10.02	13.00	3.03	0.91	−2.33	98.38	0.48	9.27
2009	9.97	12.59	3.08	1.86	−3.03	95.59	2.08	9.11
2010	10.67	14.81	3.10	2.15	−2.85	96.82	2.04	10.64
Avg.	8.73	10.63	2.52	1.28	0.01			

The parameters of the harmonics can be averaged (pooled) to create the following annual function, which can be used to estimate the temperature at any time period, t:

$$T_{mean}(t) = 8.73 + 10.63 \cos\left(\frac{\pi t}{6} + 2.52\right) + 1.28 \cos\left(\frac{\pi t}{3} + 0.01\right)$$

The previous analysis was completed for a single location near Columbus, Ohio, using National Centers for Environmental Prediction (NCEP) Reanalysis Derived data provided by the NOAA Office of Oceanic and Atmospheric Research/Earth System Research Laboratory, Physical Sciences Division (http://www.esrl.noaa.gov/psd/). However, the dataset is available globally on a 2.5 degree latitude × 2.5 degree longitude grid from 1948 to the present. With some modification of the code, this analysis could be completed for all the locations on the 2.5 degree global grid. The parameters of the harmonics could be mapped to explore their spatial variability. This global analysis could be run for each year from 1948 to the present and animated, resulting in a complete spatiotemporal analysis of temperature variability.

```
#
# Perform simplistic harmonic analysis on temperature data
#
import arcpy
import numpy as np
import math

arcpy.env.overwriteOutput = True

arcpy.MakeNetCDFTableView_md("C:/data/air.mon.mean.nc",
                             "air","mon.mean_View","time","lat 40;lon 277.5",
                             "BY_VALUE")

# Process data for years 2001 through 2010
for year in range(2001,2011):
    # Build a where clause to select twelve records for each year
    WhereClause = 'EXTRACT(YEAR FROM "time") = ' + str(year)
    arcpy.SelectLayerByAttribute_management("mon.mean_View","NEW_SELECTION",
                                                          WhereClause)
    # Covert the 12 selected records to a numpy array.
    data = arcpy.da.TableToNumPyArray("mon.mean_View","air")
    data = np.array(data)
    N = len(data)                                   # get number of data elements
    A = np.fft.rfft(data)                           # calculate discrete FFT
    A = A / math.sqrt(N)
    amplitude = np.abs(A)                           # Get amplitude
    amplitude = 2 * (amplitude / math.sqrt(N))      # Normalize amplitude
    phase = np.angle(A)                             # Get phase

    # Calculate proportion of variance explained by each harmonic
    variance = 2.0 * np.abs(A[1:])**2 / (N * np.var(data.tolist()))
    variance_proportion = variance*100
```

The numbered callouts on the right:

1 Import ArcPy site package
2 Get NetCDFFileProperties
3 Return a list of all variables in the file
4 Get the dimensions associated with the variable
5 Get the measurement units for the variable
6 Get the long description of the variable

Figure 22.4 Code to calculate a Fourier transformation. Print statements used to generate the table were removed for readability.

Summary

This chapter explored how Python can be used to manage large volumes of multidimensional data, automate workflows, and extend the analytical capabilities of GIS. For a comprehensive guide to Python scripting in a GIS environment see Zandbergen (2013). A large library of Python routines for analyzing scientific data with Python is available at http://www.scipy.org. Lin (2012) provides an introduction to using Python in the atmospheric sciences.

References

Lin, J. W. B. 2012. *A Hands-On Introduction to Using Python in the Atmospheric and Oceanic Sciences.* http://www.johnny-lin.com/pyintro/.

Zandbergen, Paul A. 2013. *Python Scripting for ArcGIS.* Redlands, CA: Esri Press.

CHAPTER 23

The Weather and Climate Toolkit

Steve Ansari, Stephen Del Greco, and Neal Lott

The Weather and Climate Toolkit (WCT) is free, platform-independent software distributed from the National Oceanic and Atmospheric Administration's (NOAA) National Climatic Data Center (NCDC). The WCT allows the visualization and data export of weather and climate data, including radar, satellite, and model data.

The WCT provides tools for custom data overlays, background maps, animations, and basic filtering. The export of images and movies is provided in multiple formats. The data export feature supports conversion of data to a variety of common formats, including shapefile, Well-Known Text (WKT), GeoTIFF, Esri grid, and Gridded netCDF (Network Common Data Form). These data export features promote the interoperability of weather and climate information with various scientific communities and common software packages such as ArcGIS, Google Earth, and MatLAB. Advanced data export support for Google Earth enables the two- and three-dimensional export of rendered data and isosurfaces.

NOAA NCDC archives many diverse datasets, including those based on station observations, radar, numerical models, and satellites. These data are in many different complicated binary formats and represent different abstract data types, such as point, time series, grid, radial, and swath. Although it is relatively easy to access the raw datasets, integration of the data into user software and applications is often difficult. Custom software must be written to decode or parse the data into formats that common software packages can read. Furthermore, these formats and software packages are different for each major scientific genre, including engineering, atmospheric science, hydrology, and environmental science. Conversion and data export tools provide easier data access and integration. The WCT is an application designed to provide simple visualization capabilities and ease the integration of weather and climate data into geographic information system (GIS) applications (Ansari, Lott, and Del Greco 2013).

Data

The WCT is based largely on the Unidata NetCDF for Java API (application programming interface; http://www.unidata.ucar.edu/software/netcdf-java/) and the Climate and Forecast (CF) conventions for netCDF (http://cfconventions.org). The NetCDF for Java API supports the direct reading of native formats, including GRIB (Gridded Binary Form), NEXRAD (Next-Generation Radar), and HDF (Hierarchical Data Format), into common data model feature types such as time series, radial, grid, and so on.

The WCT provides visualization and data export support based on these abstract feature types (http://www.ncdc.noaa.gov/wct/tutorials).

The current available release provides support for many data formats, including the following:

- Station Time Series netCDF

- Gridded netCDF, HDF, and OPeNDAP (Open-source Project for a Network Data Access Protocol)

- GRIB version 1 and 2 (Gridded Information in Binary, used in weather and climate models)

- NEXRAD Level-II Weather Radar

- NEXRAD Level-III Weather Radar

- GOES (Geostationary Operational Environmental Satellites) AREA files

- GINI (GOES Ingest and NOAA PORT Interface) format

- GEMPAK (GEneral Meteorology PAcKage) grid format

- XMRG MPE (XMRG Multisensor Precipitation Estimates)

Users may access data on any remote HTTP (Hypertext Transfer Protocol) or FTP (file transfer protocol) server in addition to local disk. Custom data access support is provided for NCDC data orders, NOAA CLASS (Comprehensive Large Array-data Stewardship) orders, and THREDDS (Thematic Real-time Environmental Distributed Data Services) catalogs (see "Unidata's Common Data Model and NetCDF Java Library API Overview": http://www.unidata.ucar.edu/software/netcdf/workshops/2008/njcdm/index.html).

Visualization

Simple two-dimensional visualization is provided for all supported datasets. The WCT includes prepackaged feature-layer data for common map layers, including states, counties, and cities (figures 23.1 and 23.2). Custom feature-layer data may be added using any NAD83/WGS84 shapefile. Background maps can be added using Web Map Services (WMS). Predefined WMS background maps for US Geological Survey (USGS) topographical maps, aerial photography, Landsat, land cover, and shaded relief are included (figure 23.3). The North American Datum 1983 (NAD83) latitude/longitude grid is used as the basis for all visualizations. Datasets are remapped for each view extent using a nearest-neighbor resampling method, if needed. Basic filtering and smoothing functionality is provided.

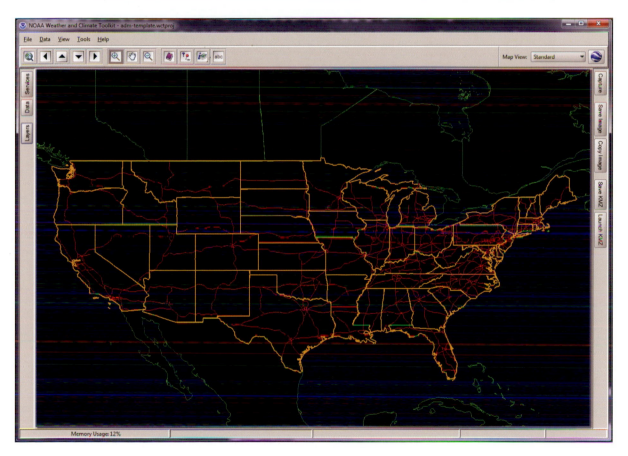

Figure 23.1   The WCT international and state/province boundaries and US roads layers. | Courtesy of NOAA. Base data from Esri.

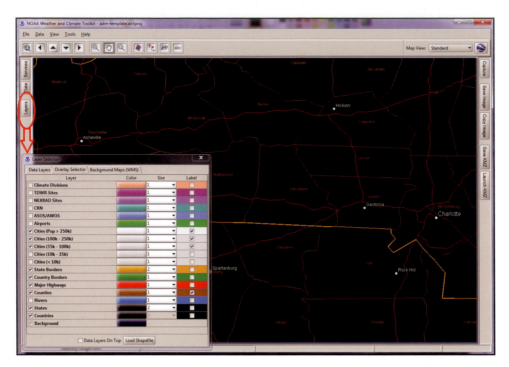

Figure 23.2   WCT layers for states, counties, and cities. | Courtesy of NOAA. Base data from Esri.

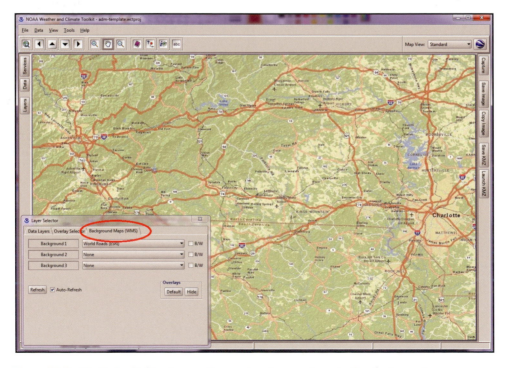

Figure 23.3   Shaded relief background map showing roads and other features. | Courtesy of NOAA. Topographic data from US Geological Survey.

Currently, a single file can be loaded as an active layer. Specific options and properties may be set based on the data type (grid, satellite, radial, station time series). These properties include the selection of grid variables, times, and heights; selection of radial elevation angles; or the selection of specific stations or observation times. Users may save map images to common file formats (such as JPEG, GIF, and PNG). Keyhole Markup language Zipped (KMZ) file export allows visualization in Google Earth or other virtual globe software (figure 23.4). Animations are supported with output in animated GIF and AVI formats in addition to KMZ. (See "Standards and file formats" at the end of the chapter.)

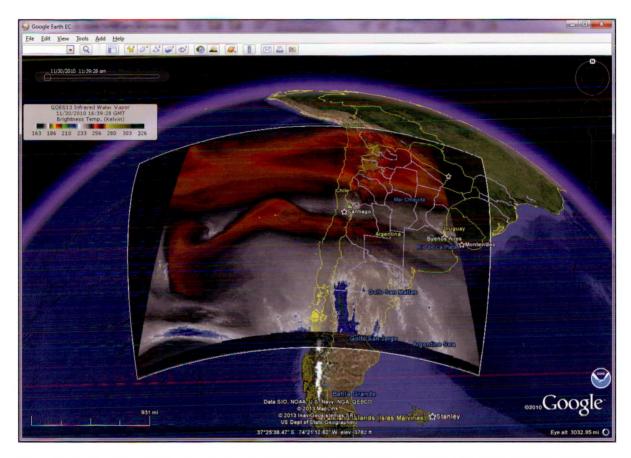

Figure 23.4   **Visualizing WCT output in Google Earth by creating a KMZ output file.** | Courtesy of NOAA. Base data from Esri Data and Maps, 2010. Data from SIO, NOAA, US Navy, NGA, and GEBCO. ©2013 MapLink. ©2013 Inav/ Geosistemas, SRL; US Department of State Geographer. ©2010 Google.

Three-dimensional rendering of radar data is supported using the COLLADA modeling syntax in conjunction with KMZ output in Google Earth (figure 23.5). The rendered data image is draped on a COLLADA model, which represents the surface of the selected beam elevation angle. Isosurface generation is also supported for radial and grid data types containing a height dimension. For radial data, a series of constant altitude slices are derived to create a latitude–longitude–height data cube. Isosurfaces are created from this data cube and are displayed as polygon or line KMZ output in Google Earth (figure 23.6). An internal instance of Google Earth provides an integrated viewing experience linked directly to the standard two-dimensional map (figure 23.7). The Google Earth instance is updated following each zoom and pan of the two-dimensional map.

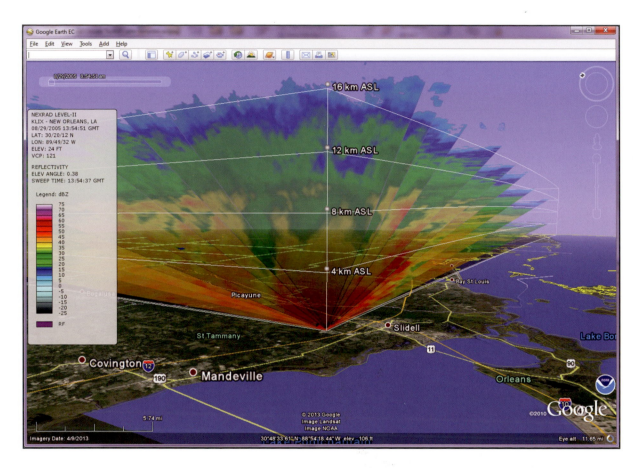

Figure 23.5 Three-dimensional rendering of radar data is supported using the COLLADA modeling syntax in conjunction with KMZ output in Google Earth. | NEXRAD data from NOAA. Base data from Esri Data and Maps, 2010. ©2010 Google, ©2013 Google. Image Landsat. Image NOAA.

Figure 23.6 Isosurfaces created from a data cube and visualized as polygon or line KMZ output in Google Earth. | NEXRAD data from NOAA. Base data from Esri Data and Maps, 2010. ©2010 Google, ©2013 Google. Image Landsat. Image NOAA.

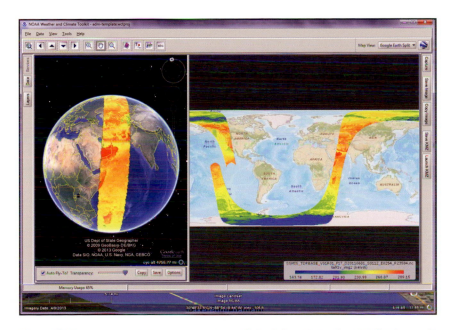

Figure 23.7 Integrated viewing experience linked directly to the standard two-dimensional map. | NOAA, The SSMI(S) CDR used in this study was acquired from NOAA's National Climatic Data Center (http://www.ncdc.noaa.gov). This CDR was originally developed by Christian Kummerow and colleagues at Colorado State University for NOAA's CDR Program. Other sources: Google Earth, US Department of State Geographer. ©2009 GeoBasic-DE/BKG. ©2013 Google. Data from SIO, NOAA, US Navy, NGA, and GEBCO. Image Landsat. Image NOAA.

Export

The WCT supports the export of data to several common scientific formats. Spatial and attribute filtering is provided, allowing users to extract subsets of the original data (figure 23.8).

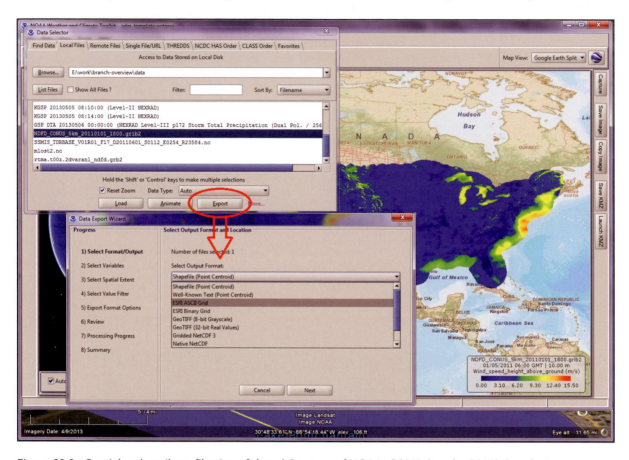

Figure 23.8   Spatial and attribute filtering of data. | Courtesy of NOAA. ©2010 Google, ©2013 Google. Image Landsat. Image NOAA. Esri.

Currently supported export formats include the following:

- Point and Polygon shapefile
- Point and Polygon WKT
- Raw netCDF (native data structure)
- Gridded netCDF (remapped, if needed)
- ArcInfo ASCII Grid
- GeoTIFF
- Comma-separated value (CSV) text
- KMZ

These export formats are readable by many software packages, including GIS applications, mathematical and statistical analysis software, engineering software, and meteorological analysis tools. Command-line batch processing is supported for all data export capabilities, which allows automation and integration of data format conversions in larger processing workflows (figure 23.9).

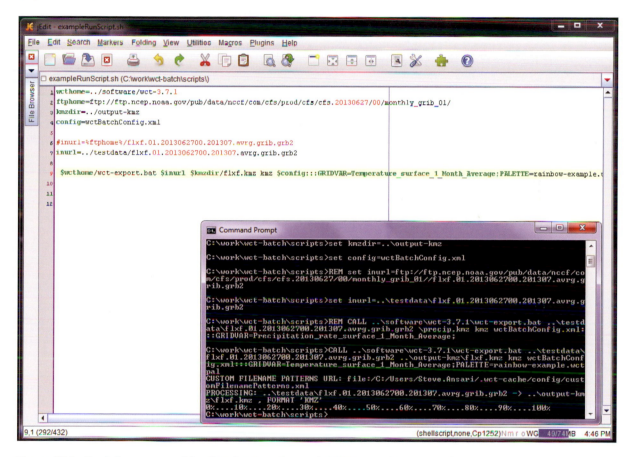

Figure 23.9 Tools for command-line batch processing and automation. | Courtesy of NOAA.

Radar data use case

In this use case, radar reflectivity and precipitation products are converted from the unique binary NEXRAD format to the shapefile format and loaded into ArcGIS using the following steps:

1. Obtain binary radar data files from NCDC, NOAA's National Weather Service (NWS), or another source, such as NOAA's Radar Data website (http://www.ncdc. noaa.gov/radar-data).

2. Load the data into the WCT.

3. Export the data into shapefile format, which creates polygon data in an NAD83 geographic coordinate system (figure 23.10).

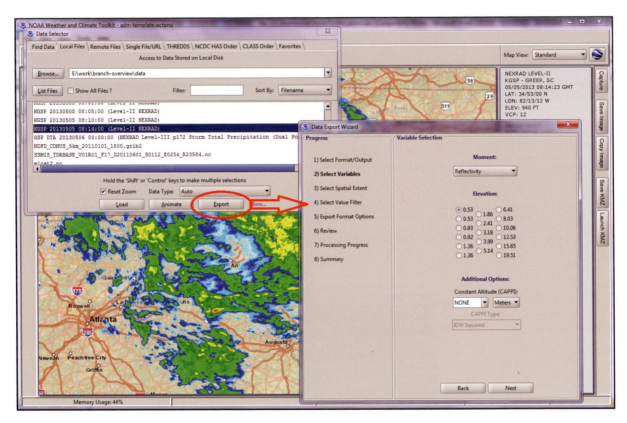

Figure 23.10   Exporting data from WCT as a shapefile. | NOAA/NCDC. Data from http://www.ncdc.noaa.gov/radar-data.

4. Load the shapefile into ArcGIS and create a custom map or conduct an analysis (figures 23.11 and 23.12).

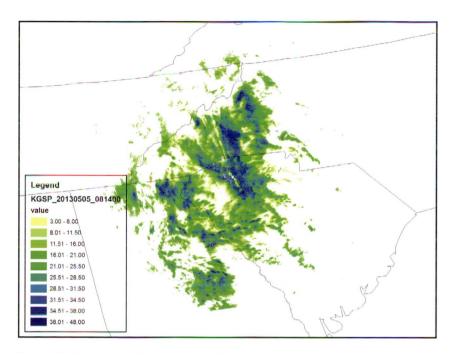

Figure 23.11   A shapefile of NEXRAD data shown in ArcGIS. | NOAA/NCDC.
Data from http://www.ncdc.noaa.gov/radar-data.

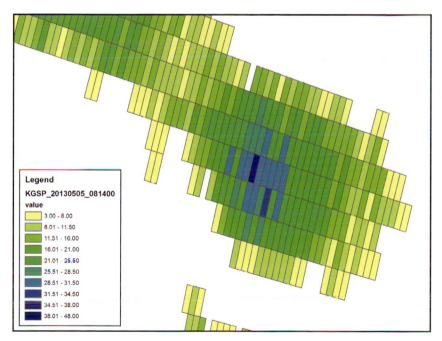

Figure 23.12   The previous dataset classified and gridded. | NOAA/NCDC.
Data from http://www.ncdc.noaa.gov/radar-data.

Satellite data use case

In this use case, GOES satellite data are converted from the McIDAS (Man computer Interactive Data Access System) AREA format to the Esri ASCII Grid (or ArcInfo ASCII Grid) format and loaded into ArcGIS using the following steps:

1. Obtain binary GOES data files in the AREA file format from the NOAA CLASS system (http://www.class.noaa.gov) or another source.

2. Load the data into the WCT.

3. Export the data into the Esri ASCII Grid format. The raster grid is resampled using the nearest-neighbor algorithm from the custom satellite projection into an NAD83 geographic coordinate system.

4. Load Esri ASCII Grid into ArcGIS and symbolize (figure 23.13).

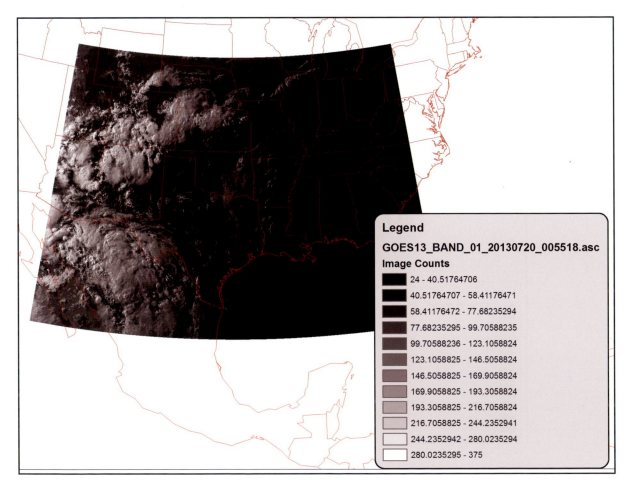

Figure 23.13   GOES satellite data as an ASCII grid in ArcGIS. | Courtesy of NOAA.

Model data use case

In this use case, the North American Regional Reanalysis (NARR) model is converted from the GRIB2 format to a shapefile and loaded into ArcGIS using the following steps:

1. Obtain binary data file (GRIB format) from the NCDC NOMADS system (http://www.nomads.ncdc.noaa.gov).

2. Load the data into the WCT (figure 23.14).

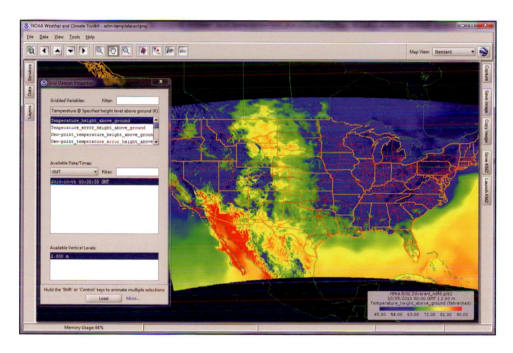

Figure 23.14 NARR data loaded into the WCT. NOAA/NCDC. Data from NCDC NOMADS system—http://www.nomads.ncdc.noaa.gov.

3. Export the data into the shapefile format, which creates point data representing the centroid of the grid cell in the NAD83 geographic coordinate system (figure 23.15).

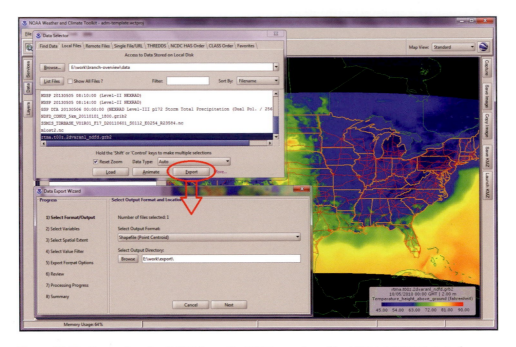

Figure 23.15   Exporting the NARR from the WCT as a shapefile. | NOAA/NCDC. Data from NCDC NOMADS system—http://www.nomads.ncdc.noaa.gov.

4. Load the shapefile into ArcGIS (figure 23.16).

5. (Optional) Interpolate into a custom raster grid and projection or create contour polylines.

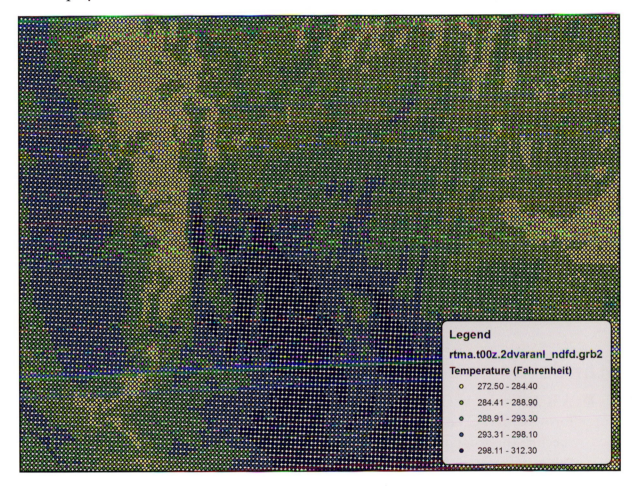

Figure 23.16 **NARR data as a shapefile displayed in ArcGIS.** | NOAA/NCDC. Data from NCDC NOMADS system—http://www.nomads.ncdc.noaa.gov.

Conclusion

The WCT provides easier access to NOAA weather and climate datasets. As free, platform-independent, stand-alone software, the WCT reaches a large audience of diverse users. By providing visualization and export capabilities, users are able to easily integrate data into their own applications and tools, including GIS software. The WCT is built on scalable, open-source, and community-driven netCDF software, which allows for flexible future development. These benefits exemplify the overall NOAA mission.

References

Ansari, S., J. N. Lott, and S. A. Del Greco. 2013. "The Weather and Climate Toolkit." Ninety-third AMS Annual Meeting, 29th Conference on Environmental Information Processing Technologies, American Meteorological Society, Presentation 5A.1, January 2013.

CF Conventions and MetaData website. http://cf-pcmdi.llnl.gov.

National Climatic Data Center, National Oceanic and Atmospheric Administration. "NOAA National Operational Model Archive and Distribution System." http://nomads.ncdc.noaa.gov.

———. "NOAA Weather and Climate Toolkit Tutorial." Last updated June 25, 2014. http://www.ncdc.noaa.gov/wct/tutorials.

———. "Radar Data." http://www.ncdc.noaa.gov/radar-data.

National Oceanic and Atmospheric Administration. "Comprehensive Large Array-Data Stewardship System (CLASS)." http://www.class.noaa.gov.

Unidata Program Center. 2008. "Unidata's Common Data Model and NetCDF Java Library API Overview." http://www.unidata.ucar.edu/software/netcdf/workshops/2008/njcdm/index.html.

———. 2014. "NetCDF for Java API." http://www.unidata.ucar.edu/software/netcdf-java/.

Standards and file formats

- **ASCII Grid:** "ARC ASCII Grid refers to a specific interchange format developed for ARC/INFO rasters in ASCII format. The format consists of a header that specifies the geographic domain and resolution, followed by the actual grid cell values. Usually the file extension is .asc, but recent versions of Esri software also recognize the extension .grd" (Ed Yu, "ArcInfo ASCII Grid format," http://docs.codehaus.org/display/GEOTOOLS/ArcInfo+ASCII+Grid+format#ASCIIGrid).

- **COLLADA:** "COLLADA is a COLLAborative Design Activity for establishing an open standard digital-asset schema for interactive 3D applications. It involves designers, developers, and interested parties from within Sony Computer Entertainment America (SCEA) as well as key third-party companies in the 3D industry. With its 1.4.0 release, COLLADA became a standard of The Khronos Group Inc., where consortium members continue to promote COLLADA to be the centerpiece of digital-asset toolchains used by the 3D interactive industry" (COLLADA Working Group, "COLLADA," https://collada.org/mediawiki/index.php/COLLADA).

- **Esri shapefile:** "A shapefile stores nontopological geometry and attribute information for the spatial features in a data set. The geometry for a feature is stored as a shape comprising a set of vector coordinates" (Esri, http://www.esri.com).

- **GeoTIFF:** "GeoTIFF represents an effort by over 160 different remote sensing, GIS, cartographic, and surveying related companies and organizations to establish a TIFF based interchange format for georeferenced raster imagery." (GeoTIFF Wiki, http://trac.osgeo.org/geotiff/).

- **GINI:** The file format and data structure used for Satellite Data in the Advanced Weather Interactive Processing System (AWIPS). For more information, see the Unisys "GINI Format for AWIPS Satellite Data" web page: http://weather.unisys.com/wxp/Appendices/Formats/GINI.html.

- **GRIB:** A format approved by the World Meteorological Organization (WMO) Commission for Basic Systems (CBS) Extraordinary Meeting Number VIII (1985) as "a general purpose, bit-oriented data exchange format, designated FM 92-VIII Ext. GRIB (GRIdded Binary). It is an efficient vehicle for transmitting large volumes of gridded data to automated centers over high-speed telecommunication lines using modern protocols. By packing information into the GRIB code, messages (or records—the terms are synonymous in this context) can be made more compact than character oriented bulletins, which will produce faster computer-to-computer transmissions. GRIB can equally well serve as a data storage format, generating the same efficiencies relative to *information* storage and retrieval devices" (World Meteorological Organization, "Part II: A Guide to the Code Form FM 92-IX Ext. GRIB," http://www.wmo.int/pages/prog/www/WDM/Guides/Guide-binary-2.html).

- **HDF (Hierarchical Data Format):** "At its lowest level, HDF is a physical file format for storing scientific data. At its highest level, HDF is a collection of utilities and applications for manipulating, viewing, and analyzing data in HDF files. Between these levels, HDF is a software library that provides high-level APIs and a low-level data interface" (The HDF Group, http://www.hdfgroup.org).

- **McIDAS (Man Computer Interactive Data Access System) AREA file description:** "In McIDAS, satellite imagery data and supplemental information are stored on disk in data structures called areas. Each area is a binary file containing all the information necessary to display and navigate the image. Complete images are often too large to be stored completely in an area file. An area may be a geographic portion of the image or a subset produced by sampling or averaging the image data. Any point in the area can be described with image coordinates, its position in the full satellite image, or with area coordinates, its position in the area or subset of the image" (McIDAS, "New AREA Format Information," http://www.ssec.wisc.edu/mcidas/doc/misc_doc/area2.html).

- **NetCDF (Network Common Data Form):** "NetCDF (network Common Data Form) is an interface for array-oriented data access and a freely-distributed collection of software libraries for C, Fortran, C++, Java, and Perl that provide implementations of the interface. The netCDF software was developed by Glenn Davis, Russ Rew, Steve Emmerson, John Caron, and Harvey Davies at the Unidata Program Center in Boulder, Colorado, and augmented by contributions from other netCDF users. The netCDF libraries define a machine-independent format for representing scientific data. Together, the interface, libraries, and format support the creation, access, and sharing of scientific data" (Unidata, "Network Common Data Form (NetCDF)," http://www.unidata.ucar.edu/software/netcdf/).

- **Unidata Common Data Model (CDM):** "Unidata's Common Data Model (CDM) is an abstract data model for scientific datasets. It merges the netCDF, OPeNDAP, and HDF5 data models to create a common API for many types of scientific data. The NetCDF Java library is an implementation of the CDM which can read many file formats besides netCDF. We call these CDM files, a shorthand for files that can be read by the NetCDF Java library and accessed through the CDM data model" (Unidata, "Unidata's Common Data Model Version 4," http://www.unidata.ucar.edu/software/netcdf-java/CDM/).

- **Well-Known Text (WKT):** An ASCII text representation of geometry data. Defined in the OpenGIS Consortium "Simple Features for SQL" specification. For more information, see the "IBM DB2 10.1 for Linux, UNIX, and Windows documentation" web page: http://publib.boulder.ibm.com/infocenter/db2help/index.jsp?topic=/com.ibm.db2.udb.doc/opt/rsbp4120.htm.

Afterword

Ted Habermann

The task of looking ahead does not get easier as we move forward with seemingly increasing speed. Nevertheless, it is the opportunity we have at this point. The work described in this book builds a strong foundation for integrating atmospheric data into geographic information systems (GIS). Like a slab of cement, this foundation provides a two-dimensional outline for future developments. Our challenge is to build that foundation into the third dimension by adding an information layer and by converging the experience and knowledge of these two communities.

The understanding continuum: A framework

One framework for discussing our task is the Continuum of Understanding originally described by Cleveland (1982) (see figure A.1). The continuum has four stages: data, information, knowledge, and wisdom. Data are observations and model results that are collected from the world around us. They are generally numbers that are critical to characterizing the environment but, by themselves, are not very useful. Structure, context, and organization are added to data to create information that can be shared and hopefully absorbed by others. Individuals create knowledge as they consume information from multiple sources and merge it with their experience. The knowledge stage of the continuum is where most human discourse happens. People share the knowledge that they have gained and present their points of view (context). This discourse hopefully leads to wisdom, the current state of the community's understanding of the object of study, the environment in this case.

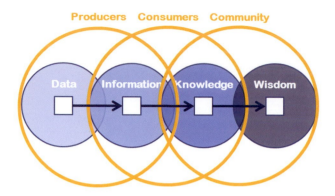

Figure A.1 The Continuum of Understanding, originally conceived by Cleveland (1982) and elaborated by Shedroff (1994), describes stages in the development of wisdom from data. Producers, consumers, and communities all contribute to different stages of that progression. | Adapted from Nathan Shedroff, "Information Interaction Design: A Unified Field Theory of Design," 1994 (http://www.nathan.com/thoughts/unified/index.html).

The groups that participate vary along the continuum. At the beginning of the spectrum, individuals (producers) formulate scientific questions and collect the data they need to answer them. They add structure and context to the observations in the form of presentations and papers and share them with other individuals (consumers). Data centers can play an important and useful mediation role in facilitating this sharing process and broadening the community of consumers. Finally, in the wisdom part of the spectrum, consumers interact with each other and community comes into play. Knowledge is shared and community wisdom is constructed.

Maps and GIS build on top of standard formats and services and are very important tools for giving data structure and context, creating information, and for sharing this information with others. The idea that sharing data is important is one of the defining characteristics of the GIS community. It is at the heart of the selection process that brought the authors of this book together. They have a deeply held belief that sharing their observations across a broad community is a critical contribution to society's understanding of the environment that we live in and affect.

The Continuum of Understanding bears a striking resemblance to the data life cycle (figure A.2), and the participants are the same. Scientists (providers) collect observations at the beginning of the life cycle; these observations are shared with other individuals (consumers) through one-on-one communication or a data center. If the data are understandable and trustworthy, they are reused by others (community) and contribute to community wisdom. The efficiency of this process is enhanced by standards throughout the creation, discovery, access, analysis, and understanding process. Standards are, therefore, a critical element in the efficient migration from data to information to knowledge to wisdom.

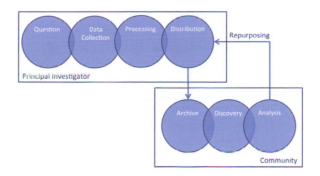

Figure A.2 The data life cycle is very similar to the Continuum of Understanding previously described, and the same individuals and groups participate.

The role of the data center is to help the data provider spread its data across a broad community. An important part of this role is to ensure that the data can be preserved and be independently understood by that community. Standards play an important role here. Custom formats and approaches make community understanding much more difficult, and many times impossible, to achieve.

Two elements are going to be critical as we look forward at the future that atmospheric scientists and data managers are building together with the GIS community: (1) the process of building information from data and sharing that knowledge with individuals that can create community wisdom and (2) understanding the benefits of standards along the path.

Building information from data

Building information from data involves adding organization, structure, and context to help users create understanding. This additional information is generally termed *documentation*, and it can take many forms. The standard and structured part of the documentation is called *metadata*.

The world of metadata has changed significantly during the last several years, and these changes will be at the center of the migration from data to information to knowledge. One of the most important changes is the concrete realization that no single metadata standard can hold all of the information required to understand all data or even a single dataset. This realization is well expressed in Annex C of the International Organization for Standardization (ISO) Metadata Standard (ISO 19115):

> The definitions and domain values are intended to be sufficiently generic to satisfy the metadata needs of various disciplines. However, the very diversity of information means that generic metadata may not accommodate all applications. This annex provides the rules for defining and applying additional metadata to better serve special user [e.g., community] needs.

Historically, a statement that a particular metadata standard does not "fit" a particular type of data has been sufficient to justify using a different standard, or even constructing a "new" one. ISO 19115 is the first metadata standard that incorporates a mechanism to plug-in extensions in a standard way. This is an important response to the "does not fit" justification for not using a particular standard and an important mechanism for increasing the breadth of the community that can use the metadata standard. More important, it increases the breadth of the community that can discover, use, and understand the data, facilitating the creation of knowledge and wisdom beyond the original intended scope of the data and information.

Annex C describes how communities can create extensions to the standard to address special needs. The ISO standard includes several other mechanisms for connecting to content outside of itself:

- The RecordType/Record mechanism supports inclusion of implementation specific metadata describing content or quality results.

- An alternativeMetadataReference citation was added to the standard to support connections to information in other metadata standards.

- An additionalDocumentation citation was added to support citations to user guides, scientific papers, data dictionaries, and other documentation.

- More than 10 new citations were added in the revision of ISO 19115 (ISO 19115-1).

The treatment of spatial/temporal extents is a second important evolutionary step in metadata standards. In the past, metadata records generally included the capability to describe a single spatial/temporal extent that applies to the data being described. This extent was used to display the dataset on a map or a time line and as support for discovery of the data.

ISO 19115 brought together the temporal and spatial bounds of the dataset into a single object and, more important, allowed multiple extents to be attached to a dataset, quality and maintenance reports, and sources that have been combined to construct an integrated dataset. This greatly improves the capability to provide complete descriptions to users, particularly for spatially and temporally disjointed datasets and for large, long-term datasets with variations in time and space. More important, it turns the metadata "record" into a collection of spatial/temporal objects that have distinct types and characteristics. The metadata record evolves from a single object to a "spatial database" of information that can be displayed and explored using the same tools used for displaying and exploring the data. This is a big step toward bridging the gap that exists because of different "metadata" and "data" tools. The adage "one person's data is another's metadata" has never been more true. This is a big step in moving us into the information and knowledge part of the continuum.

A final change in the metadata world that helps build data into information is the inclusion, for the first time, of a place in the metadata for user feedback. ISO 19115 includes the capability to describe what someone tried to do with the data, when they tried to do it, any limitations that they identified in the process, and, in ISO 19115-1, a response from the data provider. Users and reusers have always been able to identify problems and limitations of data. Now they can connect those discoveries to the ongoing discussion and improvement of the dataset. This extends the metadata creation process throughout the data life cycle and extends the range of the feedback loop to include future users who will have access to the growing metadata and documentation collection.

Data centers can take advantage of these metadata improvements to help create wisdom by managing and mediating the flow of feedback between users and data providers. This element of community and wisdom building is emerging now as an integral part of the culture of the World Wide Web, from tagging systems through social networks to wikis as elements of data discovery systems as a mechanism for collecting and sharing information from users about data. It includes the ideas and methods of citizen science and crowdsourcing to move from data to information and toward knowledge and wisdom. It will be an important way of integrating community into ongoing metadata and documentation efforts.

Community convergence

The technical process of making atmospheric data accessible to GIS tools is only a small part of converging the communities that create and use those data and tools. There are significant socialization tasks that involve bringing together members of these communities with different experiences and points of view. Important members of one community have significant expertise in that community that is less important to the other community. Losing this expertise is a difficult process, as is community convergence. Despite these difficulties, several important activities suggest that community convergence is well underway and point toward strong relationships in the future.

The National Center for Atmospheric Research (NCAR) GIS Initiative that started during 2002 was a critical first step toward converging the atmospheric science and GIS communities. NCAR is a part of the University Consortium for Atmospheric Research (UCAR), and the GIS effort there resulted in a very fruitful partnership that integrated netCDF (Network Common Data Form) into Esri products and led to this book, among other things. The success of that effort must have motivated Unidata, another part of UCAR, to set off to partner with the Open Geospatial Consortium (OGC).

The second important step toward convergence is the adoption of netCDF as an OGC standard in 2011. This adoption resulted from a long (and ongoing) process that required significant commitments from UCAR and OGC and a significant amount of work from members of each organization and others. This work involved creating and editing many documents and presentations, but, more important, it involved communication between two communities with different experiences, expectations, and expertise. Fortunately, those involved in making it happen share a belief that the result is worth the effort. They continue to forge forward and build on their success.

Another step toward convergence has recently taken place in the information rather than the data layer. It involves a tool called ncISO that initiates construction of a bridge between documentation in netCDF/THREDDS and the ISO metadata standards. This tool builds on the Unidata Attribute Convention for Data Discovery (ACDD) to make it possible to automatically generate discovery ISO metadata from netCDF files documented using this convention. Again, the technical achievement is small relative to the increased conversations between the netCDF and international standards communities. Atmospheric and ocean scientists are seeing the benefits of standard documentation and trying to bring those benefits to their datasets and users.

Finally, other major organizations are following UCAR along the road toward integrating international standards into their communities and data systems:

- The World Meteorological Organization (WMO) has adopted a profile of ISO 19115 for the WMO Information System.

- The National Oceanographic and Atmospheric Administration (NOAA) recently approved an agency-wide directive identifying the ISO Standards as the metadata standards NOAA will use.

- The next-generation geostationary satellite (GOES-R) program has developed an ISO 19115 profile for its data.

- The National Aeronautics and Space Administration's (NASA) Earth Science Data and Information System has recently committed to using the ISO standards in NASA Earth Science Data Centers and future missions.

- The Federal Geographic Data Committee (FGDC) is encouraging members to start incorporating ISO and other external standards into their data and metadata systems.

Equally important, most of these groups are considering the same standards in the data (and service) layers (netCDF/HDF5), and are thinking in terms of integrating documentation between the data and information layers (à la ncISO).

These important decisions by large organizations are critical for providing the support required to move forward. Unfortunately, they do not automatically provide the motivation for these organizations to join forces in the development of shared best practices that will ultimately be required for interoperability. Individuals in these organizations and users must seek opportunities to work outside of their organizational boundaries and keep interoperability goals in mind.

Conclusion

The evidence clearly indicates that the blueprints for building the foundation into an enduring structure of shared knowledge and community wisdom are there. The metadata standards have evolved to support integration into analysis systems and help build trust in the conclusions drawn from those analyses. They also support connections to documentation that is native to different communities. The standards are becoming tools for creating connections between communities rather than for separating them. That is a critical step toward building knowledge and wisdom.

In addition, individuals have already built strong connections between communities and organizations are now following those leaders. This institutionalization is critical for the long-term outlook. As organizational resources focus on connections, and processes integrate shared standards and technologies, the structure gains the strength it needs for longevity, hopefully while remaining open to innovation that emerges from new partners and partnerships.

The foundation is strong, and the future looks exciting!

References

Cleveland, H. 1982. "Information as Resource." *The Futurist* December (1982): 34–9.

International Organization for Standardization (ISO). 2003. "ISO 19115—Geographic Information—Metadata."

Shedroff, N. 1994. "Information Interaction Design: A Unified Field Theory of Design." http://www.nathan.com/thoughts/unified/index.html.

Contributors

Steve Ansari

Physical Scientist, National Oceanic and Atmospheric Administration's National Climatic Data Center

Steve Ansari is a graduate of the University of North Carolina at Asheville and has been a federal employee since 2005. Steve is involved in data visualization, management, interoperability, and geographic information system (GIS) applications for a variety of data types, including weather radar, satellite, model, and station.

Rich Baldwin

Project Lead, National Oceanic and Atmospheric Administration's National Climatic Data Center/Climate Data Online

Rich Baldwin received his master of science degree in geophysics from Purdue University in 1986. He spent 13 years at the National Aeronautics Space Administration's Goddard Space Flight Center (NASA/GSFC) working on numerical modeling of geomagnetic fields and a web access system for the Space Physics Data Center. He came to the National Climatic Data Center (NCDC) in 1999 to work on the development of global hourly climate data. For the past several years, he has served as the Climate Data Online (CDO) project manager. Providing access to NCDC's climate products through web-enabled system data product life-cycle development combined with user-friendly GIS and web interfaces has been his primary focus, along with the refinement of representational state transfer (REST) web services and data interoperability.

Jennifer Boehnert
GIS Coordinator, National Center for Atmospheric Research
For the past 10 years, Jennifer Boehnert has worked with the atmospheric community and Esri to make atmospheric data and GIS technology interoperable. She has also worked with National Center for Atmospheric Research (NCAR) scientists and engineers on various projects that incorporate GIS methods and tools with climate and weather model output. Boehnert has also developed several courses that focus on using GIS as an integration and communication tool for scientific data.

Kevin A. Butler
Product Engineer, Esri
Kevin A. Butler is a member of the Geoprocessing and Analysis team at Esri working primarily with the multidimension tools. He holds a doctorate in geography from Kent State University. Prior to joining Esri he was a senior lecturer and manager of GIScience research at the University of Akron, where he taught courses on spatial statistics, GIS programming, and database design.

Stephen Del Greco
Deputy Chief, Climate Services and Monitoring Division, National Oceanic and Atmospheric Administration's National Climatic Data Center
Stephen Del Greco is the deputy chief of the National Oceanic and Atmospheric Administration's (NOAA) NCDC Climate Services and Monitoring Division (CSMD). He provides leadership and management for CSMD activities that include user engagement and services, climate monitoring and assessments, data access and applications, and regional climate services. He is a graduate of the University of North Carolina at Asheville and attended Harvard University, John F. Kennedy School of Government, Public Service Executive Education program.

Ben Domenico
Unidata Outreach Coordinator
Ben Domenico establishes and maintains key Unidata relationships with external organizations, especially those in the international standards, earth science, GIS, and science education communities. As University Corporation for Atmospheric Research (UCAR) representative on the Open Geospatial Consortium Technical Committee, he edited four CF-netCDF standards specifications. He is a founding member and secretary of the American Geophysical Union's (AGU) Earth and Space Science Informatics Focus Group and was coauthor of a paper that was recognized as the outstanding 2012 publication in the *Journal of Geoscience Education*. His academic background includes a master of science in physics from Yale University and a PhD in astrophysics from the University of Colorado.

Michael J. Garay
Researcher, Multi-angle Imaging
Jet Propulsion Laboratory, California Institute of Technology

Michael Garay has been involved in satellite remote sensing and algorithm development for over 15 years. He has been a member of the Multi-angle Imaging SpectroRadiometer (MISR) team at Jet Propulsion Laboratory (JPL) since 2003, working on both aerosol and cloud retrieval algorithm development and assessment. He has a background in radiative transfer, including three-dimensional and polarimetric simulations and retrievals. Michael was also a coinvestigator on the Adaptive Sky project funded under the NASA Advanced Information Systems Technology program on multi-instrument, multiplatform data fusion. He is currently a coinvestigator on a NASA proposal studying the effects of subpixel clouds on multi-angle, spectropolarimetric retrievals of aerosol and cloud properties from the Aerosol Polarimetric Sensor.

Stephanie Granger
Research Scientist, Program Area Manager, Jet Propulsion Laboratory

Stephanie Granger has more than 25 years' experience in earth science, remote sensing studies, science data product development, and scientific visualization. As a member of an international NASA Applied Science Team she leads a project to provide satellite-based drought and crop productivity indicators to extension agents and government agencies. In 2012, Granger was a special advisor to the US Agency for International Development's (USAID) Office of Science and Technology.

She holds a bachelor of science from the University of Redlands, and a master of science in information systems and technology with an emphasis on knowledge discovery from Claremont Graduate University, California.

Ted Habermann
Director of Earth Science, The HDF Group

Ted Habermann joined The HDF Group during 2013 after working at NOAA's National Geophysical Data Center (NGDC) on interoperability projects and international documentation standards. He led the development and implementation of metadata management and data access systems at NGDC and worked closely with NOAA, Unidata, and OPeNDAP (Open-source Project for a Network Data Access Protocol) to add ISO (International Organization for Standardization) metadata capabilities to THREDDS (Thematic Real-time Environmental Distributed Data Services) and Hyrax Servers. Habermann is now focused on improving metadata and providing data and metadata services from data stored in HDF (Hierarchical Data Format). He is working to build a community that spans the many disciplines that are using HDF with community conventions to share data and metadata.

Niels Einar Jensen

Product Manager, DHI Local Area Weather Radar System

Niels Einar Jensen is a civil engineer with a degree from Aalborg University. He was an assistant professor of water resources at the Asian Institute of Technology, Bangkok, from 1989 to 1990. He has more than 30 years of professional experience in hydrological modeling. Jensen designed the MOUSE and Mike11 computational kernel at DHI and has been the product manager for the Local Area Weather Radar (LAWR) from DHI for 15 years.

Steve Kopp

Program Manager, Geoprocessing and Spatial Analysis, Esri

Steve Kopp holds a master's degree in geography from Indiana State University. He has over 20 years of experience in the GIS industry working on the management, visualization, and analysis of raster and multidimensional data.

Arlene G. Laing

Project Scientist, National Center for Atmospheric Research

Arlene Laing holds a PhD in meteorology from Pennsylvania State University. Her areas of study include large thunderstorm systems across the globe, lightning and El Niño, tropical cyclones, satellite precipitation estimates, wildfire forecasting, flash floods, volcanic ash fall, African climate variability, convection simulations, weather, and meningitis. She authored a peer-reviewed online textbook on tropical meteorology and interactive, multimedia modules at the COMET program. She has been a forecaster, postdoctoral fellow of the Cooperative Institute for Research in the Atmosphere, professor at the University of South Florida, scientist at NCAR, and an adjunct professor at North Carolina State University.

Mark LaJoie

Principal Scientist, National Oceanic and Atmospheric Administration's National Environmental Satellite, Data, and Information Service

Mark LaJoie served over 20 years in the US Air Force, primarily as a weather officer, and is currently employed at NOAA/NESDIS (National Environmental Satellite, Data, and Information Service). He has a master's degree in meteorology from the Naval Post Graduate School and a master's degree in geography from the University of South Florida. His current interests include operational meteorology, societal impacts of climate variations, Earth observation systems requirements, investment analysis, and data sharing.

Neal Lott

Chief, Data Access and Applications Branch, National Oceanic and Atmospheric Administration's National Climatic Data Center

Neal Lott is a graduate of North Carolina State University and has been a federal employee since 1982. He began his career as a civilian employee with the US Air Force, involved in various aspects of data management and climatology support for the military. He then moved to NOAA's NCDC as a software developer and continued to be involved in data management and climate applications. During the past 11 years, he has been branch chief of the Data Access and Applications Branch of NCDC.

Chris MacDermaid

Senior Research Associate, Colorado State University Cooperative Institute for Research in the Atmosphere

Chris MacDermaid earned his bachelor of science in computer science and mathematics from Colorado State University (CSU). He currently works as a senior research associate for NOAA's Earth System Research Laboratory (ESRL) in the Global Systems Division (GSD) as lead of the Data Services Group (DSG). Recently, he worked as a technical coordinator for ESRL/GSD on the Federal Aviation Administration's (FAA) CSS-Wx (Common Support Services-Weather) project and the National Weather Service's NextGen project. He is currently working as a researcher on the NEIS (NOAA Earth Information Service) project.

Henrik Madsen

Head of Innovation, DHI

Henrik Madsen is responsible for DHI's research and development activities within Rivers and Reservoirs and Climate Change Impact and Adaptation Analysis. He has 20 years of experience in water resources management and hydrological modeling. He is also adjunct professor in hydrological modeling at the Department of Geosciences and Natural Resource Management, University of Copenhagen.

Nazila Merati

Marketing Manager, ClipCard

Nazila Merati is an innovator successful at marketing and executing uses of technology in science. She focuses on peer data sharing for scientific data, integrating social media information for science research, and performing model validation. She has more than 20 years of experience in marine data discovery and integration; geospatial data modeling and visualization; data stewardship, including metadata development curation; cloud computing; and social media analytics and strategy.

Anders Peter Sloth Møller
MSc Environmental Technician, DHI
Anders Peter Sloth Møller is the coauthor of code and documentation for the MIKE URBAN Weather Radar Tool. He has contributed to the development and maintenance of the MIKE URBAN software package and was a member of the DHI Customer Support Team for MIKE URBAN for several years. Anders has also developed scripts for automated collection and processing of data.

Andrew Monaghan
Atmospheric Scientist, University Corporation for Atmospheric Research National Center for Atmospheric Research
Andrew Monaghan's research interests include a broad range of interdisciplinary regional climate topics, with an emphasis on climate-sensitive health and disease issues. He has a bachelor of science degree in civil engineering from the University of Alaska Fairbanks and master's and PhD degrees in atmospheric sciences from The Ohio State University.

Kenneth Sydney Pelman
Meteorologist and GIS Application Developer, National Oceanic and Atmospheric Administration's Climate Prediction Center
Kenneth Pelman received a master of science degree in both meteorology and geographic information systems from Pennsylvania State University. In addition to his forecasting responsibilities at the Climate Prediction Center, Pelman is responsible for the dissemination of all forecast products in geospatial formats. Pelman is also coproject manager for the Integrated Dissemination Program (IDP), which is responsible for setting up a NOAA-wide enterprise GIS.

Robert Raskin
Supervisor of the Science Data Engineering and Archiving Group, Instrument Software and Science Data Systems, Jet Propulsion Laboratory
Founding Chair of the Association of American Geographers Cyberinfrastructure Specialty Group
Robert Raskin made significant contributions to broadening the connections between cyberinfrastructure (CI) and geography over the past 20 years. He was an expert in geoinformatics, which combines theoretical knowledge of geographical science with the technical innovation of computer science, and in the field of data interoperability in the earth and environmental sciences.

Robert Raskin died in 2012, after contributing to this publication.

Steven Reader

Associate Professor of Geography, School of Geosciences, University of South Florida

Steven Reader is an associate professor of geography in the School of Geosciences at the University of South Florida (USF) in Tampa. He earned his doctorate at the University of Bristol in the United Kingdom and held positions at McMaster University in Canada prior to USF. He has been teaching GIS at senior undergraduate and graduate levels for 26 years and designed two graduate-level GIS certificate programs, one at USF and one at McMaster. His research interests include methodological developments in spatial statistics, spatial epidemiology, GIS programming, and GIScience education.

Matthew Rosencrans

Meteorologist, National Oceanic and Atmospheric Administration's Climate Prediction Center

Matthew Rosencrans's work involves production and research behind meteorological forecasts from 6 days out to 12 months, with a focus on intraseasonal variability. He is also a US Drought Monitor author. His main focus for intraseasonal variability is the variability of the tropics (Madden-Jullian Oscillation and other modes) and their potential impacts on the midlatitudes. He completed undergraduate studies in atmospheric science at SUNY-Albany, and then entered the US Air Force as a weather officer. He received a master of science degree from the Naval Postgraduate School. After leaving the US Air Force, he worked for NOAA at the Miami Center Weather Service Unit and completed an MBA before transitioning to the Climate Prediction Center in 2009.

Martin Rutherford

Director Maritime Military Geospatial Information and Services, Royal Australian Navy

Martin Rutherford is the director of maritime military geospatial information and services for the Royal Australian Navy. He is responsible for the acquisition, management, production, and dissemination of maritime environmental information to support the planning and conduct of maritime operations. He served in the Royal Australian Navy for over 30 years with senior appointments as the director of oceanography and meteorology and director of defense geospatial policy. As a senior public servant he has served as director of the Australian National Oceanographic Data Centre, and as a national delegate to a range of international oceanography, marine meteorology and remote sensing committees.

Kevin Sampson

Associate Scientist, National Center for Atmospheric Research

Kevin Sampson is an associate scientist in the GIS program at NCAR. Kevin holds a master's degree in geography from the University of Colorado and brings to NCAR experience applying geographic information systems to climate research and geographical sciences. He provides project support to UCAR scientists who use geographic data and perform geoprocessing. He develops and maintains climate products from global climate models and makes them accessible to a wide audience via open web services and web applications.

John (Jack) Settelmaier
Digital Techniques Meteorologist, National Weather Service

Jack Settelmaier earned his bachelor's degree in meteorology from Pennsylvania State University. Prior to joining the NWS, Settelmaier was a cooperative student trainee for the NWS's Meteorological (formerly Techniques) Development Laboratory (MDL). As a meteorologist and computer programmer with MDL, he focused on developing medium-range model output statistics (MOS), which are "first guess" outputs based on numerical weather model output. In 1998, he became the first science and operations officer at the NWS Forecast Office, where he served for four years. Since 2002, he has been the digital techniques meteorologist in the Science and Training Branch of the Science and Technology Services Division of the NWS's Southern Region headquarters. There he advances GIS and its use within the NWS.

Sudhir Raj Shrestha
Scientific Data Specialist, INNOVIM/National Oceanic and Atmospheric Administration's Climate Prediction Center

Sudhir Shrestha is a scientific data specialist with the INNOVIM/NOAA Climate Prediction Center. He leads the NOAA Climate Portal (http://www.climate.gov) effort on Data Access and Interoperability, which aims to become a unique platform vehicle for data discovery, access, and visualization. He has extensive experience in geospatial application development, modeling, and forecasting in the hydrology, soil, agriculture, and wildfire sectors. He has worked on projects involving the use of remote sensing and modeling methods addressing agriculture, hydrology, earthquakes, and soil erosion hazards in Nepal, Belgium, Japan, and the United States. Prior to joining INNOVIM/NOAA, he worked for the University of California–Merced, the NOAA Environmental Cooperative Science Center in Florida, the Akita Prefectural University in Japan, and the Center for the Rural Technology in Nepal. He also taught watershed management and soil science at the HICAST, Nepal Engineering College in Nepal. He completed his graduate research and training at the University of Wyoming and Ghent University (Belgium).

Amit Sinha
Senior Applications Engineer, Esri

Amit Sinha works in the Professional Services Department at Esri and is active in the integration of atmospheric data products and forecasts with GIS solutions for water, climate, and other sectors. He is one of the key authors of geospatial applications, such as HEC-GeoRAS and HEC-GeoEFM, published by the US Army Corps of Engineers' Hydrologic Engineering Center.

Paul Sliogeris
Deputy Director, METOC Geospatial Services, Navy Hydrography and METOC Branch

Paul Sliogeris is the deputy director of METOC Geospatial Services at the Royal Australian Navy's Hydrography and METOC Branch. Paul started his work in this field back in 1999 as an oceanographic data manager where he began using ArcInfo software to assist with the visualization and quality control of data. He established an enterprise geodatabase for the holistic management of Navy-collected oceanographic data. For the past few years his focus has been on interoperability and the delivery of geospatial services to defense through ArcGIS for Server and OpenGIS technologies.

Michael Squires
Climatologist, National Oceanic and Atmospheric Administration's National Climatic Data Center

Michael Squires develops new products that quantify the impact of climate on society. He worked as a weather observer and forecaster while in the Navy, producing the weather segment and forecasting for the CBS affiliate in St Louis, Missouri, and analyzing air pollution data for an electric utility company. He spent 15 years in technique development and applied climatology at the Air Force Combat Climatology Center. In 2003, he moved to NCDC. Until recently, Squires taught statistics at the University of North Carolina at Asheville. He has a master's degree in atmospheric science from St. Louis University.

Jebb Stewart
Software Engineer, Cooperative Institute for Research in the Atmosphere

Jebb Stewart has a unique background in both meteorology and computer science. He has over 15 years of experience in software development for geophysical data distribution, manipulation, and visualization. Today, he is the technical lead and project manager for NEIS, where he continues his work to improve the access and understanding of NOAA data.

Richard Tinker
Meteorologist, National Oceanic and Atmospheric Administration's Climate Prediction Center

Richard received a bachelor of science degree in meteorology from Pennsylvania State University. He began working for the Climate Prediction Center (then the Climate Analysis Center) in 1984 and has worked there since. In the past 10 years, Richard has specialized in drought studies and related impacts and statistical analyses of temperature and precipitation patterns for the past several decades.

Robert Toomey

Software Engineer, National Oceanic Atmospheric Administration's National Severe Storm Laboratory

Robert Toomey is a software developer, musician, carpenter, avid reader, and lifetime learner. Specializing in three-dimensional visualization of geographical data, he is currently studying geographic information systems and attempting to apply it to meteorological and hydrological applications. He works at the National Severe Storm Laboratory in Norman, Oklahoma, where he works on real-time display of and interaction with high-resolution weather data.

Tiffany C. Vance

Geographer/IT Specialist

National Oceanic and Atmospheric Administration's National Marine Fisheries Service/ Alaska Fisheries Science Center

Tiffany C. Vance's research addresses the application of multidimensional GIS to both scientific and historical research, with an emphasis on the use and diffusion of techniques for representing three- and four-dimensional data. Her ongoing projects include developing techniques to define and describe essential pelagic habitat; developing histories of environmental variables affecting larval pollock recruitment and survival in Shelikof Strait, Alaska; and the use of GIS and visualizations in the history of recent arctic science. She has a PhD from Oregon State University in geography and ecosystem informatics.

Kyle Wilcox

Senior Software Engineer, Axiom Data Science

Kyle Wilcox received his bachelor of science degree in computer science from the University of Rhode Island in 2006 and has since worked in the ocean sciences.

Olga Wilhelmi

Research Scientist, National Center for Atmospheric Research

Olga Wilhelmi leads NCAR's GIS program and conducts research on societal risk, vulnerability, and adaptive capacity to extreme weather events and climate change. She has many years of experience working with GIS in a variety of natural and social science applications, including water resources and drought management, extreme heat and human health, disaster risk reduction, and climate change adaptation.

May Yuan

Ashbel Smith Professor of Geospatial Information Sciences

School of Economic, Political, and Policy Science; University of Texas at Dallas

May Yuan studies temporal GIS and its applications to geographic dynamics. She is a member of the Mapping Science Committee at the National Research Council (2009–2014), associate editor of the *International Journal of Geographical Information Science*, member of the editorial boards of *Annals of American Association of Geographers and Cartography and Geographical Information Science*, and a member of the academic committee of United States Geospatial Intelligence Foundation. She holds a bachelor of science degree from the National Taiwan University and received her master's and PhD degrees from the State University of New York at Buffalo.

Index

Note: Page numbers with *f* indicate figures: those with *t* indicate tables.

web services, 188
   CDO (Climate Data Online), 69
   interoperability interfaces, 201–209, 202*f*
   maps. *See* web-based maps
   METOC. *See* METOC web services
      (meteorology and oceanography)
   NOAA Earth Information System (NEIS),
      205–209, 205*f*, 207*f*
   OGC web services interface standards,
      201–204, 202*f*
   Open Geospatial Consortium (OGC)-
      format, 193
web-based maps, 189–190, 190*f*
   analytic maps, 195–196, 196*f*
   crowsourced maps, 196–197, 197*f*, 198*f*
   distributed data sources, 194, 194*f*
   dynamically created/updated maps,
      192–194, 193*f*
   Kraak typology, 191, 191*f*
   real-time maps, 194, 194*f*
   static/animated, 191–192, 192*f*
Weekly Weather and Crop Bulletin, 114
Well-Known Text (WKT), 278
WFS (Web Feature Service), 65, 202–203
WGs (Weather generators), 108
WGS84 (World Geodetic System of 1984),
   26, 29, 31, 34, 36
wildfire data, integrating with lightning strike
   observations
   Florida, 176–177, 176*f*, 177*f*
   lightning climatologies, 178–181, 179*f*,
      180*f*, 181*f*
wind speed/direction, 237–240, 238*f*,
   239*f*, 240*f*

WKT (Well-Known Text), 278
WMO (World Meteorological Organization)
   adoption of ISO 19115, 284
   GRIB, 8, 277
   standards, 67
WMS (Web Map Service), 65, 70*f*, 114, 202
   ArcGIS support, 252
   CDR (Climate Data Record) program,
      71, 71*f*
   climate change data, 96
   GetCapabilities service section, 204
workflow automation with Python, 256–257,
   257*f*
World Geodetic System of 1984 (WGS84), 26,
   29, 31, 34, 36
World Meteorological Organization (WMO)
   adoption of ISO 19115, 284
   GRIB, 8, 277
   standards, 67
World Ocean Atlas, 217
World Weather Watch, 52
WRF Preprocessing System (WPS), 29
WSDL (Web Service Description
   Language), 203

X

Xerox PARC Map Viewer, 190
XMI (XML Metadata Interchange), 13

Y

YouTube, 86, 197